DEVELOPMENTS IN
HIGHWAY PAVEMENT ENGINEERING—1

DEVELOPMENTS IN HIGHWAY PAVEMENT ENGINEERING—1

Edited by

PETER S. PELL

Professor of Civil Engineering,
University of Nottingham, UK

APPLIED SCIENCE PUBLISHERS LTD
LONDON

APPLIED SCIENCE PUBLISHERS LTD
RIPPLE ROAD, BARKING, ESSEX, ENGLAND

British Library Cataloguing in Publication Data

Developments in highway pavement engineering.
Vol.I.
1. Pavements
I. Pell, P S
625.8   TE250

ISBN 0-85334-781-6

WITH 17 TABLES AND 136 ILLUSTRATIONS

Printed in Great Britain by Galliard (Printers) Ltd, Great Yarmouth

PREFACE

In the present and future climate of limited resources and escalating costs, highway engineers must be encouraged to obtain the economic benefits of better design, construction and maintenance of their road pavements. The aim of this book, and its companion volume, 'Developments in Highway Pavement Engineering—2', is to present some of the recent developments which have taken place in pavement engineering which are relevant to the objective of getting better value in road pavements for our money.

In books of this type it is not possible to give comprehensive coverage of all aspects of pavement engineering; the choice of topics is that of the editor and I have selected those areas in which, in my view, there have been significant developments. Each chapter deals with a particular topic and is written by an acknowledged expert in the subject. The authors contributing to both books in this series are representative of some of the many different interests involved in pavement engineering, namely, consulting, contracting, local authorities and materials suppliers, as well as research workers from government, industry and the universities.

It is now widely recognised that the traditional, largely empirical approach to flexible pavement materials and design cannot deal satisfactorily with new situations regarding changes in loading, materials and environment. The present trends in traffic loading are for more and heavier loads and it is these loads, at and above the legal limit, which cause much of the damage to a pavement structure. This heavy traffic in conjunction with unusually hot summer temperatures has exposed the shortcomings of some of our traditional materials. Factors such as these, together with the increase in costs of materials, especially oil products, have highlighted the need to be able to make more effective and efficient use of pavement materials.

In order to cope with this situation, analytically based pavement structural design methods have been developed and Chapters 1 and 2 deal with this important topic. This approach to pavement design is based on sound fundamental principles and takes cognisance of the important mechanical properties of the materials used in the various layers of the structure as well as being able to deal with any specific loading and environmental conditions. This development is particularly relevant to economic considerations as it enables the assessment of the effects of changing conditions and new materials to be made without the expense and delay of full scale road trials.

Two important aspects of bituminous materials are covered in Chapters 3 and 4. Chapter 3 describes how traditional asphalt mixes can be designed and modified to cope with today's severe conditions, while Chapter 4 shows how significant economies and improvements in performance can be ensured by better compaction which can be easily obtained by modified rolling techniques. Cement stabilised materials are dealt with comprehensively in Chapter 5. The fundamental properties, nature and behaviour of these materials, particularly lean concrete, are fully discussed as are the recent developments and changes in specifications. A careful study of this chapter should remove many of the common misconceptions regarding the properties and performance of this important road base material.

Skid resistance of road surfacings is the subject of Chapter 6, and, it should not be forgotten that safety is an important factor when considering the overall economics of pavement design, construction and maintenance.

The second book in this series, 'Developments in Highway Pavement Engineering—2', deals with other important topics such as earthworks, aggregates, frost heave, overlay design, maintenance management and pavement engineering in developing countries.

Although each chapter of this book deals with a specific topic, and is complete in itself, cross references are made to relevant subject matter in other chapters and in the second book of the series. Furthermore, each author has provided a very full list of references for the reader who wishes to study certain aspects of a topic in more detail. The new ideas and developments which have taken place in recent years, and which are presented in this book, should make it both interesting and informative for a wide range of readers. It should prove to be a useful reference work for practical civil and highway engineers as well as providing up-to-date information for students, lecturers and research workers.

Throughout this book the treatment of many topics is based on fundamental principles and measurements which allow a more analytical and quantitative approach. This is as it should be, and the words of Lord Kelvin are, I think, very relevant. 'When you can measure that of which you speak, and express it in numbers, you know something about it.'

Finally, as editor, I would like to express my thanks to the individual authors for contributing their chapters and for so cheerfully and readily accepting the editor's comments.

P.S.P.

CONTENTS

ix

LIST OF CONTRIBUTORS

D. BRIEN

Bitumen Division, Shell Research Limited, Thornton Research Centre, Chester CH1 3SH, UK.

S. F. BROWN

Department of Civil Engineering, The University of Nottingham, University Park, Nottingham NG7 2RD, UK.

G. LEES

Department of Transportation & Environmental Planning, The University of Birmingham, Birmingham B15 2TT, UK.

N. W. LISTER

Highways Department, Transport and Road Research Laboratory, Department of the Environment, Crowthorne, Berks RG11 6AU, UK.

K. R. PEATTIE

Asphalt and Coated Macadam Association, 25 Lower Belgrave Street, London SW1W 0LS, UK.

W. D. POWELL

Pavement Design Division, Highways Department, Transport and Road Research Laboratory, Department of the Environment, Crowthorne, Berks RG11 6AU, UK.

R. I. T. WILLIAMS

Department of Civil Engineering, University of Surrey, Guildford, Surrey GU2 5XH, UK.

Chapter 1

FLEXIBLE PAVEMENT DESIGN

K. R. PEATTIE

Asphalt and Coated Macadam Association, London, UK

SUMMARY

The structural design of flexible pavements deals with the determination of the thicknesses at which layers in the pavement structure have to be used having regard to the materials selected for each layer and the loads to be carried.

Following a description of the functions of each layer in a flexible pavement, the main features of empirical and analytical design procedures are reviewed. Factors that influence pavement design including traffic loading, environmental effects, materials properties and criteria of design and performance are then discussed.

The selection of models to represent flexible pavement structures and their analysis to give the distribution of stress and strain are considered. This is an area in which enormous developments have taken place in the past 25 years. Reference is made to different ways in which solutions to the equations for multi-layer structures can be obtained. The action of such structures is demonstrated by analyses of 2- and 3-layer structures. Considerable attention is given to the design criteria used in structural design procedures.

The chapter concludes by describing current design systems and the various forms in which they are presented.

INTRODUCTION

The purpose of a pavement is to carry traffic safely, conveniently and economically over its design life by protecting the subgrade from the effects

1

of traffic and climate and by ensuring that no materials used in the pavement suffer any unacceptable deterioration. The pavement surface must provide a smooth ride with adequate skid resistance. The structural design of pavements involves the selection of suitable materials for the pavement and the determination of the thicknesses at which they must be used in order to meet the objectives that have just been stated. The problem

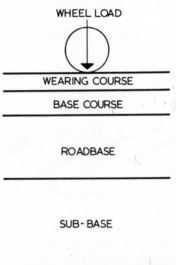

FIG. 1.   Typical flexible pavement structure.

of pavement design is essentially a structural one; to ensure that traffic loads are distributed so that the stresses and strains developed at all levels in the pavement and the subgrade are within the capabilities of the materials at each level. The design process consists of two different phases; the determination of the thicknesses of pavement layers having certain mechanical properties, and the determination of the composition of the materials that will provide these properties. Chapters 2, 3 and 5 consider the relationship between the composition and properties of various types of pavement materials.

Flexible pavements consist of a series of layers constructed on the subgrade or prepared formation as shown in Fig. 1. The top two layers, the wearing course and the basecourse, constitute the surfacing. The wearing course provides a uniform running surface whose rugosity and texture depth ensure adequate resistance to skidding. A detailed treatment of skid resistant surfacings is given in Chapter 6. The wearing course is usually impervious in order to prevent water penetrating into the pavement structure and destroying its mechanical stability. However, one method of minimising spray and improving skid resistance is to use an open-textured layer on the top of the pavement in which case the layer on which it is laid must be impervious. The wearing course must carry the high stresses induced by traffic without unacceptable deformation. The basecourse provides a good surface on which to construct the wearing course and therefore contributes to the overall riding quality of the pavement as well as to the structural strength. Occasionally the wearing course and the basecourse are combined in a single layer.

The main structural layer in the pavement is the roadbase whose purpose is to distribute traffic loads so that the stresses and strains developed by them in the subgrade and the sub-base are within the capacity of the materials in these layers. The sub-base is also a load-distributing layer but is of weaker material than the roadbase. The sub-base, in addition to reducing the stresses and strains developed in the subgrade, may help to protect it from frost action. It also provides a suitable working platform on which to construct the upper layers of the pavement. The load-distributing capacity of individual layers is a function of both their thickness and the mechanical stiffness of the materials in them.

In most flexible pavement structures the stiffness of each layer is greater than that of the layer below and smaller than that of the layer above. Layers consisting of some types of cementitious roadbase materials may be exceptions to this general rule. The overall thickness of the pavement as well as that of the individual layers depends on the traffic to be carried, the climate, the quality of the subgrade, and the mechanical properties of the materials in the pavement layers.

METHODS OF FLEXIBLE PAVEMENT DESIGN

Methods for the design of flexible pavements may be classified in two groups:

1. empirical and semi-empirical procedures;
2. analytical or theoretical methods.

Most of the significant developments in design procedures for flexible pavements that have taken place during the past 25 years have been in the

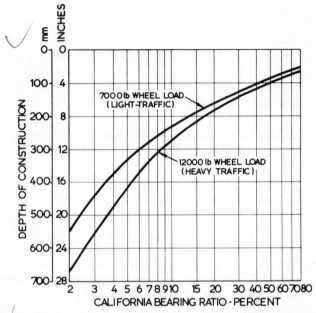

FIG. 2.   California Bearing Ratio method design curves.

second of these groups. Consequently most of the attention in this chapter
will be given to analytical methods.

Empirical Design Methods

The empirical and semi-empirical methods are based on past experience
and may include laboratory or field tests of the subgrade and pavement
materials. In some methods these tests are primarily for identification or
classification of the materials whilst in others they give quantitative
information about their mechanical properties.

   One of the most important methods in this category is the California
Bearing Ratio method[1] in which the strength of soils and unbound granular
materials is measured by the California Bearing Ratio test (CBR) in which a
circular plunger is forced into the material at a specified rate while the load
necessary to do this is recorded. The total thickness of the pavement is
related to the CBR-value of the subgrade for particular wheel loads by
curves of the type shown in Fig. 2.

   Since its introduction the CBR method has been widely adopted and
used. It has been modified to suit local materials and conditions and

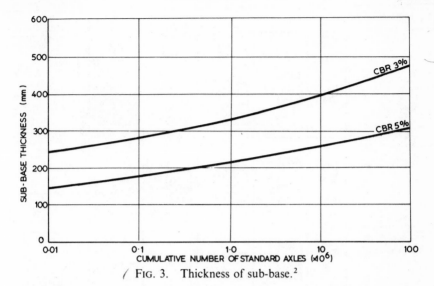

/ FIG. 3.   Thickness of sub-base.[2]

appropriate design curves have been derived. The design procedure contained in Road Note 29[2] produced by the Transport and Road Research Laboratory (TRRL) is of the CBR-type. The thickness of the sub-base is related to the CBR-value of the subgrade and to the total number of standard axle loads to be carried by curves of the type shown in Fig. 3. The

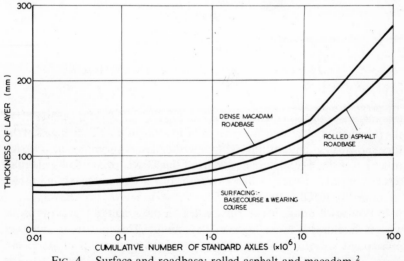

FIG. 4.   Surface and roadbase: rolled asphalt and macadam.[2]

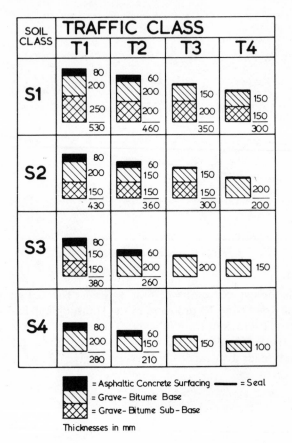

SOIL CLASS	TRAFFIC CLASS			
	T1	T2	T3	T4
S1	80 / 200 / 250 / 530	60 / 200 / 200 / 460	150 / 200 / 350	150 / 150 / 300
S2	80 / 200 / 150 / 430	60 / 150 / 150 / 360	150 / 150 / 300	200 / 200
S3	80 / 150 / 150 / 380	60 / 200 / 260	200	150
S4	80 / 200 / 280	60 / 150 / 210	150	100

■ = Asphaltic Concrete Surfacing   —— = Seal
▨ = Grave- Bitume Base
▧ = Grave- Bitume Sub-Base

Thicknesses in mm

FIG. 5.   French catalogue design—bituminous bases.

thicknesses of the other layers are related to the quality of the materials in the pavement itself as well as to the traffic loading by a series of curves of the type shown diagrammatically in Fig. 4. Other design curves are included for other pavement materials. The results of the TRRL's many full-scale road tests[3,4] have been used in the derivation of the design charts and tables contained in Road Note 29.[2]

In France the design procedure for flexible pavements involves the use of what is described as a 'catalogue of structures'.[5] This consists of a series of seven charts each of which applies to a different group of pavement materials—the catalogue for pavements having bitumen-bound bases is

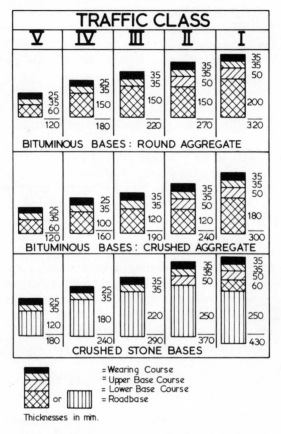

FIG. 6.   German standardised bituminous pavements.

shown diagrammatically in Fig. 5. The development of the catalogue is partially empirical and partially analytical. The subgrade is placed in one of four categories depending primarily on its CBR-value and traffic is also put in one of four categories. A similar procedure is used in the German Federal Republic.[6] A semi-empirical approach has been used to derive a series of standardised constructions similar to those illustrated in Fig. 6. The complete catalogue covers a wider range of base materials than shown here. The quality of the subgrade material does not enter directly into the German design system. Guidance is given about the quality of granular sub-bases and considerable attention is paid to providing an adequate depth of frost-resistant granular material. This appears to result in a thickness of sub-base such that the structures listed in the catalogue are all constructed on a foundation of satisfactory bearing capacity.

Empirical and semi-empirical design methods for pavements are satisfactory so long as the materials and conditions of loading for which they were developed do not change. However traffic volumes and, more particularly, traffic loadings have tended to increase quite drastically in recent years. Furthermore, the introduction of new materials may be inhibited if it is not possible to assess with any precision the thicknesses and conditions under which they should be used. The extension of semi-empirical design methods into regions of new loading and new materials can be achieved only by carrying out expensive and time-consuming full-scale pavement experiments. Analytical design methods do not suffer from these drawbacks.

Analytical Design Methods

Analytical design methods for flexible pavements are related to the design of structures since the composition and thicknesses of the layers are selected so that the stresses, strains and deformations produced by design traffic loading do not exceed the capabilities of any of the materials in the pavement. The proportions of the pavement structure are adjusted until an acceptable design results in which all the critical factors are within permissible limits.

The essential features of an analytical or structural design system for flexible pavements are:

(a) the selection of a suitable elastic or viscoelastic model to represent the pavement structure;

(b) solutions to the equations for the stresses, strains and deformations in the model;

(c) the characterisation, in fundamental terms, of the mechanical properties of the materials in the layers under appropriate climatic and loading conditions;

(d) the definition of criteria for design and performance in fundamental terms of stress, strain and deformation;

(e) the presentation of the design system in a form that is convenient for use by highway engineers.

The degree of success achieved by the various analytical design systems that have been published may be measured by assessing the extent to which these requirements have been met.

FACTORS AFFECTING DESIGN

Traffic

Both the magnitude and numbers of traffic loads contribute to damage in flexible pavements. The importance of traffic loading is recognised in most countries by the specification of statutory limits for axle loads. Although the overall vehicle weight may also be limited it is usual to consider vehicle loadings in terms of axle loads for pavement design purposes. Tyre pressure and the wheel or axle configuration also influence pavement performance.

Tyre pressure affects primarily the wearing course, and the composition of the material in this layer is selected accordingly. So far as the structural design of pavements is concerned only commercial vehicles need be considered and their tyre pressures do not cover a very wide range—500 kN m^{-2} may be taken as typical. Tyre pressures in aircraft cover a considerably greater range. Values of around 1·0 to 1·5 MN m^{-2} are found in commercial aircraft and pressures up to 3·0 MN m^{-2} are used in military aircraft. This must be taken into account when designing airfield pavements. Wheel and axle configurations influence mainly the conditions in the upper layers of the pavement. However, the AASHO Road Test[9] showed that an 80 kN (18 000 lb) single axle load had the same structural effect as a 142 kN (32 000 lb) tandem axle load and required the same pavement structure for equivalent performance. Similar differences were observed for other values of single and tandem axle loads. Most commercial road vehicles have dual wheels at both ends of each axle. There are some variations in the spacings adopted. An analytical study has been made of load equivalency factors for road vehicles having different wheel and axle configurations.[7] Aircraft employ highly complex multiple-wheel landing gear in order to reduce individual wheel loads to acceptable values. This can cause difficulties in the structural analysis of flexible airfield pavements, particularly in locating the positions at which maximum critical stresses and strains are developed. A study of the strain patterns developed by current commercial aircraft has led to the developments of design charts for heavy-duty airfield pavements.[8]

Normal traffic on conventional roads is mixed in composition and various attempts have been made to reduce it to a single parameter for pavement design purposes. At the AASHO Road Test,[9] each test lane or loop carried traffic of only one axle weight and configuration. The damaging effects of different axle loads could therefore be assessed and a detailed series of equivalence factors for flexible pavements and single and tandem axles was developed.[10] The technique of expressing mixed traffic in terms of its equivalent number of standard axle loads is now regularly accepted as being convenient and suitable for both the design of pavements and the assessment of pavement performance. The concept of equivalent load means that one application of a load (L) is equivalent in terms of pavement damage to (F) applications of a standard load (L_s), where

$$F = \left(\frac{L}{L_s}\right)^a$$

The value of the power a found by most investigators, is about 4 and the standard load (L_s) most generally used is 80 kN (18 000 lb). A series of equivalency factors based on a standard axle load of 80 kN and the fourth power relationship is given in Table 1.

TABLE 1
EQUIVALENT AXLE LOAD FACTORS

Single axle load (kN)	Factor
20	0·0039
40	0·063
60	0·316
80	1·000
100	2·441
120	5·06
140	9·38
160	16·00
180	25·63
200	39·06

In some countries the statutory axle load is used as the standard for pavement design purposes.

If the composition of traffic is expressed in terms of the numbers of axle loads in each of a range of categories the damaging power of the traffic flow may be assessed. The proportion of pavement damage caused by each load category is obtained by multiplying the number of axle loads in that category by the appropriate equivalence factor. An example taken from the traffic on the M1 Motorway in Hertfordshire during 1968 to 1969[11] is given in Table 2.

The sum of the equivalent number of 80 kN axles listed in the right-hand column gives the damaging effect of the total vehicle flow in standard axles. The damaging effect of small axle loads is insignificant in spite of their large

TABLE 2

AXLE LOAD DATA FROM M1 MOTORWAY AT FRIAR'S WASH, HERTS. AVERAGE WEEKLY DATA OVER 18 WEEKS IN 1968 to 1969[11]

Axle load class (kN)	Number of axles	Percentage per class	Equivalence factor	Equivalent number of 80 kN axles
0–17·8	57 642	44·81	0·0002	11
17·8–35·6	26 973	20·97	0·01	270
35·6–53·4	16 004	12·44	0·09	1 440
53·4–71·2	10 949	8·51	0·35	3 832
71·2–89·0	9 277	7·21	1·00	9 277
89·0–106·8	5 545	4·31	2·30	12 754
106·8–124·6	1 796	1·40	4·40	7 902
124·6–142·4	319	0·25	7·60	2 424
142·4–160·2	66	0·05	12·10	799
over 160·2	60	0·05	22·80	1 368
Total	128 631	100·00		40 077

numbers. Consequently, private cars may be ignored for the purposes of pavement design and it is common to assess traffic loading solely in terms of the numbers of commercial vehicles. A study of the damaging power of traffic and its effect on the design of flexible pavement overlays under British conditions was made in 1974.[12]

Where accurate information about the composition of traffic flows is not available an estimate has to be made of the average number of standard axles per commercial vehicle. This is a function of both commercial vehicle loading and the percentage of commercial vehicles in the traffic flow and consequently its value depends on the type of road. Typical values for design purposes in the UK are given in Road Note 29[2] and these are summarised in Table 3.

TABLE 3

COMMERCIAL VEHICLE AXLE LOADING IN THE UK[2]

Type of road	Standard (80 kN) axles per commercial vehicle
Motorways and roads carrying more than 1 000 commercial vehicles per day in each direction	1·08
Roads carrying between 250 and 1 000 commercial vehicles per day in each direction	0·72
All other public roads	0·45

The speed of traffic has an influence on the design of flexible pavements because it affects the mechanical properties of bituminous materials. The critical factor is the time for which a load pulse due to a moving vehicle affects the bituminous layer. This is a function of both vehicle speed and the thickness of the bituminous layer.

A relationship connecting the loading time with these two factors has been developed.[13] An approximate value for the loading time in seconds is given by the reciprocal of the speed of the vehicle in $km\,h^{-1}$. In assessing loading times the average speed of commercial vehicles should be used since they are critical in design from the point of view of the magnitude of traffic loading.

In addition to the structurally damaging effects of individual wheel loads their numbers are also important because the pavement is influenced by the cumulative effect of traffic over a period of years. It is therefore necessary to estimate the growth of traffic as well as its composition. Techniques exist for forecasting future traffic volumes but it has proved to be difficult to achieve high precision. When the New Jersey Turnpike was designed in 1951 it was estimated that there would be 10 million vehicles in 1952 and 20 million by 1970. The actual traffic in these years was 18 and 100 million vehicles respectively. This point is discussed in more detail elsewhere.[12]

The difficulty in predicting future traffic flow with precision is important in two aspects of pavement construction: the number of years for which the pavement should be designed and the use of the technique of stage construction. Current practice in the UK is to recommend that flexible pavements be designed for a life of 20 years and rigid pavements for 40 years. It is highly doubtful that the data on which traffic forecasts are based can be established with sufficient precision to justify a prediction covering 40 years. Indeed past experience not only in highway engineering but also in water supply, sewerage systems and population growth in relation to education and other social phenomena suggests that a much shorter period would be more realistic.

Not only is it difficult to forecast future traffic volumes but commercial vehicle loadings will also probably change. In addition, planning and similar decisions frequently alter drastically the traffic loading on existing roads. It may therefore be more realistic and economic to design roads for an initial modest increase in traffic loading and to strengthen them by applying overlays if and when traffic growth makes this necessary. The principle may be applied successively giving rise to the name of stage construction. The techniques of designing overlays are dealt with in detail elsewhere.[46] The flexible pavement can readily be strengthened and is very well suited to stage construction. The postponement of some road construction costs until traffic intensity makes it necessary to incur them makes the most effective use of resources and is economically attractive, particularly where interest rates are high.

Environmental Effects

The environmental effects important in pavement design are moisture and the position of the water table which influence subgrade performance and temperature which strongly affects the properties of bituminous materials.

Moisture influences primarily the subgrade and unbound pavement materials. The properties of these materials should therefore be determined for critical conditions existing after the construction of the pavement. This point is discussed elsewhere.[47] The stiffnesses of subgrade soils are related to their moisture contents. Frost can significantly affect soils and unbound pavement materials. This effect can be minimised by selecting unbound materials having low susceptibility to frost action (see ref. 48) and by ensuring that any materials which might be so affected are located below the likely frost penetration depth. Damage from water can adversely affect the performance of bituminous materials if it is able to penetrate into the pavement structure as a result of poor drainage, excessive permeability in the bituminous layers or cracks in the pavement.

Temperature has a strong influence on the stiffness and behaviour of bituminous materials. Increasing temperature decreases the stiffness with the result that more load is transferred to the lower parts of the pavement structure. Stiffness increases with decreasing temperature with the opposite effect. Temperature variations are likely to have only minor effects on unbound pavement materials.

Because of the importance of temperature in determining the stiffness and other mechanical properties of bituminous materials it is desirable to have information about temperature variation over a complete year so that the mechanical properties, and hence the pavement performance, can be assessed on an annual basis. Some pavement design methods assume an average annual pavement temperature when evaluating stresses and strains. Other design procedures divide the year into seasons or months and evaluate the pavement properties over each of these periods.

Materials Properties

Information on a wide range of mechanical properties for all the materials in a pavement is necessary for the proper application of analytical design methods. This subject is treated fully in Chapter 2 but in order to appreciate the development of analytical pavement design methods it is discussed briefly here.

Because the properties, particularly those of bituminous materials, depend principally on temperature and time of loading they do not have single, unique values like purely elastic engineering materials. It is generally assumed that the stress–strain relationship of bituminous materials is linear under the dynamic conditions existing in pavements carrying moving traffic. The ratio of stress to strain is termed stiffness.[14] This property is analogous to Young's modulus E but its magnitude depends on temperature and time of loading and the appropriate values must be used having regard to the aspect of pavement behaviour under consideration. Stiffness permits the use of the concept of Young's modulus with materials that are viscoelastic.

The majority of the models used to represent flexible pavements assume elastic behaviour and the properties of the materials involved are stiffness at the appropriate temperature and time of loading and Poisson's ratio. Experimental work has provided suitable average values for this latter parameter for all pavement materials. Both stiffness and Poisson's ratio are used in carrying out stress analyses under load. To give proper consideration to aspects of performance such as surface cracking and permanent deformation induced by traffic loads, knowledge of the fatigue behaviour under repeated flexure and deformation behaviour under repeated direct loading are also required. Extensive laboratory investigations of the fatigue properties of bituminous materials have been carried out since the early 1950s and relationships between the value of tensile strain and the number of load applications necessary to initiate cracking have been derived. Much attention is currently being given to the correlation between fatigue behaviour in the laboratory and that in pavements. The analysis of permanent deformation has been studied more recently and several approaches to the problem are being used. In some, the properties of the pavement materials are determined by creep tests while in others triaxial cells designed to apply repetitive loads are used. In all this work precise temperature control of the laboratory tests is essential.

Design and Performance Criteria

The serviceability of a pavement is a measure of its state of fitness to carry traffic comfortably, safely and economically. The level of serviceability of a pavement declines gradually and continuously as shown in Fig. 7. If no remedial action is taken it will ultimately reach a state in which it can no longer carry traffic acceptably and will have to be withdrawn from service.

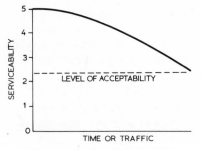

FIG. 7.   Serviceability history.

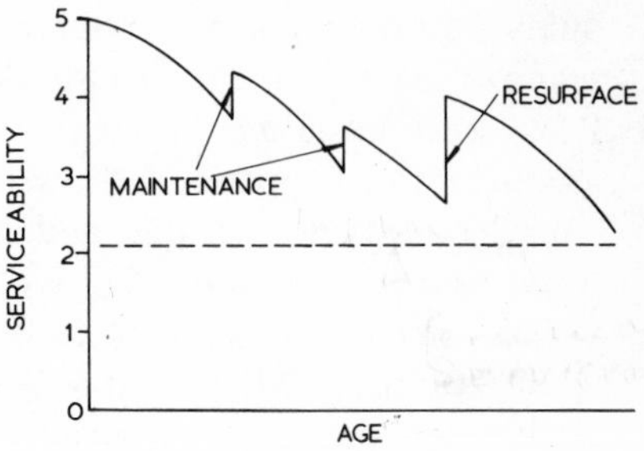

FIG. 8.   Effect of maintenance.

More generally, a pavement receives treatment such as surface dressing, overlaying or reconstruction at intervals throughout its life so that the level of serviceability is always maintained above the acceptable minimum as shown in Fig. 8. Serviceability can be assessed from a number of points of view such as structural condition, and the safety and comfort of occupants of vehicles travelling on the pavement. Safety is controlled predominantly by skid resistance although it may also be affected by very poor riding quality. The structural condition of the pavement may be assessed by measuring surface cracking, permanent deformation, transient surface deflection and curvature. A study of the behaviour of flexible pavements under traffic indicates those criteria that should be incorporated in design procedures.

Attempts have been made to combine the different measurements of serviceability listed above into a single index representing the overall state of the quality of the pavement. At the AASHO Road Test[9] a rating system involving the measurement of permanent deformation, riding quality and the extent of cracking and patching was developed. Formulae were devised for both flexible and rigid pavements to give a Present Serviceability Index (PSI) based on these measurements. For flexible pavements the formula was:

$$p = 5{\cdot}03 - 1{\cdot}91 \log (1 + \overline{SV}) - 0{\cdot}01(C + P)^{1/2} - 1{\cdot}38(\overline{RD})^2$$

where $p = $ PSI, $\overline{SV} = $ mean slope variance in both wheel paths (an assessment of riding quality), $C + P = $ cracking and patching (ft^2 per 100 ft^2 of surface area), and $\overline{RD} = $ rutting in wheel paths (an assessment of permanent deformation).

The initial value of PSI for flexible sections was 4·2 and it was considered that repair or replacement was necessary when it had dropped to 1·5. A 'mid-fair' rating, corresponding to a value of 2·5 was used to determine many of the design relationships derived from the data from the AASHO Road Test.[9] The use of such a system allows a convenient numerical assessment to be made of the serviceability of a pavement section over considerable periods of time and, in addition, comparisons can readily be made between the serviceability of different sections.

Following its development in the USA the PSI system has been adopted in different parts of the world. It has been criticised on the grounds that the factors and the functions included in the equations are not necessarily applicable to other parts of the world. This may be true but it is possible to devise an index appropriate to any locality by following the procedure used at AASHO. Such an investigation has been carried out in Germany.[15]

In the UK the predominant mode of distress in flexible pavements is permanent deformation appearing at the road surface in the form of ruts. Consequently this factor is used as a criterion of performance and once a rut depth of 10 mm, measured under a 1·8 m straight edge, has been reached the pavement is considered to have reached a 'critical' condition and to require maintenance if satisfactory performance is to be obtained in the future.[16] Once a rut depth of 20 mm has developed the pavement is considered to have failed. In making this assessment of performance note is also taken of any cracks that have developed in the pavement surface.

Deformation and cracking induced by traffic loading are the criteria most commonly used for assessing the state of serviceability of a pavement and hence for deciding when maintenance is necessary. Cracking due to thermal stresses can occur but it seems to be confined to countries having very cold climates.

Transient deflection under moving wheel loads is commonly used to assess serviceability in connection with maintenance programmes. This measurement tends to be related to the future behaviour of the pavement whereas rut depth is more a manifestation of the cumulative effect of past traffic loads. However, the two factors are clearly related as Fig. 9, taken from results of the AASHO Road Test,[9] shows. The excellent correlation occurs because all the sections, indicated by different symbols in this figure, were of the same type; asphaltic concrete surfacing, crushed limestone roadbase and sand–gravel sub-base. Only the thicknesses of the layers and traffic loading varied from section to section. If a wider range of types of pavement materials is included in such a study the level of correlation obtained is considerably reduced. The significance of surface deflection in the evaluation of flexible pavements is dealt with by Lister and Kennedy[46] and has also been examined in detail elsewhere.[17]

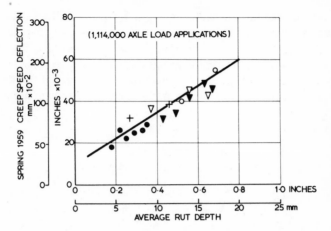

FIG. 9. Relationship between rut depth and deflection: AASHO Road Test.[9]

PAVEMENT MODELS AND STRESS ANALYSIS

There have been enormous developments in this area of pavement design during the past 25 years.

The adoption of suitable pavement models has been influenced by the constant conflict between the desire to represent the pavement structure by a comprehensive and realistic model and the considerable difficulties encountered in solving the equations for stress and strain as the complexity of the model increases. Much early work on flexible pavement design was seriously inhibited by mathematical and computational problems and only since electronic computers became widely available has it been possible to adopt fairly representative models. Even at the present time there can be problems, not so much of a mathematical nature, but arising from the time and cost of the computations required.

Most of the work on the development of design systems for flexible pavements is based on the assumptions that all the materials are elastic, homogeneous and isotropic in spite of the contradiction between these assumptions and the actual behaviour which leads to permanent surface deformation. Some models incorporating visco-elastic materials have been investigated. However, they have had limited application up to the present time because of mathematical and computational difficulties as well as problems in characterising the properties of the pavement materials in a form suitable for inclusion in the analysis. Equations for stress distribution in an elastic semi-infinite mass were put forward by Boussinesq.[18] To represent flexible pavement structures the first step was to adopt models of the 2- or 3-layer type in which either one or two layers of finite thickness lie on a semi-infinite mass representing the subgrade. A typical 3-layer structure is shown in Fig. 10. It is commonly assumed that full friction is developed between adjacent layers at the interfaces although a number of

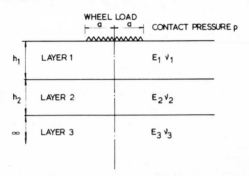

FIG. 10.   Three layer road structure.

investigators have considered the case where no friction whatsoever is developed there. The loading is commonly assumed to be applied in the form of a uniform stress acting over a circular contact area as shown in Fig. 10. The earliest attempt to deal with elastic systems on a rigorous basis was by Burmister[19,20] who formulated equations for the deflection and stresses in 2- and 3-layer structures but gave solutions only to the equations for surface deflection in a 2-layer structure.

In this type of analysis of a 3-layer system four non-dimensional parameters defined as follows are used:

Two geometric parameters

$$a_1 = \frac{a}{h_2} \quad \text{and} \quad H = \frac{h_1}{h_2}$$

where a = radius of loaded area, h_1 = thickness of layer 1, and h_2 = thickness of layer 2.

Two structural parameters

$$K1 = \frac{E1}{E2} \quad \text{and} \quad K2 = \frac{E2}{E3}$$

where $E1$, $E2$ and $E3$ are the elastic moduli of layers 1, 2 and 3 respectively.

The value of Poisson's ratio v, in each layer also enters into the analysis. In early work a value of 0·5 in all layers was commonly assumed in order to simplify computation. Subsequent developments in analysis enabled any value of Poisson's ratio to be used for any layer.

The first successful attempt to obtain solutions for 3-layer structures was by Acum and Fox.[21] This work gave solutions based on the Burmister method for a 3-layer system and tabular values of stresses at the interfaces on the central axis were provided for a limited range of the geometric parameters.

Up to this time all computation was done by mechanical or electrical desk calculators. The first major application of the electronic computer to this work was by Jones[22] who published extensive tabular solutions for the stresses on the central axis at the interfaces of 3-layer structures. The ranges of parameters covered were:

$$a_1 = 0\cdot1,\ 0\cdot2,\ 0\cdot4,\ 0\cdot8,\ 1\cdot6,\ 3\cdot2$$

$$H = 0\cdot125,\ 0\cdot25,\ 0\cdot5,\ 1,\ 2,\ 4,\ 8$$

$$K1 \text{ and } K2 = 0\cdot2,\ 2\cdot0,\ 20,\ 200$$

The extended range of the geometric parameters a_1 and H greatly increased the practical applicability of the solutions and all the values of the parameters were selected with a view to interpolation on a logarithmic basis.

Tabular solutions to the equations for surface deflection on the central axis were also evaluated by Jones.[23] The solutions to the stress equations were obtained on the assumption of a value of 0·5 for Poisson's ratio in all layers. Developments in the procedure enabled a value of 0·35 for Poisson's ratio in all layers to be used in obtaining the solutions to the deflection equations. This value was chosen as representing more closely the materials involved.

A difficulty with the tabular solutions is the amount of interpolation required for normal analyses. To reduce the effort involved a series of graphs of the type shown in Fig. 11 which permit direct interpolation for a_1 (shown as A in Fig. 11) and H were developed by Peattie.[24] One such chart was required for each pair of values of $K1$ and $K2$. This work was based on Jones' solutions,[22] and also included some additional factors which simplified the determination of the horizontal strain at the bottom of the top layer on the central axis which is important in the investigation of fatigue behaviour.

There was subsequently a proliferation of solutions for multi-layer elastic and, to a lesser extent, viscoelastic systems. Most of the more recent work

K. R. PEATTIE

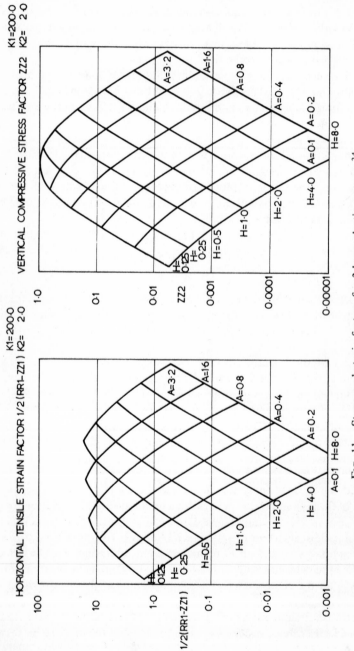

FIG. 11. Stress and strain factors for 3-layer elastic systems.[24]

has been presented in the form of computer programs. Many are capable of handling quite complex multi-layer systems and conditions of loading and give considerable freedom in the interfacial conditions and materials properties that can be used. Modern computer programs are characterised by BISTRO[25] and its later derivative BISAR.

Solutions in the form of computer programs are very useful and capable of great versatility provided ready access to a suitable computer is available. However, this is not always so and easily used solutions, even if of limited scope, can be attractive when making initial assessments of a range of structures. The tabular and graphical solutions referred to are rather cumbersome. Brown[26] has developed a simple computer program for interpolation in the Jones' tables.[22] Another approach is to simplify the model by restricting the range of parameters covered so that convenient graphical solutions can be provided. This will be referred to later.

The elastic pavement models can be used to demonstrate the action of layered pavement structures. An examination of 2-layer systems shows that increasing the modulus of the top layer reduces the level of vertical stress developed in the lower layer and concentrates contours of vertical stress within its own boundaries. The horizontal stress in the top layer varies from compression at the surface to tension at the bottom and the magnitude of stresses at the upper and lower boundaries of the top layer increases with increasing values of the modular ratio $E1/E2$. That is to say, a stiffer upper

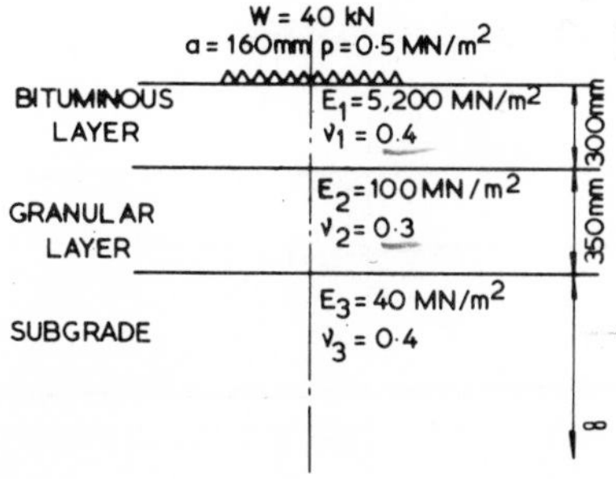

FIG. 12.   Typical pavement structure with details for analysis.

layer protects the subgrade from the effect of traffic stresses and achieves this at the expense of the larger horizontal tensile and compressive stresses developed at its upper and lower boundaries. A typical 3-layer pavement structure is shown in Fig. 12 together with the stiffnesses and values of Poisson's ratio for the materials in each layer. The stresses and strains in this structure have been analysed[27] by the BISTRO computer program and

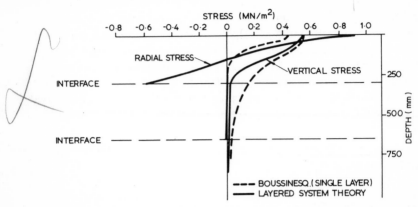

FIG. 13. Variation of vertical and radial stress with depth on centre line of load.

are shown in Figs. 13 and 14. Figure 13 also shows the stress distribution in a homogeneous semi-infinite mass according to the Boussinesq analysis. It should be noted that the vertical stress in the layered system is lower than that developed in the semi-infinite mass whereas the radial stresses are larger and, in addition, tensile stresses of significiant magnitude are developed at the bottom of the top layer.

The strain distribution throughout this structure is shown in Fig. 14. When evaluating strains it has to be recognised that vertically-oriented elements in the layered structure are subjected to a 3-dimensional stress system. Direct stresses σ_v, σ_r and σ_t act in the vertical, radial and tangential

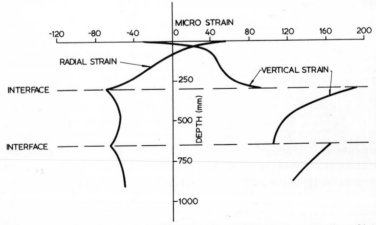

FIG. 14. Variation of vertical and radial strain with depth on centre line of load.

directions respectively. In addition shear stresses exist on the vertical and radial planes except when the element under consideration lies on the vertical axis through the centre of the loaded area. Because of the symmetry of the system the tangential stress is always a principal stress. Once the values of the stresses have been obtained the strains can be derived by using Hooke's law:

$$\varepsilon_v = \frac{1}{E}(\sigma_v - v(\sigma_r + \sigma_t))$$

Similar equations exist for the radial and tangential strains, ε_r and ε_t respectively. It should be noted that where strains are being evaluated in elements on the vertical axis through the centre of the loaded area, σ_r and σ_t are equal in magnitude. The values of stresses developed depend on the modular ratios $K1$ and $K2$ and the values of Poisson's ratio v whereas the values of strains depend in addition on the value of the modulus at the element under consideration. In the model used for this analysis it is assumed that full friction is developed at both interfaces and consequently vertical stress and radial strain are continuous across each interface. These two Figures illustrate some of the features of layer system pavement action mentioned.

CRITERIA FOR DESIGN

The main features of pavement distress are cracking and permanent deformation resulting from the repeated application of traffic loads.

Surface cracking unaccompanied by any deformation associated with deep-seated failure in the pavement structure is attributed to fatigue failure in the bituminous layers. Cracking of this type has been said to be the most common mode of distress in flexible pavements in the USA.[28] It is also reported to be widespread in South Africa.[29] Attention has also been given to the fatigue performance of bituminous materials in other parts of the world including Europe. The determination of the fatigue properties of bituminous materials is discussed in Chapter 2.

Investigations of fatigue phenomena in bituminous pavements have shown that strain is a good indicator of fatigue performance both in the laboratory[30] and in pavements.[31] The relationship between the number of load applications, N, causing the initiation of cracking and the tensile strain ε is

$$N = C\left(\frac{1}{\varepsilon}\right)^m$$

C and m are constants whose values depend on the type and composition of the bituminous mix. When assessing the fatigue performance of flexible pavements in structural design, layered system analysis is used to determine the maximum value of the tensile strain. This is usually developed at the bottom of the bituminous layer on the vertical line through the centre of the loaded area. However, under certain conditions the critical position may be elsewhere in the structure. The results of the analysis depend on the elastic moduli assumed for the pavement layers and in the case of bituminous layers this depends on temperature.

The temperature variation over a 12-month period may be obtained and the corresponding stiffness of the materials evaluated. This procedure has been used to predict the annual variations in stiffness of asphaltic concrete pavements in Texas and Winnipeg.[32] It has been extended to predict the monthly damage by fatigue in Iowa. This latter work was compared with the monthly variation in fatigue damage observed at the AASHO Road Test.[9] Where the annual temperature range is not too large and when a simplified design procedure is being used an average temperature typical of a 12-month period may be used in the analysis. This approach has been used in a simplified analytical procedure developed for conditions in the UK.[33] The average temperature in the bituminous layer is taken as the same as the average air temperature which is 15 °C.

The fatigue problem has been investigated in great detail in the laboratory and attention is now being directed to the relationship between these results and the fatigue performance of bituminous materials on the road. It has been found that the fatigue life of bituminous materials under traffic conditions in flexible pavements is considerably longer than that found in the laboratory. It is believed that this results from differences between conditions in the road and the test procedures adopted in the laboratory. It has been suggested that a factor of 100 times is appropriate for conditions in the UK.[33] This relationship is discussed in detail in Chapter 2.

It has been much more difficult to comprehensively include permanent deformation in structural design procedures although it is actually a more common form of distress than cracking in the UK and other European countries. There are problems in assessing the contribution made by each individual layer to the total rut depth visible at the pavement surface. It has also been difficult to select a suitable model to represent the phenomenon and to analyse its behaviour.

The deformation that appears at the surface of a pavement is the sum of the deformation of each of the pavement layers together with that in the subgrade. The distribution of this deformation is not fully known but measurements in different parts of the world have shown that the proportions vary from road to road although it appears that about half develops in the surfacing and roadbase and half in the sub-base and subgrade. The figures given in Table 4 are average values obtained from measurements made at the AASHO Road Test[9] and at trials carried out by the Transport and Road Research Laboratory.[34]

TABLE 4

CONTRIBUTION OF INDIVIDUAL LAYERS TO PERMANENT DEFORMATION IN FLEXIBLE PAVEMENTS

AASHO Road Test		TRRL trial	
Layer	Contribution (%)	Layer	Contribution (%)
Asphaltic concrete	32	Rolled asphalt surfacing and crushed stone	
Crushed stone roadbase	14	roadbase	54
Sub-base	45	Sub-base	13
Subgrade	9	Subgrade	33

These figures support the general statement made above that about half the deformation develops in the surfacing and roadbase and half in the sub-base and subgrade. It is noticeable in the examples given in Table 4 that the contributions to deformation made by the sub-base and subgrade are almost reversed between the AASHO and TRRL trials. This is a result of differences in stiffness and resistance to deformation of the individual layers and in the stress distribution in the two structures. Examples taken from other trials may show different distributions of deformation and the figures in Table 4 are given as examples of the type of variation that exists rather than as typical of any particular kind of pavement structure. While it is clear that some of the deformation in the individual layers is caused by a reduction in air voids and a corresponding increase in density this accounts for a relatively small proportion of the total deformation observed in layers of material that has been well compacted. At the AASHO Road Test[9] it was found that only 20% of the change in thickness of the surfacing and 4% of the change in thickness of the sub-base could be attributed to increases in the density of the materials. The contribution of densification to changes in the thickness of the crushed stone roadbase was more variable. In the spring

of 1960 it accounted for all the decrease in thickness but in the summer of
the same year it contributed only 30 %. Until the mechanism of permanent
deformation in flexible pavement structures is fully understood
approximate methods of dealing with this design criterion must be adopted.

    On the basis that the function of a pavement is to protect the underlying
subgrade permanent deformation may be minimised by limiting the value
of the vertical stresses and strains developed in this by traffic loads. One of

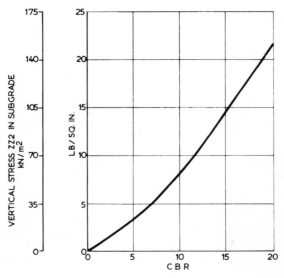

FIG. 15.   Relationship between permissible vertical stress and CBR of subgrade.

the earliest attempts[35] to incorporate permanent deformation as a criterion
in the structural design of asphalt pavements involved relating the
permissible value of vertical stress developed in the subgrade to its CBR-
value as shown in Fig. 15 and providing an additional relationship
involving the number of load applications. The curve of permissible stress
was obtained by analysing a number of pavement structures known to have
performed satisfactorily and data from the AASHO Road Test[9] were used
to produce the relationship involving the numbers of loads. A later
approach to this problem was to use the value of the vertical compressive
strain reaching the subgrade thereby eliminating the need to involve the
quality of the subgrade material. A relationship connecting this strain with
the number of load applications was developed[36] and is shown in Fig. 16.

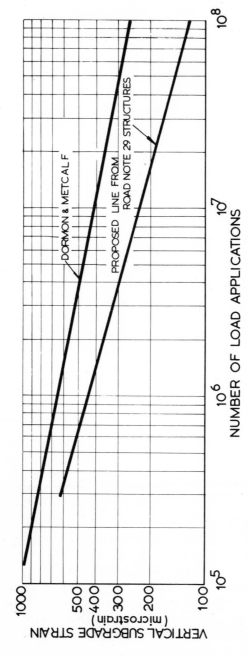

Fig. 16. Relationship between maximum allowable subgrade strain and number of load applications.

Also shown in Fig. 16 is another line developed[33] from an analysis of pavement structures with bituminous bases proportioned according to Road Note 29.[2] This second line is therefore limited in its applicability to the geographical area covered by Road Note 29.[2] The analyses of the latter structures showed that the vertical compressive strain developed in the subgrade was not completely independent of its CBR-value but the range of values found was sufficiently small to justify the use of a single line.

The methods just described confine their attention to conditions in the subgrade although, in principle, they might also be applied to other granular layers. A more detailed treatment of the permanent deformation of unbound granular roadbase materials involves the use of repeated load triaxial tests.[37] The primary objective of this work was to compare the performance of different granular roadbase materials with respect to rut formation. It was also extended to develop a rut index which is approximately proportional to the change in thickness of the layer under repeated load application. The results of the triaxial tests are given in the form of curves of deviator stress against permanent axial strain after 100 000 load applications. Data in this form cannot be used to predict directly the permanent deformation of the layer and a procedure similar to that developed elsewhere[38] is used. Each layer is divided into sub-layers in which the values of stresses are calculated using non-linear elastic or viscoelastic theory. The permanent strain developed in each sub-layer can then be determined from the data obtained from the triaxial tests. The total deformation in the layer is the sum of the deformations developed in the individual sub-layers. The procedure may be applied to all layers in the pavement structure including those of bound materials and the sum of the deformations gives the total surface deformation.

A similar approach[38] has been made to determine the total rut depth in flexible pavements. Each layer of the pavement structure is divided into a number of sub-layers which are also divided horizontally into a series of elements. The stresses developed in each element by wheel loads can be calculated and variations in both the types of wheel load and their transverse distribution across the pavement can be taken into account. The stresses are evaluated by using a computer program developed for elastic layered systems. It has been found that the amount of calculation can be minimised by considering stresses developed within a region extending radially from the axis of the loaded area to a distance of 20 times the radius of that area and to a depth of 20 times this radius below the surface of the subgrade. Further minimisation of computation is achieved by determining stresses at a number of discrete points, both horizontally and vertically, and obtaining the intermediate values of stress by interpolation. The stress-permanent strain relationships for the materials in each layer are obtained by carrying out triaxial tests under repeated loading. The calculated values of stress and the stress-permanent strain relationships enable the permanent strains developed in each element and layer to be calculated. The sum of the deformations in each layer gives the total deformation at the surface of the pavement.

A procedure has been recently developed[39] for predicting the deformation in the bitumen-bound layers of a flexible pavement using elastic layer system analysis[25] to determine the average value of the vertical compressive stress developed in the bituminous layer of a 2-layer pavement structure, i.e. a full-depth bituminous construction. The viscous component of the stiffness of the bitumen is calculated under appropriate conditions of temperature and time of loading and for the number of load applications for which the permanent deformation is to be determined. Specimens of the bituminous mix are manufactured in the laboratory or cored from a pavement and are then subjected to a creep test which enables the stiffness of the mix to be obtained. The permanent deformation in the bituminous layer is given by

$$C_M H_0 \frac{\sigma_{av}}{S_{mix}}$$

where C_M = a correction factor whose value depends upon the type of mix, H_0 = the initial thickness of the bituminous layer obtained from a structural design procedure using the vertical compressive strain in the subgrade and the horizontal tensile strain in the bituminous layer as criteria, σ_{av} = the average value of the vertical compressive stress in the bituminous layer, and S_{mix} = the stiffness of the bituminous mix obtained from the creep test.

It has been found experimentally that the depth of rut appearing in the pavement structure is about 1·5 times the value of the permanent deformation in the bituminous layer. This rut depth is defined as the vertical distance between the bottom of the rut and the top of any lateral swelling. If the value of rut depth so calculated is acceptable the design is satisfactory. If not, the composition of the bituminous mix is changed and the procedure is repeated until an acceptable value of rut depth results.

A fully rigorous treatment of the deformation criterion requires the adoption of a model consisting of viscoelastic materials together with the determination of the appropriate mechanical properties of the materials in the model. Approaches of this type have been developed[40] to predict the performance of pavements under repeated loads and to include time-dependent properties of materials evaluated from laboratory tests. Permanent deformations can therefore be predicted. However, it is rather complicated to apply the viscoelastic approach in practice and, furthermore, some of the materials used in flexible pavements behave in a complex and non-linear manner so that the use of linear viscoelastic theory does not predict performance with sufficient precision. Consequently attention is currently being given to the development of approaches for the prediction of permanent deformation of the types described in the previous paragraphs.

DESIGN SYSTEMS

To provide a direct method of pavement design the elements comprising the pavement model, the procedure for stress analysis, the properties of the pavement materials, the traffic loading and climate, and the design criteria have to be combined into a comprehensive system. To reduce the amount of work involved while still representing a pavement realistically some of the structural design systems have adopted a 3-layer model such as that shown in Fig. 12. All the bituminous layers are considered together as the top layer, all the unbound granular layers as the second layer and the subgrade as the semi-infinite mass. The principles of such a system in which the design criteria are the vertical compressive stress at the top of the subgrade and the horizontal tensile strain at the bottom of the bituminous layer were enunciated by the author.[35] Traffic loading was assumed to apply a uniform stress over a circular contact area.

The operation of such systems is illustrated in the flow chart in Fig. 17. The basic data required are the temperature and time of loading of the bituminous material, the quality of the subgrade and the number of axle loads to be carried during the design life of the pavement. The temperature used may be an average annual pavement temperature in the simpler approaches or the year may be divided into shorter periods and the appropriate temperatures used for each as mentioned earlier. The time of loading will normally be taken as that given by the average speed of commercial vehicles. The estimated traffic flow over the design life of the pavement is converted into the equivalent number of standard axle loads. The standard value used is commonly 80 kN although some countries employ their statutory axle load. The subgrade is generally characterised by its CBR-value which enables the stiffness to be estimated. The next step in

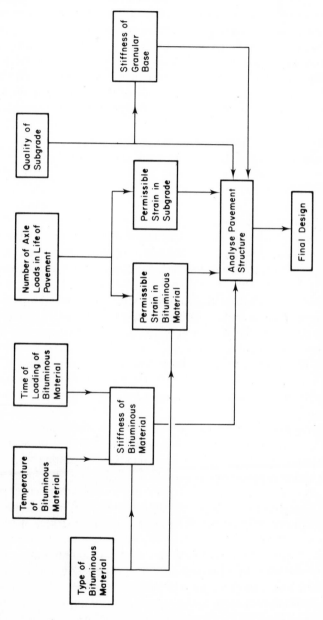

FIG. 17. Flow chart for pavement design system.

the design process is to select the type of bituminous material and to determine its stiffness under the design conditions. The factors influencing this are shown in the flow chart. The stiffness of the granular base is affected by its support conditions and it has been proposed[41] that a modular ratio of 2·5 between granular base and subgrade is appropriate for design purposes. The maximum permissible tensile strain in the bituminous material is determined from the fatigue characteristics of the particular bituminous mix selected and the number of load applications to be carried. The permissible value of compressive strain in the subgrade depends on the number of axle loads. Having determined the stiffness of the pavement materials and the permissible values of strain in them a trial selection of the thicknesses of the layers is made and the values of the critical strains calculated and compared with the permissible levels. The thicknesses of the layers are adjusted until both criteria are economically satisfied. The principles of this approach were used in the construction of the Shell design charts[42] from which the appropriate thicknesses of bituminous and unbound granular layers can be obtained for particular conditions of subgrade and of traffic loading. Traffic is expressed in its equivalent number of (10-ton) axle loads. Different values of modulus for the bituminous layer are used when investigating the subgrade strain and fatigue criteria—a value corresponding to a relatively high temperature is used for the former and a value corresponding to a lower temperature for the latter. The charts give guidance on protecting the unbound granular layers by indicating minimum CBR-values required under particular conditions of design. This work was extended to cover the design of runways for airports handling heavy aircraft and subjected to complex loading[8] and also to enable designs appropriate for higher temperatures to be obtained.[43]

The large amount of information now available about the mechanical properties of bituminous materials has led to the development of a simplified design system[33] for flexible pavements incorporating bituminous surfacings and roadbases which gives greater freedom in the choice of the characteristics of the bituminous material. It is assumed that the pavement may be represented by a 3-layer elastic structure carrying a single load uniformly distributed over a circular area. A constant thickness of 200 mm is used for the unbound granular sub-base whose modulus is taken as 2·5 times that of the subgrade. Once the type and composition of the bituminous mix have been selected its stiffness can be obtained either by calculation or from charts of the type shown in Fig. 18. The permissible levels of fatigue strain in the bituminous mix and compressive strain in the subgrade can be obtained graphically from charts of the type shown in Figs.

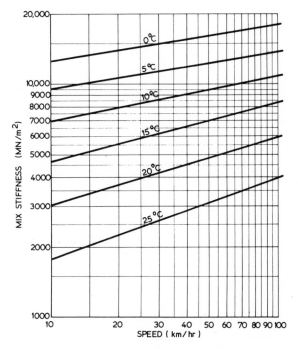

FIG. 18. Stiffness for a typical hot rolled asphalt.

19 and 20 respectively. A series of design charts of the type shown in Fig. 21 relating the thickness of the bituminous layer to the tensile strain developed in that layer and to the compressive strain developed in the subgrade is provided for a range of CBR-values. The greater of the thicknesses given by the two design criteria is selected as the design value. This method has been extended by developing a computer program which gives directly the necessary thickness of the bituminous layer once the load conditions, design life, average temperature and mix composition have been determined.[44]

The design procedures and systems mentioned above have all been checked to ensure that when applied to conventional structures designed for conventional conditions they give results comparable with that obtained by existing methods. The particular merit of the structural design methods is their ability to handle unconventional conditions of loading and climate and to handle a wide range of pavement materials without the necessity for expensive and lengthy full-scale trials.

More complex multi-layer models than those just described may be

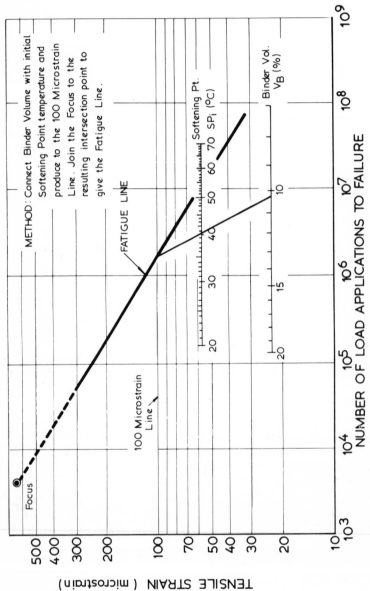

FIG. 19.   Nomograph for prediction of *in situ* fatigue performance of bituminous materials.

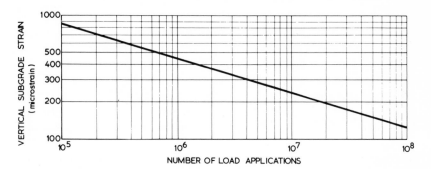

FIG. 20. Relationship between maximum allowable subgrade strain and number of load applications.

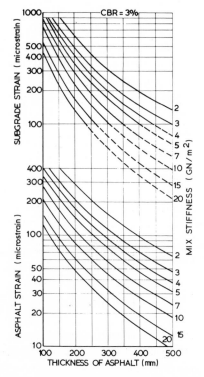

FIG. 21. Relationships between critical strains and thickness and stiffness of the bituminous layer (CBR = 3 %).

adopted for design systems. In addition to permitting a greater range of materials characteristics and layer thicknesses to be investigated this also allows more complicated multi-wheel loading to be considered. However, no direct system of this type has yet been produced and it is necessary to carry out a trial and error approach involving a series of selections of trial structures and check calculations with appropriate modifications to layer thicknesses where required. More comprehensive methods of including permanent deformation in pavement design systems have been introduced.[38,39,45] However, these also require an iterative approach and, in addition, are relatively inconvenient to use. The multi-layer models have been very effectively employed in analysing existing pavements to assess the probable effects of altering the properties of certain layers or portions of layers and have been helpful in the investigation of pavement failures.[27]

Increasing attention is being given to the form in which structural design methods are presented. The development of these methods has led to the production of procedures that are oriented towards structural analysis rather than to structural design. A trial-and-error iterative approach which is both lengthy and cumbersome has therefore to be employed for design. Furthermore, the more comprehensive analytical systems require the use of sophisticated computer programs which can not always readily be used by road engineers and, indeed, would not be justified for much design work. The most effective application of the analytical design approach may therefore be in the production of a series of standardised structures for a limited range of conditions covering most requirements similar to those produced in France.[5] Standardised structures involving either new design conditions or new pavement materials could readily be prepared. An alternative approach is that typified by present work in the UK,[33,44] which gives the engineer greater freedom of choice of materials and conditions while still, in its graphical form, being reasonably convenient to use. The computer program developed as part of this work is ideally suited for the rapid production of catalogues of standardised structures.

CONCLUSIONS

The major development in the design of flexible pavements over the past 25 years has been the extensive growth of the analytical design approach. A number of design systems based on this procedure have been produced. The models used do not fully represent real road structures and so general acceptance of these design methods will depend on the extent to which it can be shown that calculated values of stresses, strains and deformation agree with those measured in pavements. Much of the information on this aspect of the analytical design of flexible pavements is to be found in the 'Proceedings of the International Conferences on the Structural Design of Asphalt Pavements' published by the University of Michigan, USA in 1962, 1967, 1972 and 1977. These Proceedings also contain the most extensive collection of papers dealing with all aspects of the analytical design of flexible pavements available anywhere.

Analytical methods are being increasingly used to assess the probable effects of changes in loading or materials properties on the performance of flexible pavements without the necessity of carrying out expensive and lengthy full-scale road trials. The information so obtained may then be used to modify existing empirical design procedures. Analytical procedures have also been valuable in the investigation of structural difficulties with pavements since they allow the identification of the part of the structure most likely to be contributing to the observed effect and may indicate the type of remedial action most likely to be effective.

The more complex design systems are likely to be presented in the form of computer programs or comprehensive sets of design charts. Both these approaches may be too involved and slow for general use by highway engineers on routine work. It therefore seems probable that a fruitful application of the analytical design approach will be in the construction of catalogues of structures or some other simplified form of presentation. This will allow convenient assessment of comparative designs involving different materials or loading conditions.

REFERENCES

1. PORTER, O. J. Proc. Hwy Res. Brd, **18**(2), 324, 1938; **22**, 100, 1942.
2. TRANSPORT AND ROAD RESEARCH LABORATORY. *Road Note No.* 29—A guide to the structural design of pavements for new roads, 3rd ed., HMSO, London, 1970.
3. LEIGH, J. V. and CRONEY, D. Proc. 3rd Int. Conf. on the struct. design of asphalt pavements, **1**, 1039, 1972.
4. THOMPSON, P. D., CRONEY, D. and CURRER, E. W. H. Proc. 3rd Int. Conf. on the struct. design of asphalt pavements, **1**, 920, 1972.
5. CHANTEREAU, M. and LEGER, PH. Proc. 3rd Int. Conf. on the struct. design of asphalt pavements, **1**, 990, 1972.
6. VOGT, H. and VON BECKER, P. Proc. 3rd Int. Conf. on the struct. design of asphalt pavements, **1**, 1102, 1972.
7. DEACON, J. A. Proc. Ass. of Asphalt Paving Technol., **38**, 465, 1969.

8. EDWARDS, J. M. and VALKERING, C. P. *Structural design of asphalt pavements for heavy aircraft*, Shell Int. Pet. Co. Ltd, London, 1971.
9. HIGHWAY RESEARCH BOARD. The AASHO road test: pavement research, Special Report 61E, 1962.
10. LIDDLE, W. J. Proc. 1st Int. Conf. on the struct. design of asphalt pavements, **1**, 42, 1962.
11. WHIFFIN, A. C. and GRAINGER, J. W. Axle loads on the M1 Motorway at Friar's Wash, Hertfordshire, TRRL Report LR 537, Transport and Road Research Laboratory, 1973.
12. PEATTIE, K. R. *J. Inst. Hwy Engrs*, **XXI**, 9, 1974.
13. BROWN, S. F. Hwy Res. Brd, Record No. 431, 38, 1973.
14. VAN DER POEL, C. *J. App. Chem.*, **4**, Part 5, 1954.
15. SCHWADERER, W. Proc. 3rd Int. Conf. on the struct. design of asphalt pavements, **1**, 711, 1972.
16. NORMAN, P. J., SNOWDON, R. A. and JACOBS, J. C. Pavement deflection measurements and their application to structural maintenance and overlay design, TRRL Report LR 571. Transport and Road Research Laboratory, 1973.
17. PEATTIE, K. R. *The Queen's Hwy*, **33**, 1, 27, 1967.
18. BOUSSINESQ, V. J. *Application des potentiels à l'étude de l'équilibre et du mouvement des solides élastiques*, Gauthier-Villard, Paris, 1885.
19. BURMISTER, D. M. Proc. Hwy Res. Brd, **23**, 126, 1943.
20. BURMISTER, D. M. *J. App. Physics*, **16**, 89, 126, 296, 1945.
21. ACUM, W. E. A. and FOX, L. *Geotechnique*, **2**, 4, 293, 1951.
22. JONES, A. Hwy Res. Brd, Bulletin No. 342, 176, 1962.
23. PEATTIE, K. R. and JONES, A. Proc. Symp. road tests for pavement design, Lisbon, **VIII**, 1, 1962.
24. PEATTIE, K. R. Hwy Res. Brd, Bulletin No. 342, 215, 1962.
25. PEUTZ, M. G. F., VAN KEMPEN, H. P. M. and JONES, A. Hwy Res. Brd, Record No. 228, 34, 1968.
26. BROWN, S. F. Hwy Res. Brd, Record No. 407, 55, 1972.
27. BROWN, S. F. and PELL, P. S. *The Queen's Hwy*, 107, 11, 1976.
28. MONISMITH, C. L. Hwy Res. Brd, Special Report 140, 1, 1973.
29. FREEME, C. R. and MARAIS, C. P. Hwy Res. Brd, Special Report 140, 158, 1973.
30. PELL, P. S. Proc. 1st Int. Conf. on the struct. design of asphalt pavements, 310, 1962.
31. KINGHAM, R. I. Proc. 3rd Int. Conf. on the struct. design of asphalt pavements, **1**, 656, 1972.
32. WITCZAK, M. W. Hwy Res. Brd, Special Report 140, 112, 1973.
33. BROWN, S. F. *J. Inst. Hwy Engrs*, **XXI**, 8–9, 14, 1974.
34. LISTER, N. W. Proc. 3rd Int. Conf. on the struct. design of asphalt pavements, **1**, 94, 1972.
35. PEATTIE, K. R. Proc. 1st Int. Conf. on the struct. design of asphalt pavements, 403, 1962.
36. DORMON, G. M. and METCALF, C. T. Hwy Res. Brd, Record No. 71, 69, 1965.
37. BARKSDALE, R. D. Proc. 3rd Int. Conf. on the struct. design of asphalt pavements, **1**, 161, 1972.

38. ROMAIN, J. E. Proc. 3rd Int. Conf. on the struct. design of asphalt pavements, **1**, 705, 1972.

39. VAN DE LOO, P. J. Trans. Res. Brd, Symposium on Rutting, 1976.

40. BARKSDALE, R. D. and LEONARDS, G. A. Proc. 2nd Int. Conf. on the struct. design of asphalt pavements, **1**, 321, 1967.

41. HEUKELOM, W. and KLOMP, A. J. G. Proc. 1st Int. Conf. on the struct. design of asphalt pavements, **1**, 667, 1962.

42. SHELL INTERNATIONAL PETROLEUM CO. LTD. *Shell* 1963 *design charts for flexible pavements*, Shell Int. Pet. Co. Ltd, London, 1963.

43. EDWARDS, J. M. and VALKERING, C. P. *Hwys and Road Constr.*, **42**, 3–9, Feb. 1974.

44. BROWN, S. F., PELL, P. S. and STOCK, A. F. Proc. 4th Int. Conf. on the struct. design of asphalt pavements, **1**, 327, 1977.

45. CELARD, B. Proc. 4th Int. Conf. on the struct. design of asphalt pavements, **1**, 249, 1977.

46. LISTER, N. W. and KENNEDY, C. K. Assessment of performance and overlay design of flexible pavements, Chapter 4, in *Developments in Highway Pavement Engineering*—2, P. S. Pell (ed.), Applied Science Publishers, London, 1978.

47. HIGHT, D. W. and GREEN, P. A. Earthworks, Chapter 1, in *Developments in Highway Pavement Engineering*—2, P. S. Pell (ed.), Applied Science Publishers, London, 1978.

48. JONES, R. H. Frost heave damage and its prevention, Chapter 3, in *Developments in Highway Pavement Engineering*—2, P. S. Pell (ed.), Applied Science Publishers, London, 1978.

Chapter 2

MATERIAL CHARACTERISTICS FOR ANALYTICAL PAVEMENT DESIGN

S. F. BROWN

The University of Nottingham, UK

SUMMARY

The overall objective of this chapter is to present a summary of current knowledge about the various materials used to build flexible pavements within the context of developing analytically based methods for pavement design of the type discussed in Chapter 1.

A large part of the chapter is concerned with the properties of bituminous materials since these have been more extensively researched than others. The other materials considered are unbound aggregates and soils. For each material, the characteristics of interest for pavement design are discussed, these being stress–strain relationships and failure criteria. Both elastic and permanent strains are considered since the former are relevant to elastic analysis of pavements and fatigue cracking of bituminous materials and the latter relate to the development of permanent deformation in the various layers which causes the observed surface deformation used as the principal failure criterion in Great Britain.

INTRODUCTION

The materials which are used to build flexible pavements in Great Britain are many and various. In addition to the underlying soil, either cut or fill, they fall into three categories; bituminous materials, unbound granular materials, and cement bound materials. The current practice is to specify individual materials using a 'recipe approach', the details being described in the 'specification for road and bridge works', produced by the Department of Transport[1] and in several British Standards.[2,3] This approach to materials together with the recommendations for layer thickness contained in Road Note No. 29[4] represents the empirical approach to pavement design that has emerged from long experience of British conditions. The need for a more fundamental and scientific approach to the structural design of pavements is outlined in Chapter 1. The analytically based method which is described therein requires a knowledge of the mechanical properties of all the materials in the pavement structure and the success of the method relies very heavily on these being accurately known. These mechanical properties, which basically include the stress–strain relationships and failure conditions for the materials, have been extensively investigated and the current state of knowledge is outlined in this chapter.

As a preamble to the detailed consideration of each type of material and in order to correlate this chapter with others in this book, a brief description of the various specified materials currently in use in Great Britain follows.

Bituminous Materials

There is a very large number of different bituminous materials which may be used in various circumstances. The term includes materials which consist of mineral aggregate mixed with either tar or bitumen or with one of the low viscosity cut back bitumen or bitumen emulsion binders. These latter are not used for major structural components of heavy duty pavements and will not be considered further.

There are three basic mix types:

1. *Hot rolled asphalt* (BS 594):[2] is a gap graded material including filler and a relatively hard grade of bitumen. The bitumen content is high and the mechanical properties of the material are influenced primarily by those of the bitumen–sand–filler mortar. Hot rolled asphalt is extensively used for wearing courses on heavily trafficked roads, but can also be used for base courses and roadbases. It is relatively easy to compact on site. A mix design method for this material involving a performance test is a recent development and this, together with other information, is presented in Chapter 3.

2. *Dense bitumen (or tar) macadam* (BS 4987):[3] is a continuously graded material using a softer binder than rolled asphalt. Its properties are partly influenced by interparticle friction and interlock, which is the characteristic of a 'macadam', and partly by the viscosity of the binder. The bitumen content is relatively low and this makes it a cheaper material than rolled asphalt. The use of

even lower binder contents and the consequent problems of achieving adequate compaction are discussed in Chapter 4. These materials tend to be used for roadbase and base course layers, though they may also be used for surfacing. Significant developments in this area are described in Chapter 6.

3.   *Open textured macadam* (BS 4987):[3] is a uniformly graded material with low binder content sometimes referred to as 'coated stone'. It has a high void content when compacted and therefore is not of use as a major structural layer. However, it is used for surfacing minor roads and has the advantage of providing a relatively 'dry' surface under wet conditions. The ability of very open textured mixes to drain surface water has been exploited for surfacing runways when the material is underlaid by an impermeable layer and this development, which is described in Chapter 6, is being extended to use on highways.

Cement Bound Materials[1]

These are of three types of which the most widely used is 'lean concrete', a material which uses normal concreting aggregate within a fairly strict grading and for which a crushing strength is specified. It is used in roadbase construction. A lower quality material is 'cement bound granular material' which has wider grading limits than lean concrete and contains less cement. Again a crushing strength is specified and it is usual for a trial section to be laid prior to acceptance of the material on site. 'Soil–cement' is a stabilised soil type of material which can include a wide range of aggregates and soils.

Each of these materials may be used for roadbase or sub-base construction under various circumstances. Full details on their use and properties are given in Chapter 5.

Unbound Materials[1]

These are used for base and sub-base construction. For bases, the specification includes two alternatives, wet mix macadam and dry bound macadam. Wet mix is a well graded crushed rock compacted at optimum moisture content while dry bound macadam is placed in two operations, the larger stone followed by finer material which is vibrated into the voids until refusal. For sub-base construction, material similar to wet mix macadam but with wider grading limits and greater choice of aggregate is specified either as 'Type 1' or 'Type 2' in descending order of quality. The current specifications for these unbound materials are discussed elsewhere.[74]

MATERIALS TESTING PHILOSOPHY

In Situ Stress Conditions

An understanding of the stress regime to which pavement materials are subjected is a necessary preliminary to any discussion of present practices and the recent developments associated with using analytical design methods.

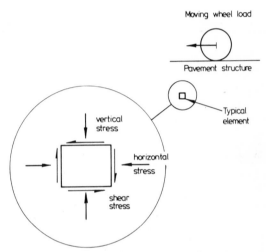

FIG. 1.   Stresses on a pavement element.

Figure 1 shows a typical pavement element and the stresses acting on it due to the approaching wheel load. These stresses change with time as the wheel passes over and the variations of vertical, horizontal and shear stress are shown qualitatively in Fig. 2. This pattern is repeated for every wheel and the magnitudes of the stresses are a function of the wheel load and its contact pressure with the pavement surface together with the geometry and mechanical characteristics of the structure (see Chapter 1).

For using the analytical approach to pavement design outlined in Chapter 1, the response of each of the constituent materials in the structure to the type of loading regime shown in Fig. 2 is required. Furthermore, it is the behaviour of the material as it exists in the pavement which is of importance. The necessary *in situ* testing to obtain this information would be very complex and expensive. Hence engineers usually rely on the testing of samples of materials in the laboratory in such a way as to simulate the *in situ* situation.

For this to be successful, it follows that care must be taken to reproduce the conditions of sample state in terms of density and aggregate packing, the environmental conditions of temperature or moisture, and the repeated loading conditions expressed as stress or strain pulses applied at an appropriate rate.

The information required from a laboratory test of this type to provide the necessary data for an analytical approach to pavement design is

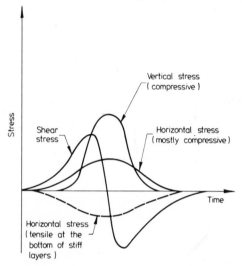

FIG. 2.   *In situ* stresses caused by moving wheel load.

twofold. Firstly, the elastic response of the material expressed in terms of a stress-elastic strain relationship and secondly, the failure conditions in terms of stress or elastic strain related to the mode of failure for the material which is likely to occur in the road. There are two traffic associated failure situations possible for bituminous material, cracking and excessive permanent deformation. For granular materials and soils, permanent deformation is the main criterion since complete shear failure is unlikely except in very unusual circumstances. In the case of cement bound materials, cracking is the main criterion. Each of these modes of failure is discussed in subsequent sections of this chapter.

Reference to Fig. 2 indicates that even under laboratory conditions the reproduction of an *in situ* stress regime in all its aspects would require most complex equipment and this, even for research purposes, has not yet successfully been done. Hence, simplifications have been introduced with

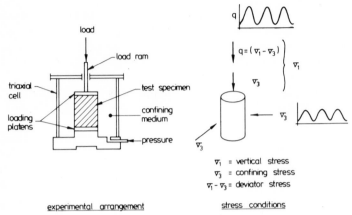

v_1 = vertical stress
v_3 = confining stress
$v_1 - v_3$ = deviator stress

experimental arrangement   stress conditions

FIG. 3. The repeated load triaxial test.

the object of reproducing those aspects of the *in situ* situation which are likely to be of most significance.

Laboratory Tests

There are four basic types of test which have been used to a greater or lesser extent for research purposes. The repeated load triaxial test shown diagrammatically in Fig. 3 is a development of the test configuration long regarded as standard in soil mechanics. However, instead of testing materials monotonically to failure, it is used under repeated load conditions to examine the relationship between applied stress and the resulting elastic and permanent strain. The type of stress regime which can be obtained in this test is shown in Fig. 4. Although this shows a continuous sinusoidal variation in stress, it is possible to provide rest periods between pulses.

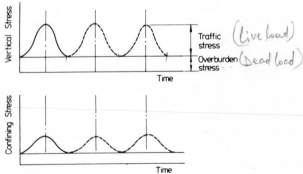

FIG. 4. Stresses in repeated load triaxial test.

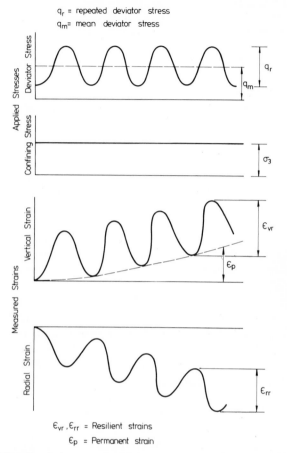

FIG. 5.   Stresses and strains in repeated load triaxial test.

Comparison with Fig. 2 indicates that only the normal stresses are being reproduced and not the shear stress reversal occurring *in situ*. Furthermore, it is easier to apply repeated stresses of constant amplitude in a particular test rather than attempt the reproduction of the random loading which occurs *in situ*.

A simpler version of the repeated load triaxial test involves the application of cyclic deviator stress under constant confining stress. It is in this form which it has been most widely used and is indeed recommended by the Asphalt Institute in their aircraft pavement design manual.[5] Under this simpler condition, Fig. 5 shows the applied stresses and the form of the measured strain response. The elastic components of strain ε_{1r} and ε_{3r} can be used to determine what is known as a resilient modulus for the material defined as

$$E_r = \frac{q_r}{\varepsilon_{1r}} \tag{1}$$

where q_r = cyclic deviator stress, and a resilient Poisson's ratio

$$v_r = \frac{\varepsilon_{3r}}{\varepsilon_{1r}} \tag{2}$$

Under these simple test conditions the resilient modulus is identical to Young's modulus and may be used as such for carrying out structural analysis of pavements.

The resilient strains which have to be measured are often very small and experimental accuracy is important. Because of end effects in the triaxial test, which would cause errors to overall measurements of deformation, direct 'on-sample' techniques have been developed for most paving materials.[5-8]

The permanent strain ε_p which gradually builds up during testing can also be related to the stress conditions and such data provides the basis for a prediction method for *in situ* permanent deformation as outlined in Chapter 1.

For bituminous or cement bound materials the repeated load triaxial test can be used in tension as well as compression. Figure 2 shows that tensile stresses develop at the bottom of bound layers and Fig. 13 in Chapter 1 shows that these can be substantial. The response of these materials under tensile stress is therefore of importance for design.

In the direct stress test which has most often been used in this context, loading platens are glued to the sample and an axial repeated stress is cycled between equal tensile and compressive values under uniaxial conditions. This provides data on elastic response including some influence from both the tension and compression zones. A version of this test involving only compressive stress has been adopted by ASTM[9] for evaluating the resilient modulus, or stiffness as it is more properly termed, for bituminous materials. A review of the detailed use of repeated load triaxial and uniaxial testing of materials, including experimental techniques, has been presented by Brown.[10]

Under the repeated tensile stresses which occur at the bottom of a bituminous layer, failure by cracking is a possibility and extensive research on this subject has shown that it is a fatigue phenomenon. This means that

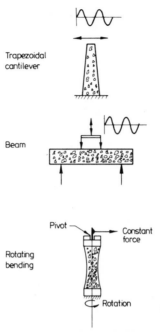

Trapezoidal
cantilever

Beam

Pivot

Constant
force

Rotating
bending

Rotation

FIG. 6.   Flexure tests for bituminous materials.

the incidence of failure is associated with both the magnitude and the
number of applications of load; maximum allowable stresses and strains
decreasing as number of applications increases. The uniaxial tension-
compression test has been used to investigate this since it reproduces those
aspects of the *in situ* stress-regime of most significance to the problem.

Fatigue cracking and the evaluation of stiffness have also been
investigated by various forms of flexure test illustrated in Fig. 6. This
approach recognises that the stiff bound layer in a pavement is to some
extent resisting the applied vertical loads by bending action which induces
compression at the top and tension at the botton, both of which vary with
time.

The indirect tensile test has been developed for the application of
repeated loading to evaluate stiffness, fatigue characteristics and
permanent strain.[6,11,12] The stress conditions in this test are ill-defined.
However, under elastic conditions involving low strains, the assumptions
inherent in the calculation of tensile stress and hence stiffness will not be as
inappropriate as seems to be the case when investigating failure
conditions.[13] One of the merits of this test is that it is simple to perform and

involves the use of test specimens of the same dimensions as those used in the well established Marshall test, discussed in a subsequent section and in Chapter 3.

The reversal of shear stress illustrated in Fig. 2 is not reproduced in either the triaxial test or the flexure test but requires a different configuration, the simple shear test providing the most straightforward arrangement although it is not particularly 'simple'. The principle of this test is illustrated in Fig. 7

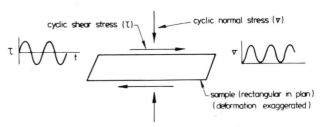

Fig. 7.   Cyclic simple shear test.

from which it can be seen that direct shear is applied to the test specimen together with normal stress and that each can be applied cyclically. Apparatus of this type is only just being introduced to the pavement problem at a research level. It should be noted that the stress regimes of this test and the repeated load triaxial test (Fig. 4) taken together come close to reproducing *in situ* conditions (Fig. 2).

With the foregoing background, it is of interest to examine those tests which are currently used in pavement design to evaluate mechanical properties of materials other than cement bound materials, which are dealt with in Chapter 5. There are primarily two of them, the Marshall test for bituminous mixes[2,14] and the California Bearing Ratio test (CBR) for soils and granular materials.[15] These tests are illustrated in Fig. 8. Both are tests of the materials to failure under monotonic loading conditions, and in each the stress system set up in the material is very complex. In the Marshall test, the ultimate load and the associated deformation are determined and known as the 'stability' and 'flow' respectively. In the CBR test the load against plunger penetration is plotted so that the relationship between these two parameters can be obtained at two fixed values of penetration for comparison with a high quality standard material established originally by the California State Highway Authority.

Neither of these tests is intended to produce fundamental information on the stress–strain characteristics of paving materials, since each is associated with an empirical procedure for either mix design, in the case of the

Marshall test, or pavement thickness design, in the case of the CBR test. It is apparent, furthermore, that the conditions in these tests are such as to make them of little direct use for evaluating those mechanical properties of materials needed for the analytical approach to pavement design. However, these tests exist and are widely used by highway engineers. Attempts have

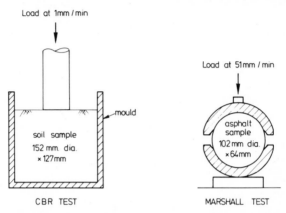

FIG. 8.   The CBR and Marshall tests.

been made to correlate the results which they produce with the elastic or permanent deformation characteristics required for analytical design and such relationships are discussed in subsequent sections.

A more positive approach to materials testing is to be found in the development of simplified, practical pieces of test apparatus derived from the more complex equipment discussed above, which has been used for research purposes. American agencies are beginning to adopt such an approach and in the case of tests for elastic properties of materials, the Transportation Research Board has brought out a manual describing several possible tests for different materials.[6]

BITUMINOUS MATERIALS

General Behaviour

Bituminous materials, as used in highway engineering, consist of a mixture of tar or bitumen with mineral aggregate. Their mechanical characteristics are hence very much influenced by those of the binders which are viscoelastic in their response to load. This means that the deformation depends on both temperature and the time for which the load is applied.

Temperature is important because of the effect it has on the viscosity of the binder and this property is therefore something which needs to be measured and specified. Although viscosity can be measured directly by use of one of various viscometers, the test is not used in British practice. Instead, bitumens are specified by the use of two empirical tests which relate to the viscosity and the influence which temperature has upon it. The penetration test[16] is carried out at a standard temperature of 25 °C and gives a measure of viscosity at this temperature; the penetration (P). The ring and ball softening point[17] determines a temperature (SP) at which each bitumen has the same viscosity, i.e. an equiviscous temperature.

The results of these two tests can be combined to obtain a measure of the temperature susceptibility of a bitumen and this is known as the penetration index (PI). It is a simple function of the slope of the penetration against temperature relationship and can be calculated from the following equation:

$$PI = \frac{1951 \cdot 4 - 500 \log P - 20\, SP}{50 \log P - SP - 120 \cdot 14} \tag{3}$$

or from a nomograph developed by Van der Poel.[18] For most bitumens used in road construction, values of PI range from about -1 to $+1$. Temperature susceptibility increases with decreasing PI and, hence, low temperature susceptibility can be produced by using a binder with a high PI. Tars have values of PI down to -3 and are therefore more affected by temperature changes than most bitumens.

Stiffness
Definition
The relationship between stress and strain under given conditions of loading time and temperature was defined by Van der Poel[18] as 'Stiffness'. This is a concept of considerable engineering significance, since it is of immense help in developing the fundamental approach to design, both for mixes and pavements.

Stiffness of pure bitumen
Figure 9 shows how the stiffness of a bitumen is affected by loading time and temperature. Under short loading times the curves become horizontal, indicating elastic behaviour, while under very long loading times

$$S = \frac{3\eta}{t} \tag{4}$$

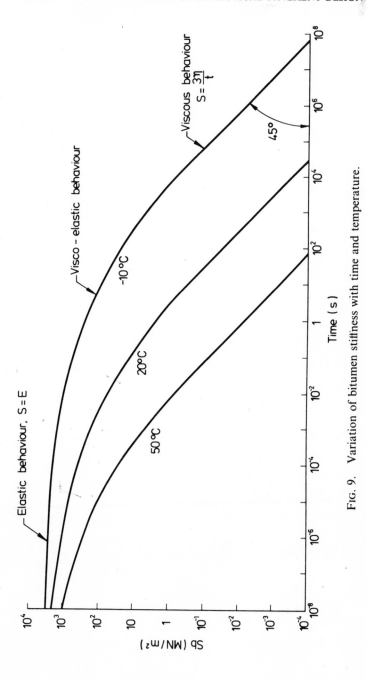

FIG. 9.   Variation of bitumen stiffness with time and temperature.

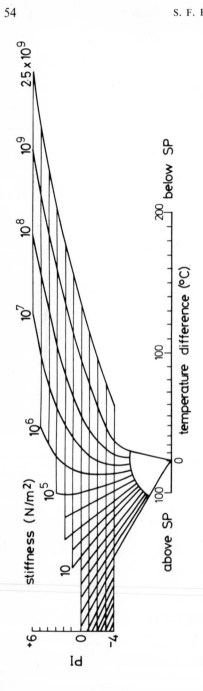

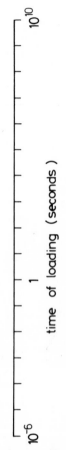

Fig. 10. The Van der Poel[18] nomograph for bitumen stiffness.

where η = dynamic viscosity indicating purely viscous behaviour. At intermediate loading times, the behaviour is viscoelastic with significant contributions to strain coming from both elastic and viscous deformations. Figure 9 also shows the influence which temperature has through its effect on viscosity. The very large range of values on the logarithmic scales of Fig. 9 should be noted. Furthermore, a similarity of shape in the curves is apparent and this indicates that the curves could be made coincident by 'shifting' them in the horizontal direction. In other words, there is a value of temperature which has the same effect on the response of the material as a certain loading time. This interchangeability of time and temperature is an important property of bituminous materials and indicates that they are 'thermorheologically simple'.

The principal use which can be made of this property is that it enables laboratory testing over a limited time scale to be extended to very large times by carrying out tests at different temperatures.

In his investigation of stiffness of pure bitumens, Van der Poel[18] carried out a large number of tests under a wide range of loading time and temperature conditions and included bitumens of 47 different rheological types, i.e. various combinations of penetration and softening point or penetration index.

The outcome of this research was the production of the well known Van der Poel Nomograph which allows the stiffness of a particular bitumen under given time (t) and temperature (T) conditions to be predicted to an accuracy of a factor of 2, which is considered reasonable in view of the large range of values noted in connection with Fig. 9. In more detail, the parameters required to use the nomograph are:

1. the temperature difference, $(SP - T)$;
2. loading time or frequency, t or f;
3. penetration index, PI.

A simplified version of the nomograph is shown in Fig. 10.

Stiffness of Bituminous Mixes

As a general principle, in materials engineering, it is always better to carry out appropriate tests for mechanical properties rather than rely on predictive methods. This certainly applies to highway materials whose characteristics can vary so much with composition and environmental effects. However, methods of estimating important parameters such as stiffness are very useful, particularly where laboratory facilities are not readily available. As an extension of Van der Poel's work on pure bitumen, the Shell organisation have developed useful predictive methods for the stiffness of bituminous mixes.

In testing a range of dense bituminous mixes, Van der Poel[19] established that mix stiffness was a function of the bitumen stiffness and the quantity of aggregate in the mix expressed as C_v where

$$C_v = \frac{\text{Vol. of aggregate}}{\text{Vol. of aggregate} + \text{Vol. of bitumen}}$$

$$= \frac{(M_A/G_a)}{(M_A/G_a) + (M_B/G_b)} \tag{5}$$

where M_A, M_B = percentage aggregate and binder contents by mass, and G_a, G_b = specific gravities of aggregate and binder. His work was extended by colleagues in Shell[20] and it resulted in a prediction procedure for mix stiffness (S_m) represented by the following equations:

$$S_m = S_b \left[1 + \frac{2 \cdot 5}{n} \frac{C_v'}{(1 - C_v')} \right]^n \tag{6}$$

in which S_b = bitumen stiffness in MN m^{-2}, for the material in its mixed and laid condition which implies that recovered properties of the binder (SP_r and PI_r) should be used in estimating S_b from the Van der Poel nomograph (Fig. 9).

$$C_v' = \frac{C_v}{1 + (0 \cdot 01 V_V - 0 \cdot 03)}$$

for a void content $V_V \%$. This represents a correction to C_v for mixes having void contents in excess of 3 %; and

$$n = 0 \cdot 83 \log \left(\frac{4 \times 10^4}{S_b} \right)$$

An important restriction to the applicability of the above relationship is that it only applies under dynamic conditions defined by $S_b \geq 10$ MN m^{-2} and for values of C_v between 0·7 and 0·9.

More recent work by Shell[21] has resulted in a similar procedure for predicting mix stiffness by use of a chart which requires a knowledge of S_b (from the Van der Poel nomograph), the volume of aggregate and the volume of bitumen in the mix. The two procedures give similar results, though the second is applicable for a wider range of mix types.

At high temperatures or long loading times when the bitumen stiffness is less than 10 MN m^{-2}, there are many more factors which affect mix

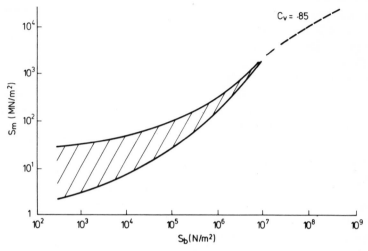

FIG. 11.   Relationship between mix stiffness and binder stiffness.

stiffness than simply C_v. As the influence of the binder becomes less, so the following factors become important:

1.   aggregate type, shape, texture and grading;
2.   compaction method and resulting void content;
3.   confining conditions.

The situation is illustrated by Fig. 11 which shows how the unique $S_b - S_m$ line for a given C_v above $S_b = 10\,\text{MN m}^{-2}$ splits up to cover a zone which reflects the influence of the above factors. A further point to note in Fig. 11 is that at very low values of S_b the lines flatten out, indicating that, for a particular mix, there is some minimum stiffness applicable when the binder viscosity is too low to provide any strength; resistance to deformation coming entirely from the aggregate matrix.

In general, the simple situation to the right of Fig. 11 represents elastic behaviour and the values of stiffness are of interest for the structural analysis of pavements using elastic theory. The loading time involved will be that resulting from the passage of a single wheel load and this may be obtained approximately from

$$t = \frac{1}{V} \text{seconds} \tag{7}$$

where V = vehicle speed in km h^{-1}.

Values of stiffness for a typical dense bitumen macadam roadbase, which has been properly compacted, are given in Fig. 18 of Chapter 1 for a range of temperatures and vehicle speeds. A representative average temperature for most parts of Great Britain is regarded as 15 °C.[22]

The details in Chapter 1 indicate that a value of Poisson's ratio is required for pavement analysis as well as the dynamic stiffness or Young's modulus of the mix. Poisson's ratio has been shown to vary between 0·35 and 0·5, higher values being appropriate for high temperatures. However, values of this parameter have not been measured as often as those of stiffness.

The more complex situation to the left of Fig. 11 is of interest for studying the problem of permanent deformation in roads since in this zone the viscous deformation of the mix becomes significant. In view of the high temperature (60 °C) and relatively long loading times associated with the Marshall test, its test conditions fall into this zone. Brien[23] has reported a correlation between mix stiffness and a term known as the Marshall quotient which is simply the stability divided by the flow.

Permanent Deformation

Introduction

Pavement failure in Great Britain is usually a result of excessive permanent deformation building up to produce a rut in the nearside lane which at 10 mm depth is regarded as critical and at 20 mm constitutes failure when it is often accompanied by cracking.[24] The surface deformation is a summation of the vertical deformations developing in each layer of the pavement structure. In view of the known viscous response of bituminous materials, they can be expected to contribute substantially to this, particularly under high temperature conditions. However, figures quoted in Chapter 1 from full scale experiments show that the bituminous layers may not contribute more than about half the surface deformation under normal conditions. During the unusually hot summers of 1975 and 1976 in Great Britain deformation developed rapidly and there is evidence to suggest[25] that the hot rolled asphalt surfacings were contributing substantially to it because of the very high surface temperatures which developed (50 to 60 °C) over relatively long periods.

Creep Testing

The simplest way to investigate the permanent deformation characteristics of bituminous materials is by use of the static creep test. The relevance of results from this test to the repeated load situation which actually occurs in the road has to be demonstrated for the results to be applicable. Evidence on this point is not complete at the time of writing but results obtained for a

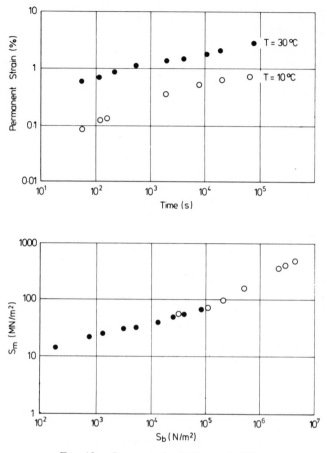

FIG. 12. Creep results (Hills *et al.*, 29).

dense bitumen macadam roadbase mix indicate good correlation of results from the two test modes.[26,27]

Whether or not creep test results are quantitatively correct, the test can indicate the important characteristics of bituminous materials. The Shell laboratories conducted a large number of creep tests involving simple uniaxial loading in compression in order to study the effects of mix parameters on permanent deformation.[28-30] They showed that the effects of temperature, binder type and applied stress could effectively be eliminated if the results were presented in terms of a mix stiffness against binder stiffness plot such as Fig. 11. This point is illustrated in Fig. 12 for tests carried out at two different temperatures. On an S_m against S_b plot the creep test results move from right to left since increasing time implies decreasing bitumen stiffness. This method of presentation is successful because it eliminates, as separate variables, those factors which just affect one or other of the two ordinates.

The three factors noted in the previous section as influencing mix stiffness under low binder stiffness conditions have been investigated with the creep

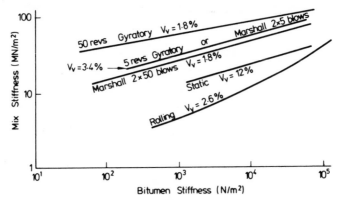

FIG. 13.   Effect of compaction on creep behaviour of bituminous materials (Hills,[28]).

test. The influence of aggregate characteristics has been demonstrated in that mixes made with a crushed sand provided higher mix stiffnesses and, therefore, lower permanent deformations than mixes with rounded sand.[28]

Figure 13 shows the important effect of compaction method and compactive effort on the characteristics of a single mix type. It is clear that density expressed in terms of air void content is not the sole determinant but that the different packing arrangement of particles resulting from different compaction techniques is just as significant. This highlights one of the problems of sample preparation in the laboratory for work of this type and points to the need for tests to be carried out on samples cored from a test section of pavement.

Relatively few creep tests seem to have been done with the application of a confining stress. Although this adds to the complexity of the test, the material *in situ* is certainly confined and the effect of a three-dimensional, or even a two-dimensional, stress system on the deformation characteristics of mixes is likely to be most important.

Repeated Load Testing

The repeated load triaxial test has been used to investigate permanent deformation characteristics under more realistic conditions than those of the creep test. Additional evidence that the permanent strain which gradually accumulates under repeated loading, is essentially a creep phenomenon, was provided by Brown and Snaith[26] who showed that total loading time rather than the number of load applications was the parameter

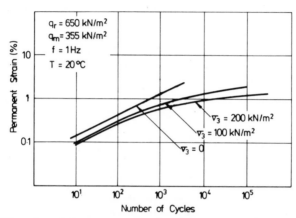

FIG. 14.   Effect of confining stress on the development of permanent strain in a dense bitumen macadam.

which controlled permanent strain. Their results indicated that frequency of loading between 1 and 10 Hz (6 and 63 km h^{-1}) did not affect the relationship between permanent strain and time.

The effect of confining stress has been clearly demonstrated under repeated load conditions as the results in Fig. 14 show. Although the tests involved used a static confining stress, similar effects have been noted when the confining stress is applied cyclically in phase with the vertical stress. Indeed, a simplification to test technique has been suggested by this work[26] in that a static confining stress equal to the mean value of the desirable cyclic stress produces essentially the same response from the material.

The influence of rest periods between load cycles has also been investigated and the conclusion drawn that they do not affect the basic permanent strain against time relationship where the latter refers to the time when the material is actually being loaded.

In practice, both load and temperature vary whereas most laboratory testing involves simple constant conditions for these parameters. The material behaviour can be predicted from the simple test curves using the basic principle that permanent strain is indeed permanent. Figure 15, which uses a natural scale for permanent strain, illustrates the point diagrammatically for various stress levels. A similar procedure would apply for various temperatures.

Most of the above conclusions have been drawn from tests on a dense bitumen macadam roadbase mix. Repeated load tests on hot rolled asphalt

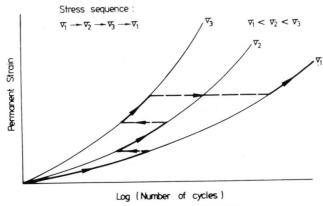

FIG. 15.   Compound loading.

base make an interesting comparison and highlight some basic principles. Figure 16 shows that at 10 °C similar permanent strains are observed in each material but that at 20 °C the rolled asphalt deforms more. Resistance to permanent deformation comes from a combination of binder viscosity, which is highest in the rolled asphalt, and interparticle action which is highest in the dense bitumen macadam. At the lower temperature the net effects in each material are the same, but at the higher temperature the decrease in binder viscosity is not compensated for in the rolled asphalt though it is in the macadam because of its better aggregate grading characteristics.

Figure 16 also shows the important direct influence which temperature has on permanent deformation, even for the well graded dense macadam. In the road a secondary temperature effect is also apparent. In hot weather the dynamic stiffness of the bituminous layer decreases and hence higher stresses are transmitted to the layers below, resulting in greater deformations from them.

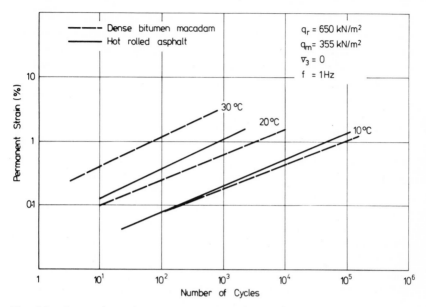

FIG. 16.   Comparison of permanent strain for dense bitumen macadam and hot rolled asphalt base mixes.

Fatigue Cracking

Introduction

The subject of fatigue cracking in bituminous materials has been extensively investigated and a state-of-the-art on the design of pavements to minimise the possibility of its occurrence was published in 1973.[31] The problem has not been a particularly British one since failures in this country have generally been caused by excessive deformation. However, in the USA where practice has tended to incorporate thinner layers of leaner mixes, cracking has long been regarded as a major problem in many areas. It is possible that economic pressures and the need for mixes with better resistance to deformation may cause British practice to move in this direction and hence an appreciation of the problem is necessary.

In many ways the design problem relating to fatigue cracking is rather simpler than that concerning deformation. The respective procedures are outlined in Chapter 1 from which it will be noted that a simple design criterion, maximum tensile strain in the bituminous layer, applies, whereas the prediction of permanent deformation requires detailed data on the stress-permanent strain relationships for all constituent layers. The fatigue cracking problem arises from the fact that under repeated applications of tensile stress and strain, a bituminous material will eventually fracture—the life of the material decreasing with increasing magnitude of stress and strain. The actual number of load cycles which a particular mix can withstand before failure depends on a variety of factors which are discussed in the following sections.

Stress and Strain Conditions
Fundamental studies of fatigue cracking using flexural or direct stress testing have indicated important differences in material response depending on whether a test is carried out under controlled stress or controlled strain conditions.[32, 33] The former involves application of a repeated stress of constant amplitude while in the latter the strain amplitude is kept constant.

Typical results from controlled stress tests at 10 °C are shown in Fig. 17. A large number of tests were involved and several different stress amplitudes were used. The large amount of scatter at each stress level should be noted pointing to the need for plenty of tests to provide a reliable mean result. A straight line relationship was obtained for these mean lives and this pattern

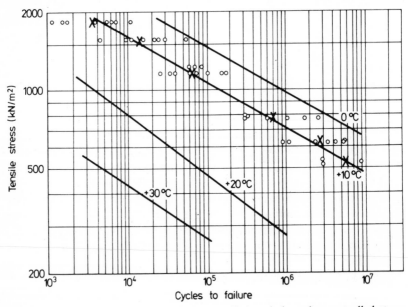

FIG. 17.   Typical fatigue test results for a rolled asphalt under controlled stress conditions.

has been generally observed in fatigue testing. The other lines on Fig. 17 show results at other temperatures which implies different stiffnesses.

The contrast between controlled stress and controlled strain tests is illustrated in Fig. 18. The top figure shows the same pattern as in Fig. 17, indicating longest lives for the highest stiffness, while the bottom figure

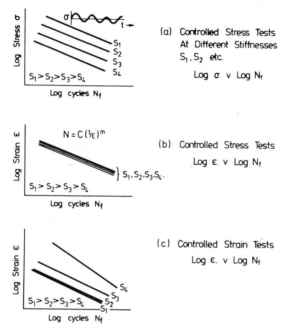

FIG. 18.   Controlled stress and controlled strain fatigue tests.

indicates that for controlled strain tests stiffness has the opposite effect; longest lives being associated with lowest stiffness.

A further point of considerable significance which is shown in Fig. 18 is that if controlled stress results are expressed in terms of the resulting strain applicable to the early part of a test before any damage has been incurred, then stiffness apparently has no influence on the results. This finding which establishes the tensile strain criterion is discussed more fully in the next section.

The difference in behaviour between the two test methods can be explained in terms of the mechanism of failure. This is initiated by the formation of cracks at points of stress concentration and during the subsequent part of a test these cracks propagate through the material until

S. F. BROWN

fracture occurs. These two phases of a test are illustrated in Fig. 19. The propagation of a crack depends on the tensile stress at its tip so that in a stress controlled test crack propagation is very rapid. In a strain controlled test, however, the stress will gradually decrease after crack initiation as the stiffness of the material is effectively decreased. Therefore, these tests can include long periods of crack propagation and these will increase with

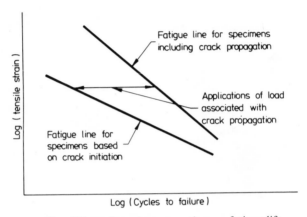

FIG. 19.   Effect of crack propagation on fatigue life.

decreasing stiffness as shown in Fig. 18. Some stress controlled tests include a certain amount of crack propagation time and the fatigue line obtained with a particular apparatus will depend on the extent of this.

From a pavement design point of view it is obviously important to define which test is most relevant. Monismith and Deacon[32] showed that for pavements with thin layers of bituminous material (less than 50 mm) strain control was appropriate while layers in excess of 150 mm produced a stress controlled situation. The intermediate thicknesses required intermediate conditions which would be impracticable from a laboratory testing viewpoint.

These conclusions have a simple physical explanation. The pavement as a whole is subjected to a stress controlled loading system, since vehicles apply axle loads and contact pressures rather than deformations, which depend on the pavement characteristics. Those layers which have considerable structural significance will hence also be stress controlled. However, thin surfacings are essentially 'moved' by the lower structural layers which results in a strain control situation.

It should be noted that under low temperature conditions when stiffnesses are high, crack propagation times will be short even under strain controlled testing and the two modes will produce rather similar results.

The Strain Criterion

Maximum principal tensile strain has been established as the criterion for fatigue cracking from a variety of tests on a wide range of mixes.[34,35] There is, however, some evidence to suggest that the unique strain life line from controlled stress testing may not embrace results at temperatures above 25 °C and is not obtained with all test methods.[36] For British conditions the average temperature is only 15 °C and 25 °C is not maintained at the bottom of a bituminous layer of reasonable thickness for very long periods.[22,37]

The convenience of having a unique fatigue line for a particular mix is obvious for design purposes and has been clearly demonstrated for a wide range of mixes using flexure tests.[34,35] Under these circumstances, fatigue life can therefore be evaluated from the following equation:

$$N_f = C\left(\frac{1}{\varepsilon}\right)^m \tag{8}$$

where N_f = number of strain cycles to failure, ε = maximum tensile strain, and C, m = constants which depend on the mix characteristics.

Results for a range of typical mixes are shown in Fig. 20 and details of the mix compositions are given in Table 1, together with values of the constants C and m. These results indicate that resistance to fatigue cracking is best for rich, stiff, dense bitumen bound mixes of rolled asphalt type; that macadams, with higher void contents, give poorer performance and that tar bound mixes are more susceptible to cracking than those made with bitumen. It is interesting to note that wearing courses are more resistant than base courses and therefore roadbase mixes, but that Chapter 1 showed the maximum tensile strains as occurring at the bottom of the bituminous layers taken as a whole. Hence the notion that from a fatigue cracking point of view roads are built upside down!

Effect of mix variables

The constants C and m in eqn. (8) are influenced by the large number of variables associated with mix composition together with the test method. The influence of mix parameters can conveniently be explained by use of a general relationship for the prediction of fatigue perfomance developed by Cooper and Pell.[34] They analysed a very substantial number of fatigue

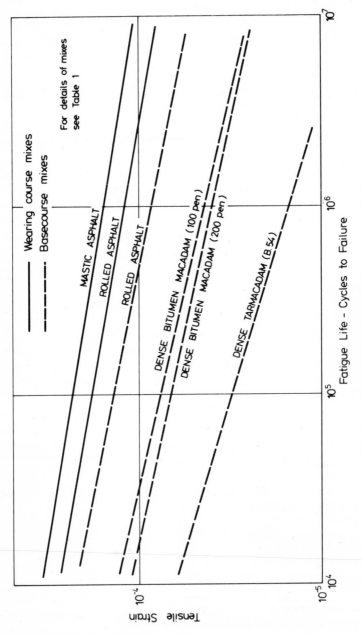

FIG. 20.   Controlled stress results for a range of mixes.

TABLE 1

DETAILS OF MIXES REPRESENTED IN FIG. 20

Description of mix	Coarse aggregate (% by mass)	Fine aggregate (% by mass)	Filler (% by mass)	Binder (% by mass)	Mean void content (%)	Fatigue line constants	
						C	m
Mastic asphalt wearing course	42 crushed rock	23 limestone	20 limestone	15:70/30 TLA^a/20 pen. bit.	0	$1 \cdot 1 \times 10^{-15}$	5·5
Rolled asphalt wearing course	30 crushed rock	53·2 sand	8·9 limestone	7·9 45 pen.	2·9	$1 \cdot 3 \times 10^{-14}$	5·1
Rolled asphalt basecourse	65 crushed rock	29·3 sand	—	5·7 45 pen.	4·0	$3 \cdot 2 \times 10^{-8}$	3·2
Dense bitumen macadam basecourse	62 crushed rock	28·6 crushed rock	4·7 crushed rock	4·7 100 pen.	6·8	$2 \cdot 0 \times 10^{-11}$	3·8
Dense bitumen macadam basecourse	62·3 crushed rock	28·7 crushed rock	4·7 crushed rock	4·3 200 pen.	6·9	$2 \cdot 5 \times 10^{-12}$	4·0
Dense tar macadam basecourse	61·7 crushed rock	28·4 crushed rock	4·7 crushed rock	5·2 B54	7·5	$1 \cdot 0 \times 10^{-7}$	2·7

^{a} Trinidad Lake Asphalt.

results and came to the conclusion that the constants defining the fatigue line depended on just two parameters:

1. The binder content of the mix by volume (V_B) which can be calculated from

$$V_B = (100 - V_V) \frac{(M_B/G_b)}{(M_B/G_b) + (M_A/G_a)} \qquad (9)$$

where V_V = void content (%) and the other parameters were defined for eqn. (5).

2. The initial ring and ball softening point of the binder (SP_i) according to the British standard test.[17]

This simplified situation allowed the development of the nomograph shown in Fig. 19 of Chapter 1, for predicting fatigue performance.[34] This procedure applies for binder contents between 3·5 and 15% by mass and softening points between 33 and 61 °C. It should also be emphasised that the method is associated with the rotating bending test although a similar general relationship has been found by Verstraeten[35] for trapezoidal cantilever tests.

Although only two mix parameters feature in the general relationship, the effect of all the others can be explained either by their influence on V_B or SP_i or by the effect they have on stiffness.

Void content is clearly an important variable and eqn. (9) shows that it influences V_B. Furthermore, the interaction of aggregate type and compactive effort and temperature combine to produce an effect on V_V and hence V_B. Fatigue is essentially a tensile phenomenon and hence aggregate type does not have a direct bearing on fatigue performance. The tensile behaviour, however, is clearly dependent on the binder and high binder contents produce good fatigue resistance. On the other hand, stiffness is decreased by higher binder contents and higher strains arise. These conflicting effects result in an optimum binder content for a particular mix which is generally higher than that currently used in practice.[34] It coincides with the maximum density which occurs when the voids in the mixed aggregate (VMA = $V_V + V_B$) are a minimum.

Whilst the addition of filler increases stiffness and hence reduces strain leading to a longer life, it does not have an effect on the position of the fatigue line unless it causes a change in V_B. Filler may, therefore, be regarded as part of the overall aggregate content as far as fatigue resistance is concerned.

The foregoing discussion has indicated the influence which stiffness has on fatigue performance. For a given mix, stiffness can be changed by temperature or loading time, the effect of which, in a controlled stress situation, is simply to alter the strain, i.e. to move up or down a particular fatigue line.

Conclusions about *in situ* fatigue performance cannot be arrived at simply on the basis of laboratory fatigue lines and stiffnesses. The actual tensile strain to which the material will be subjected in the road depends on the details of the pavement structure as a whole together with the loading and environmental conditions. The effect of changing a mix parameter on the relative life of a pavement can only be assessed when the pavement is analysed under both conditions. Figures 21 and 22 show contrasting examples of the effect of binder and void contents on a dense bitumen macadam base and a hot rolled asphalt surfacing.[38]

In Fig. 21 the importance of compaction is emphasised since void content is shown to have more influence on the fatigue life than binder content. The

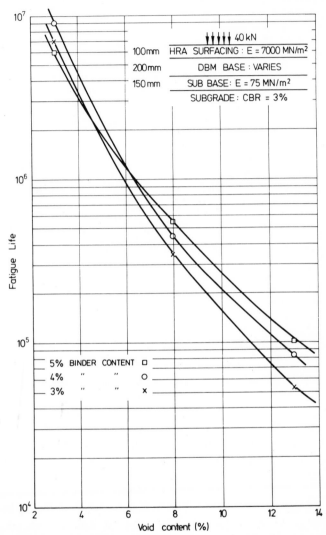

FIG. 21. Effect of mix variables on fatigue life of a dense bitumen macadam base.

reason for this is that increasing void content causes a decrease in both stiffness and fatigue life while a drop in binder content decreases fatigue life but, provided compaction is adequate, increases stiffness. Hence in the latter case the effects tend to cancel each other out.

For the hot rolled asphalt surfacing, Fig. 22 shows that binder content is

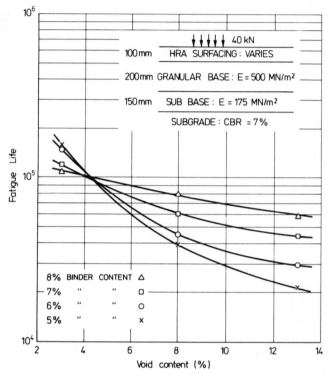

Fig. 22.   Effect of mix variables on fatigue life of a hot rolled asphalt surfacing.

more important at high void contents and that void content has generally less influence. This arises from the fact that the hot rolled asphalt is less significant structurally (100 mm) than the dense bitumen macadam (200 mm) and, therefore, its stiffness has less influence on the tensile strains which are induced.

In Situ Conditions

There are three major differences between the simple stress controlled laboratory repeated load fatigue test and the situation in a road. Traffic loads vary so that strain pulses will be of variable magnitude, vehicles do not come at regular short intervals so that rest periods often occur between strain pulses, and since stress controlled tests essentially determine lives to crack initiation some allowance should be made for the time it takes for a crack to propagate up through the bituminous layer.

Factors which affect the magnitude of the tensile strain, such as vehicle speed, wheel load and temperature (the last two via their effect on stiffness) can be handled by using Miner's law developed for cumulative damage in metal fatigue.[39,40] When applied to bituminous materials this states that failure will occur when

$$\sum_{i=1}^{r} \frac{n_i}{N_i} = 1 \qquad (10)$$

Cumulative damage hypothesis

where n_i = number of cycles at strain ε_i, N_i = number of cycles to failure at strain ε_i, and r = number of different strain levels involved.

A number of laboratory studies have investigated the effect of rest periods between load pulses.[41-43] The results show a variety of effects but the general conclusion has been reached that for British conditions, lives are increased by a factor of about 5 compared with continuous cycling tests.

The prediction of crack propagation time is much more complex and simple rules for design purposes have not yet been produced. A further problem which arises in extending laboratory results to practice is the likely influence of the lateral distribution of wheel loads. Not all wheels pass exactly over the most heavily trafficked part of the pavement and some extension of fatigue life should be allowed for this fact. An increase in life by a factor of about 20 seems appropriate to allow for this together with the effects of crack propagation. Combining this with the rest period effect produces the factor of 100 quoted in Chapter 1 for design purposes. It should be emphasised that this factor is based on very little data and, while it appears appropriate as an adjustment for rotating bending results to British conditions, other test methods and environments are likely to require other factors. The bridging of this gap between laboratory data and *in situ* behaviour is one of the most urgent research problems in this field at the time of writing.

Design Considerations
The foregoing discussion concerning the interaction of stiffness and fatigue resistance in determining the potential life of a bituminous mix in the pavement highlighted one aspect of pavement design based on the use of analysis. However, a more complete view is required to embrace the dual problems of fatigue and deformation and the general approach to design for this is discussed in Chapter 1. Deformation can develop in all layers of the structure and the vertical strain (ε_z) at the top of the subgrade has been extensively used as an overall criterion for limiting deformation of the whole pavement. The magnitude of both ε_z and ε_r, the fatigue strain

criterion in the bituminous layer, will depend on the stiffness of that layer, particularly for pavements with bituminous bases.

The analytical approach can be used to investigate the effect of changing the major mix variables, binder content and void content on the thickness of base required for a given life expressed in standard axles (see Chapter 1). Figure 23 shows some typical results obtained by Brown et al.[44] for a mix

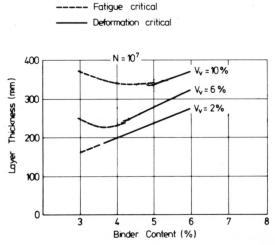

FIG. 23. Effect of binder and void contents on design thickness (dense bitumen macadam with 100 pen binder, 10^7 standard axles, 15 °C, 80 km h^{-1}).

made with 100 pen binder wherein the binder content has been varied between 3 and 6 % and the void content between 2 and 10 %. Those thicknesses where the design is controlled by the fatigue criterion (ε_r) are distinguished from those where the deformation criterion (ε_z) was critical.

Moving from right to left on the line for good compaction ($V_v = 2$ %), as the binder content decreases the stiffness increases, and smaller thicknesses become adequate. As compaction gets worse, $V_v = 6$ or 10 %, the pattern changes since at low binder content, the improved stiffness cannot counter the deteriorating fatigue resistance and thickness requirements increase.

This example shows the important interactions between material behaviour and structural response and, incidentally, emphasises the importance of good compaction. In the context of the potential for low binder content mixes Fig. 23 indicates that compaction levels need to be adequate if any benefit is to be obtained in terms of equal or smaller thicknesses.

In considering the role played by the bituminous base, conflicting requirements are apparent. Good resistance to deformation requires low binder content, a hard binder and good compaction. Good fatigue resistance for thick construction requires a high binder content together with the other two factors.

The two bituminous materials currently used most often for roadbases in Great Britain are not ideal when viewed in this light. Hot rolled asphalt has good fatigue resistance but is expensive and does not have sufficient stiffness or resistance to deformation under elevated temperatures. It could be improved by use of a harder binder. Dense bitumen macadam offers reasonable resistance to deformation if it is adequately compacted, but its fatigue resistance is not high. This material could also be improved by use of a harder binder which would make it more like grave bitume, the material developed in France.[45]

In using a knowledge of the mechanical characteristics of bituminous materials it is important that any decisions concerning mix design are related to what is possible on site in terms of compaction, this being discussed in Chapter 4.

⌣ SOILS AND GRANULAR MATERIALS

Introduction

Soils, being naturally occurring materials, have more variable properties than the man made mixes, either bound or unbound, which are used in the pavement structure. The mechanical properties of subgrades, whether cut or fill, have an important bearing on the design of the pavement since the latter is essentially required to protect the former from excessive stresses.

Granular materials used in the base and sub-base layers have constituents which are controlled to some extent, but the nature of current British specifications is such that density checks, for instance, are not used and wide variations in mechanical properties are possible. Tighter control is effected in many countries, particularly where the granular base is only covered by a modest thickness of bituminous material and its behaviour is therefore the controlling factor in the performance of the pavement.

In view of the variability of soils and granular materials it is not surprising that their mechanical properties are not so conveniently characterised in predictive forms as bituminous materials. None the less, general behaviour patterns and the important variables affecting them have been determined and these are reviewed below.

Non-linearity

The stiffness or elastic modulus of bituminous materials was shown to depend primarily on temperature and loading time. Stress level was not discussed as a variable of particular importance for pavement design, since bituminous materials are essentially linear elastic under dynamic conditions except at high stress levels when there is some decrease in

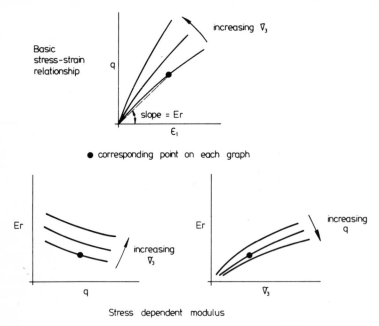

FIG. 24.   General representation of non-linearity for soils and granular materials.

stiffness. This behaviour is very much a function of the properties of the bituminous binder. Unbound aggregates and soils, on the other hand, generally contain water in their pore spaces and its influence is rather different since it cannot directly offer resistance to shear deformation like a bituminous binder. The most important difference in response between this type of material and bituminous ones is that soils and granular materials are markedly non-linear. Their stress–strain curves are indeed curves and the resulting resilient modulus of elasticity is very stress-dependent.

The non-linearity of soils and granular materials can be represented in a simple general way by the curves in Fig. 24. Consider a repeated load triaxial test in which a series of specimens, or even a single specimen if the stresses are not too high, are subjected to various magnitudes of repeated deviator stress under various static confining stresses. Figure 24 indicates that the resilient modulus, being the secant modulus, will be affected both by deviator stress and confining stress or

$$E_r = f(q, \sigma_3) \tag{11}$$

More generally it can be said that the modulus depends on both shear stress $(= q/2)$ and mean normal stress, p, which is related to confining stress $\{p = \frac{1}{3}(\sigma_1 + 2\sigma_3) = \frac{1}{3}q + \sigma_3\}$.

The relative influence of these two basic types of stress depends very much on the material and the conditions of test and these will be discussed in the following sections.

Cohesive Soils
Resilient Strain

The non-linearity of cohesive soils in terms of the stress dependence of resilient modulus is of the form shown in Fig. 25.[46] These tests were on samples of saturated silty clay having various consolidation stress histories

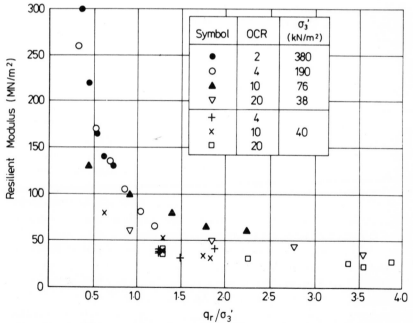

FIG. 25.   Resilient modulus of a saturated silty clay as a function of stress.

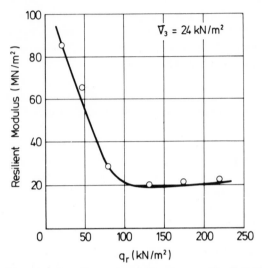

FIG. 26.   Resilient modulus of compacted silty clay as a function of deviator stress
(Seed *et al.*,[47]).

from normally consolidated to an over-consolidation ratio of 20. The
relationship is of the form

$$E_r = K / \left(\frac{q_r}{\sigma_3'}\right)^n \tag{12}$$

where σ_3' = initial effective confining stress, q_r = cyclic deviator stress, and
K and n = constants which depend on the soil type.

The frequency of load application has little effect on resilient strains over
the practical range relevant to pavement design. Most tests have been
carried out at frequencies of between 1 and 10 Hz either with continuous
sinusoidal wave forms or with pulses of some 0·1 s duration applied at
intervals of 3 s. The rest periods incorporated in the more realistic second
case allow some delayed elastic recovery in a clay analogous to that which is
characteristic of bituminous materials. The resulting values of resilient
modulus will tend to be somewhat lower than from a continuously loaded
test. Unless failure conditions are approached, the resilient strain settles
down to a reasonably constant value after 200 to 2000 cycles, depending on
the soil and loading conditions. Discussion in this section relates to resilient
modulus values based on these 'equilibrium' values of strain.

Numerous tests have been conducted on partially saturated compacted
silty clays producing results of the type shown in Fig. 26.[47] Here the

dependence of resilient modulus on deviator stress is clear, particularly at the low stress levels likely to occur *in situ*. Confining stresses in tests of this type have usually been small to represent the effect of overburden pressure but variations in this parameter have not influenced the resilient modulus significantly.

However, for the partially saturated condition, soil suction has been shown to correlate well with resilient modulus[48-50] for a particular deviator stress as can be seen from Fig. 27.[48]

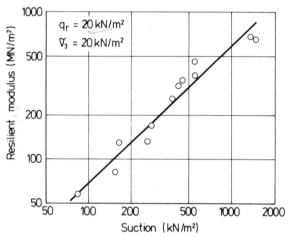

FIG. 27.   Relationship between resilient modulus and soil suction (Dehlen,[48]).

A general similarity in behaviour between saturated and partially saturated soils is apparent since in addition to the deviator stress, the resilient modulus seems to be dependent on the initial effective confining stress (σ'_3). In the triaxial test

$$\sigma'_3 = \sigma_3 - u \qquad (13)$$

where σ_3 = applied confining stress and u = initial pore pressure.

The soil suction (s) may be regarded as providing an initial negative pore pressure which in the case of soils with low degrees of saturation will be very large. Hence, for these soils

$$\sigma'_3 \approx s$$

since $-u = s$ and $s \gg \sigma_3$.

There are various methods for measuring[48,51] and estimating soil

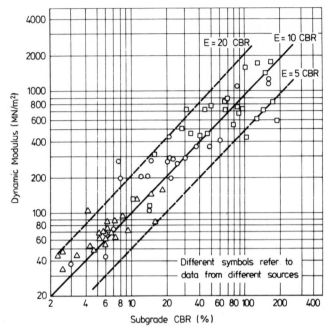

FIG. 28. Relationship between dynamic soil modulus and CBR (Heukelom and Klomp,[55]).

suction[52] which could prove useful in this context. The position of the water table is critical, and British conditions generally involve high water tables, a situation which more readily lends itself to accurate predictions of suction than that occurring in arid regions with low water tables.

Work at the Transport and Road Research Laboratory (TRRL)[53,54] has produced empirical correlations of soil suction with plasticity index and CBR for a range of soils. However, convincing relationships between resilient modulus and fundamental soil properties have yet to be developed. A useful empirical relationship, referred to in Chapter 1, between CBR and dynamic modulus from wave propagation testing[55] has been established, viz:

$$E = 10 \times CBR\,(MN\,m^{-2}) \tag{14}$$

The data used to produce this equation is shown in Fig. 28.

In addition, Kirwan and Snaith[56] have developed a simple chart for the prediction of resilient modulus from moisture and density information which is applicable in the plasticity index range from 14 to 20 but is based on only one soil type (glacial till).

The current situation is that no accurate substitute exists for actual repeated load testing of soils if a reliable value of resilient modulus is required. A standardised procedure has been developed for this test in the USA.[5,6]

Values of Poisson's ratio have not been quoted very often. Under undrained conditions appropriate to traffic loading on an impermeable soil, a value of 0·5 will be applicable for the saturated condition. Lower values will apply as the degree of saturation decreases and 0·4 is often taken for analysis.

Permanent Strain

The development of permanent strain under repeated loading depends not only on the applied deviator stress but also on the stress history of the soil. Figures 29 and 30 show the contrasting behaviour of a silty clay when normally consolidated and when heavily over-consolidated.[46,57] Compacted, partially saturated soils show behaviour rather similar to that of the normally consolidated case (Fig. 29).[58,59]

Several investigators[57,58,60] have reported a threshold deviator stress, or zone of stress, above which the material will eventually fail, and below which the sample will not fail. Furthermore, the shear stress at failure under repeated loading has been shown to be about 70% of that under conventional static undrained test conditions.[57]

For heavily over-consolidated clays (Fig. 30) a well defined failure condition is not reached, but strain levels are about twice as high as in the normally consolidated case.

The pavement design process requires detailed information relating permanent strain to applied stresses for the detailed deformation prediction procedure outlined in Chapter 1. A potential aid for obtaining this kind of data more easily is represented by the creep test as is the case for bituminous materials. Hyde and Brown[61] have shown that reasonable predictions of permanent strain rate under repeated load conditions can be obtained from creep tests.

Alternatively, Monismith *et al.*[59] have suggested a framework which could be used if repeated loading facilities are available. They showed that the permanent strain (ε_p) after a given number of cycles was related to deviator stress by a hyperbolic equation of the form

$$q_r = \frac{\varepsilon_p}{l + m\varepsilon_p} \qquad (15)$$

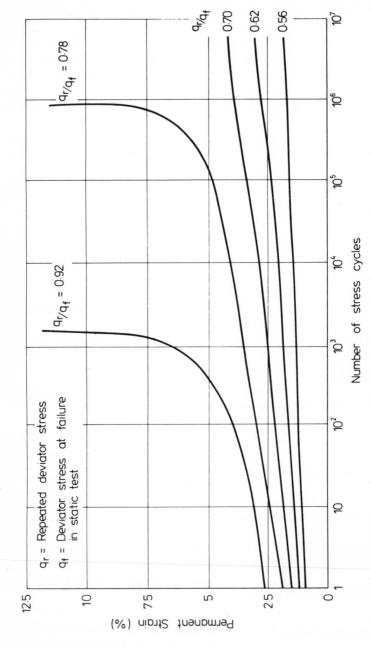

FIG. 29.   Permanent strain development in a normally consolidated, saturated silty clay.

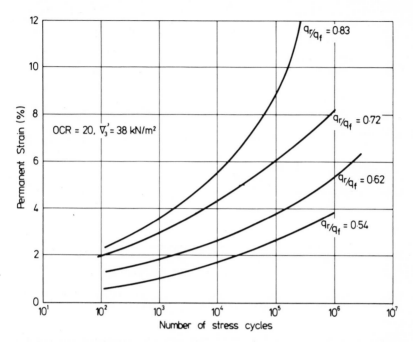

FIG. 30.   Permanent strain development in a heavily over-consolidated, saturated silty clay.

where l and m are constants which will depend on the soil type and possibly the suction or effective stress. Furthermore, the build up of permanent strain during repeated loading was shown to obey a simple exponential law:

$$\varepsilon_p = AN^b \tag{16}$$

where N is the number of stress applications and A and b could be experimentally determined.

The subgrade stresses below well designed pavements are likely to be low and, therefore, the question of failure is unlikely to arise. Permanent strains could also be small and the relationship of eqn. (15) gives a method of predicting such strains from data produced in tests at higher stress and strain levels which would be more reliable.

Granular Materials
Resilient Strain
For the purposes of this discussion, granular material embraces both the

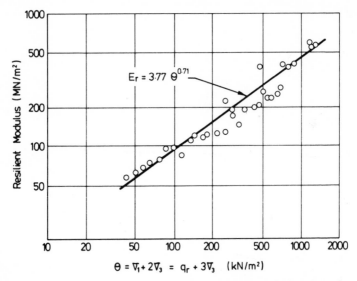

FIG. 31.   Resilient modulus of a dry crushed aggregate as a function of normal
stress (Hicks and Monismith,[62]).

unbound aggregate used in base and sub-base construction and non-cohesive soils. As for cohesive soils, frequency of loading has no effect on resilient strain and an equilibrium level of strain develops under sub-failure conditions after a reasonable number of load applications.

The non-linearity of granular materials is typically represented by the results in Fig. 31.[62] This shows a well defined relationship of the form

$$E_r = K_1 \theta^{K_2} \tag{17}$$

where θ = sum of the principal stresses which for the triaxial test is $\sigma_1 + 2\sigma_3 = q + 3\sigma_3$, and K_1, K_2 = constants which depend on the material.

More recent research[63] has shown that the resilient behaviour is much more complex than eqn. (17) suggests but that under conditions well removed from failure this equation seems appropriate. It has been incorporated into non-linear analysis procedures for pavement structures using either finite elements[64,65] or layered systems.[66] With reference to eqn. (11) the resilient modulus of granular materials has been found to depend strongly on normal stress but to be relatively independent of shear stress level.

Poisson's ratio has been shown to depend on the principal stress ratio[62] or the ratio of deviator stress to mean normal stress, p ($= \frac{1}{3}\theta$), with a better defined relationship resulting from the use of effective stress rather than total stress.[67] Its magnitude increases with increasing q_r/p but a value of 0·3 is considered appropriate for simple design calculations.

The precise form of the stress-dependent equations for resilient modulus and Poisson's ratio depends on the aggregate grading, density, particle shape and texture and moisture conditions. In general, higher density produces higher resilient modulus and the dependence on normal stress is greater with rounded aggregate than angular.

The role of moisture in granular materials is not well defined but it appears to be limited to its effect, via suction or pore pressure, on effective stress. Results analysed in terms of effective stress show that moisture content has little effect on the constitutive equations.

The likely response of a granular material in a pavement is complicated by the fact that the density which can be achieved depends on the stiffness of the supporting material. Furthermore, its non-linearity and lack of tensile strength results in very low or zero modulus towards the bottom of the layer because of the tendency for tensile stress to develop in this zone. Wave propagation testing of various combinations of granular material and subgrade soil[55] has indicated that for design purposes a modular ratio between the two layers of about 2·5 is appropriate for linear elastic analysis. This reflects the effective modulus of the granular layer and the effect which it has on other layers. It is not suitable for use in calculating the stresses and strains in the granular layer itself for which purpose a non-linear analysis should be used, and this is discussed at the end of this chapter.

Permanent Strain

For well graded materials the development of permanent strain is of the type shown in Fig. 32.[68] This illustrates the importance of adequate drainage and that equilibrium strains develop after some 10^4 cycles in drained tests unless the stress level approaches a failure condition. For poorly graded, single size material, which is not recommended for road construction, permanent strain continues to build up even after very large numbers of cycles.[69] The value of this equilibrium strain depends on the ratio q_r/σ_3[68,70] and, since drainage has been allowed, σ_3 is in fact the effective stress. Figure 33 shows that similar results are obtained for both static and cyclic confining stresses if the former is equated to the mean value of the latter.

Barksdale[71] tested a range of granular materials and aggregate-soil mixes from which it is apparent that the percentage of fines should not

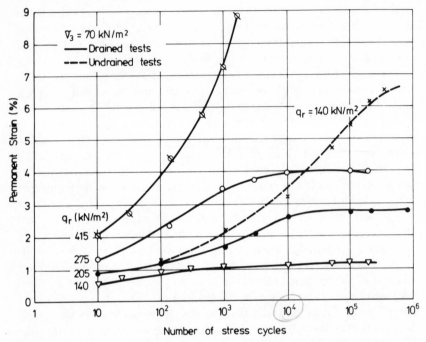

FIG. 32.   Permanent strain development in a granular material under drained and
undrained conditions.

exceed that required to provide high density, if low deformations are
required. He also established the validity of a hyperbolic stress–strain curve
of the type discussed above for cohesive soils. In order to compare his
materials in the context of the pavement, Barksdale used a 'rut index' which
was defined as the sum of the permanent strains at the centre of the top and
botton halves of the granular layer multiplied by 10^4. The figures are based
on the strains after 10^5 load repetitions in a repeated load triaxial test under
stress conditions dictated by a non-linear analysis of the pavement
structure. Typical stresses could probably be developed for standard types
of structures and environments to obviate the need for analysis on every
occasion.

Design Considerations

The previous sections have shown the importance of non-linearity for soils
and unbound aggregates and thus the assumptions of linear elasticity
incorporated in layered system analysis of the type outlined in Chapter 1 are

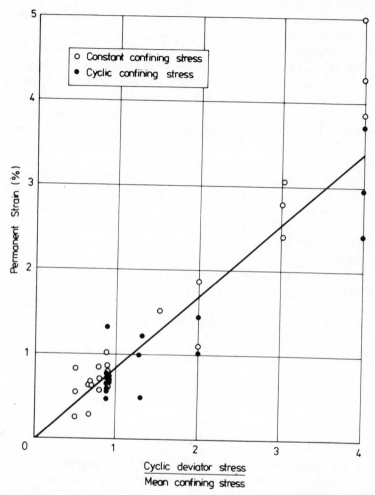

Fig. 33.   Permanent strain in a granular material as a function of applied stresses.

clearly questionable. In pavements with thick bituminous construction, the non-linear soils and granular materials have a relatively small influence on the overall pavement response to load. Under these circumstances linear elastic theory is valid provided high temperatures are not involved. If they are, then the bitumen viscosity becomes low and the mix properties will tend towards those of an unbound material, i.e. non-linear. For these circumstances, together with those involving thin bituminous layers over unbound bases when the response of the granular material dominates, non-linearity needs to be considered in design calculations.

A simple engineering approach to non-linear analysis[66] involves the use of linear elastic theory to calculate stresses in the relevant layers based on estimated values of modulus in the first instance. This is followed, in a successive approximation procedure, by re-analyses of the structure using modulus values which are adjusted in the light of the non-linear characteristics of the materials as expressed by relationships such as the ones in Figs. 26 and 31.

A more sophisticated approach utilises finite element analysis[64,65] wherein the pavement can be divided into a large number of elements each of which can have its own modulus. This is also a successive approximation procedure and involves a large amount of computing time. However, it has the potential to model the *in situ* material more accurately than the layered system approach since the modulus can vary in the horizontal as well as the vertical directions.

In the foregoing sections, resilient properties of materials have been expressed in terms of a resilient modulus (analogous to Young's modulus, E) and a resilient Poisson's ratio. However, when dealing with non-linear response, it is better to characterise materials in terms of their bulk and shear moduli, K and G, where

$$K = \frac{\text{mean normal stress}}{\text{volumetric strain}} \tag{18}$$

and

$$G = \frac{\text{shear stress}}{\text{shear strain}} \tag{19}$$

This is fundamentally a sounder approach since it is based on separating the two basic modes of behaviour although for particulate materials there is an important interaction between them. Shear stress can cause volume change and the application of normal stress affects the shear characteristics via interparticle friction. Further details about this approach can be found in Brown and Hyde, and Thrower.[70,72] It is more suitable for finite element analysis than the use of E and v. For non-linear materials K and G will be stress dependent and in general

$$K = \varphi(p, q) \tag{20}$$

and

$$G = \varphi'(q, p) \tag{21}$$

where in these functional relationships the first parameter is the most significant.

CONCLUDING SUMMARY

This chapter has described those aspects of pavement material behaviour related to the development of analytically based methods of flexible pavement design, which are fairly well established at the time of writing.

It is apparent that more information is available about bituminous materials reflecting the greater relevant research effort which has gone into this subject compared with soils and granular materials.

The stiffness concept was shown to be well established and to be a useful concept for bituminous material. Methods are available for estimating it under a range of time and temperature conditions and for various mix parameters. Permanent deformation is essentially a creep phenomenon and therefore relates to stiffness under very long loading times. The problem of fatigue cracking is well understood under laboratory conditions and the tensile strain criterion is a useful parameter for pavement design. More data is required on the incidence of fatigue cracking in roads to bridge the gap with the laboratory orientated findings.

The need for relevant laboratory testing of soils and unbound aggregates is greater than for bituminous materials since predictive methods have not yet been sufficiently developed for the former. However, there are some simplifications which can be used when designing pavements having thick bituminous layers. Under these circumstances the marked non-linear response of soils and granular materials will be relatively unimportant. However, when dealing with pavements in which granular materials play a dominant structural role, their non-linear stress–strain characteristics should be taken into account.

These non-linear resilient properties are quite well understood qualitatively but because of the variable nature of soils in particular, quantitative information requires the use of relevant tests.

The importance of the principle of effective stress has been demonstrated and should always be borne in mind when dealing with saturated or partially saturated materials. In this context the influence of soil suction has been recognised.

In essence, all the materials discussed in this chapter are particulate and there is, therefore, an underlying similarity in their mechanical characteristics. The differences arise because of the roles of viscoelastic bitumen or tar in the pore spaces on the one hand, and water, or just air, on the other.

For bituminous materials, the viscous nature of the binder tends to dominate its behaviour for most road building situations and the stiffness concept provides a good basis for evaluating likely performance. Relatively simple equipment has been developed for measuring this parameter[6, 9, 73] under service conditions and the introduction of such a test would be of immense assistance to future implementation of a more scientific approach to pavement design. Other mechanical tests which should be considered by highway authorities are the creep test and the repeated load triaxial test both for bound and unbound materials. None of these tests is much more complex than many currently regarded as standard in soil mechanics.

REFERENCES

1. DEPARTMENT OF TRANSPORT. Specification for road and bridge works, HMSO, London, 1976.
2. BS 594. British Standards Institution, London, 1973.
3. BS 4987. British Standards Institution, London, 1973.
4. TRANSPORT AND ROAD RESEARCH LABORATORY. Road Note No. 29—A guide to the structural design of pavements for new roads, 3rd ed., HMSO, London, 1970.
5. THE ASPHALT INSTITUTE. Manual series No. 11 (MS-11), 1973.
6. TRANSPORTATION RESEARCH BOARD. Special Report 162, 1975.
7. BROWN, S. F. and SNAITH, M. S. *Geotechnique*, **24**, 255–9, 1974.
8. BOYCE, J. R. and BROWN, S. F. *Geotechnique*, **26**, 637–40, 1976.
9. ASTM. *Annual book of ASTM standards: Part 11, bituminous materials; soil and rock; skid resistance*, 1976.
10. BROWN, S. F. Transportation Research Record No. 616, 22–7, 1976.
11. ADEDIMILA, A. S. and KENNEDY, T. W. Transportation Research Record No. 595, 25–33, 1976.
12. SCHMIDT, R. J. Highway Research Record No. 404, 22–32, 1972.
13. HANNANT, D. J. *Concrete*, **3**, 260, July 1969.
14. THE ASPHALT INSTITUTE. Manual Series MS-2, 4th ed., Maryland, USA, 1974.
15. BS 1377. British Standards Institution, London, 1975.
16. BS 4691. British Standards Institution, London, 1974.
17. BS 4692. British Standards Institution, London, 1971.
18. VAN DER POEL, C. *J. App. Chem.*, **4**, 221–36, 1954.
19. VAN DER POEL, C. *J. Soc. Plastics Engrs*, **11**, 47–64, 1955.
20. HEUKELOM, W. and KLOMP, A. J. G. Proc. Ass. of Asphalt Paving Technol., **33**, 92–123, 1964.
21. BONNAURE, F., GEST, G., GRAVAIS, A. and UGÉ, P. Proc. Ass. of Asphalt Paving Technol., **46**, 1977.

22. WILSON, A. N. TRRL Report LR 719, Crowthorne, 1976.
23. BRIEN, D. *The Hwy. Engr.*, **24**, 1977.
24. CRONEY, D. Proc. 3rd Int. Conf. on the struct. design of asphalt pavements, **1**, 608–12, 1972.
25. KNIGHT, V. A. Seminar 76, Asphalt & Coated Macadam Assn., 1976.
26. BROWN, S. F. and SNAITH, M. S. Proc. Ass. of Asphalt Paving Technol., **43**, 224–52, 1974.
27. KIRWAN, R. W., SNAITH, M. S. and GLYNN, T. E. Proc. 4th Int. Conf. on the struct. design of asphalt pavements, **1**, 509–18, 1977.
28. HILLS, J. F. *J. Inst. Pet.*, **59**, 247–62, 1973.
29. HILLS, J. F., BRIEN, D. and VAN DE LOO, P. J. Inst. Pet. paper IP 74–001. 1974.
30. VAN DE LOO, P. J. Proc. Ass. of Asphalt Paving Technol., **43**, 253–84, 1974.
31. HIGHWAY RESEARCH BOARD, Special Report 140, 1973.
32. MONISMITH, C. L. and DEACON, J. A. *J. Transp. Eng. Div.*, ASCE, **95**, 317–46, 1969.
33. PELL, P. S. Proc. 2nd Int. Conf. on the struct. design of asphalt pavements, 577–93, 1967.
34. COOPER, K. E. and PELL, P. S. TRRL Report LR 633, Crowthorne, 1974.
35. VERSTRAETEN, J. Proc. 3rd Int. Conf. on the struct. design of asphalt pavements, **1**, 729–38, 1972.
36. RAITHBY, K. D. and STIRLING, A. B. *Roads and Road Const.*, **50**, 219–23, 1972.
37. FORSGATE, J. TRRL Report LR 438, Crowthorne, 1972.
38. PELL, P. S. Proc. Ass. of Asphalt Paving Technol., **44**, 111–14, 1975.
39. DEACON, J. A. Ph.D. thesis, Univ. of California, 1965.
40. MCELVANEY, J. and PELL, P. S. *J. Trans. Eng. Div.*, ASCE, **100**, 701–18, 1974.
41. MCELVANEY, J. and PELL, P. S. *Hwys and Road Const.*, **41**, 16–20, 1973.
42. RAITHBY, K. D. and STERLING, A. B. Proc. Ass. of Asphalt Paving Technol., **39**, 134–47, 1970.
43. VAN DIJK, W., MOREAUD, H., QUEDEVILLE, A. and UGÉ, P. Proc. 3rd Int. Conf. on the struct. design of asphalt pavements, **1**, 354–66, 1972.
44. BROWN, S. F., PELL, P. S. and STOCK, A. F. Proc. 4th Int. Conf. on the struct. design of asphalt pavements, **1**, 325–41, 1977.
45. HINGLEY, C. E., PEATTIE, K. R. and POWELL, W. D. TRRL Supplementary Report 242, 1976.
46. BROWN, S. F., LASHINE, A. K. F. and HYDE, A. F. L. *Geotechnique*, **25**, 95–114, 1975.
47. SEED, H. B., CHAN, C. K. and LEE· C. E. Proc. Int. Conf. on the struct. design of asphalt pavements, 611–36, 1962.
48. DEHLEN, G. L. Ph.D. thesis, Univ. of California, 1969.
49. RICHARDS, B. G. and GORDON, R. Proc. 3rd Int. Conf. on the struct. design of asphalt pavements, **1**, 133–43, 1972.
50. FREDLUND, D. G., BERGAN, A. T. and SAUER, E. K. *Canadian Geot. J.* **12**, 213–23, 1975.
51. RICHARDS, B. G. Proc. Aust.-NZ Conf. on geomech., **1**, 387–94, 1971.
52. CRONEY, D., COLEMAN, J. D. and BLACK, W. P. M. Hwy Res. Brd, Special Report 40, 226–52, 1958.
53. BLACK, W. P. M. *Geotechnique*, **12**, 271–82, 1962.
54. RUSSAM, K. R. TRRL Report LR 110, Crowthorne, 1967.

55. HEUKELOM, W. and KLOMP, A. J. G. Proc. Int. Conf. on the struct. design of asphalt pavements, 667–79, 1962.

56. KIRWAN, R. W. and SNAITH, M. S. *Geotechnique*, **26**, 212–15, 1976.

57. PELL, P. S. and BROWN, S. F. Proc. 3rd Int. Conf. on the struct. design of asphalt pavements, **1**, 326–42, 1972.

58. LAREW, H. G. and LEONARDS, G. A. Proc. Hwy Res. Brd, **41**, 529–56, 1962.

59. MONISMITH, C. L., OGAWA, N. and FREEME, C. R. Transportation Research Record No. 537, 1–17, 1975.

60. WATERS, J. M. and SHENTON, M. J. *The Railway Gazette*, **124**, 734–37, 1968.

61. HYDE, A. F. L. and BROWN, S. F. *Geotechnique*, **26**, 173–84, 1976.

62. HICKS, R. G. and MONISMITH, C. L. Proc. 3rd Int. Conf. on the struct. design of asphalt pavements, **1**, 410–29, 1972.

63. BOYCE, J. R., BROWN, S. F. and PELL. P. S. Proc. Aust. Road Res. Brd, **8**, 8–19, 1976.

64. DUNCAN, J. M., MONISMITH, C. L. and WILSON, E. L. Highway Research Record No. 228, 18–32, 1968.

65. DEHLEN, G. L. and MONISMITH, C. L. Highway Research Record No. 310, 1–16, 1970.

66. MONISMITH, C. L., SEED, H. B., MITRY, F. G. and CHAN, C. K. Proc. 2nd Int. Conf. on the struct. design of asphalt pavements, 109–40, 1967.

67. BOYCE, J. R. Ph.D. thesis, Univ. of Nottingham, 1976.

68. BROWN, S. F. *J. Geot. Eng. Div.*, ASCE, **100**, 825–41, 1974.

69. SHENTON, M. J. Report No. R15, British Rail, Derby, 1974.

70. BROWN, S. F. and HYDE, A. F. L. Transportation Research Record, No. 537, 49–58, 1975.

71. BARKSDALE, R. D. Proc. 3rd Int. Conf. on the struct. design of asphalt pavements, **1**, 161–74, 1972.

72. THROWER, E. N. *Aust. Road Res.*, **7**, 2, 55–6, 1977.

73. FREEME, C. R. Proc. 3rd Int. Conf. on the struct. design of asphalt pavements, **2**, 72–3, 1972.

74. FRY, J. W. Aggregates in base construction, Chapter 2, in *Developments in Highway Pavement Engineering*—2, P. S. Pell (ed.), Applied Science Publishers, London, 1978.

Chapter 3

ASPHALT MIX DESIGN

D. Brien

Shell Research Limited, Chester, UK

SUMMARY

This chapter considers the two types of dense asphaltic mixes in common use for road surfacings. These are gap-graded mixes (such as hot rolled asphalt) and continuously graded mixes (such as asphaltic concrete). In both cases, the effect that the various components can have on the performance of the complete mix is first discussed, and a suitable design procedure is then described. In the case of the gap-graded mixes the procedure described, which uses parts of the Marshall test, is flexible in that it can be used to produce either conventional hot rolled asphalts to BS 594,[8] or less conventional mixes outside the limits of that specification. For continuously graded mixes, two versions of the Marshall test are described.

Desirable values of the performance parameters are given, although for the gap-graded mixes it is suggested that field trials are needed to confirm these.

INTRODUCTION

Asphalt in UK terminology is generally taken to be any dense mixture of bitumen and aggregate in which the composition is such that the mix when compacted obtains its strength by virtue of a strong and stiff mortar. Such mixes are usually gap-graded—that is to say they consist of mortar of bitumen and fine aggregate together with single sized stone that is considerably larger than the fine aggregate. The function of the stone is mainly to extend the mortar, thus making the mix more economical. All this

93

is in contrast to coated macadam, in which the strength comes principally from the interlock between a large amount of relatively coarse aggregate and only to a small extent from the viscosity or stiffness of the bitumen.

The high quality bituminous surfacing material used in the USA known as asphaltic concrete is not an asphalt as defined above. It is a mixture of aggregate, continuously graded from a maximum size that depends on its position in the road structure to a fine filler of about 0·05 mm, together with sufficient bitumen to reduce the voids between the aggregate to a value of about 4 % (vol). Because of the aggregate content and grading this too gets its strength mainly from the aggregate interlock. Nevertheless because of the void filling effect of the finer aggregate and the bitumen, when it deforms it does so in a plastic manner, and in this respect is more like a gap-graded UK asphalt than a macadam. Both 'asphalt' and 'asphaltic concrete' will be considered in this chapter.

In passing it may be noted that dense bitumen macadam, which is also used for wearing courses and base courses in the UK, is in effect similar in grading and bitumen content to asphaltic concrete. However, it has never been the practice to use a design procedure with this material; instead a recipe specification is used and as a result, material of widely varying properties can be produced. There might be some merit in extending the design procedures described in this chapter to dense bitumen macadams, though some modifications would be needed to deal with the larger sizes of stone involved.

Bituminous mixes when used in a road structure have a number of different functions to fulfil. They must:

1.   resist deformation by traffic;
2.   be impervious—to protect the lower layers of the road structure from water;
3.   be durable, resisting both effects of weather and abrasion by traffic;
4.   give a skid-resistant surface;
5.   contribute to the strength of the complete road structure.

In addition to having these properties when laid, they must be tolerant to the inevitable manufacturing variations that occur. They must also be capable of being handled and laid in the conditions that are found on contracting sites.

Mix design procedures must therefore be able to optimise any or all of these properties, the importance of which may vary from one road to another. Before the big increases in road traffic that began after 1945 the main requirements for a road surface were that it should be impervious and durable. Since these properties could easily be obtained by the use of high bitumen contents in recipe formulations, there was no need for, and no interest in, design procedures. It was, in fact, the big increase in aircraft wheel loadings that took place during the 1939–45 war, coupled with the fact that the US Air Force, operating outside the USA had to build airfields often using materials with which it was not familiar that led to the need for a mix design procedure for aircraft pavements. The Marshall procedure which was investigated and adopted by the US Corps of Engineers for this purpose was only slowly adopted for designing bituminous road materials. When the method was first described by the US Asphalt Institute in 1956, criteria were given for tyres of 100 and 200 psi pressure, i.e. typical aircraft tyres. It was not until the 1962 edition that these criteria were replaced by criteria for light, medium and heavy road traffic.

In the UK a design procedure for asphaltic concrete airfield pavings was introduced as a result of war-time experience, but its adoption by road builders was even slower than in the USA. This was partly because it was argued that the Marshall procedure was neither applicable to nor necessary for hot rolled asphalt mixes. It was not until the British Standard for hot rolled asphalt was revised in 1973[8] that a form of design procedure which used the Marshall test was included. Even then the procedure was only used to evaluate the sand used in an asphalt, and not to design the complete mix. In France, as a result of some instances when bitumen bound roadbases had deformed when made with river gravels, a new material 'grave-bitume' was introduced around 1972. This was designed with the aid of the Duriez test[17]—a loading test carried out on compacted asphalt specimens.

It should be noted that all the design procedures that will be discussed in this chapter do not design mixes in the full sense of the word. A complete design procedure should:

(a) Measure the relevant characteristics of the component materials that are available.

(b) Measure (or estimate) the properties that are required in the completed and compacted mix. (As indicated previously, these properties may relate to deformation resistance, durability, elastic modulus, surface texture, etc.).

(c) Knowing (a) and (b) the procedure should then indicate the proportions in which the components should be mixed in order to produce the required properties as economically as possible.

It will be seen for example that the Marshall test as applied to asphaltic concrete consists of making a series of mixes in which only the bitumen content is varied. From these mixes the bitumen content giving a mix that most nearly meets the requirements is selected. However, if this mix does not completely meet the requirements there is no part of the procedure to indicate what changes in aggregate grading or type are necessary. Only the designer's own experience plus a few general rules are available for this.

GAP-GRADED MIXES

Gap-graded mixes normally consist of bitumen plus three separate and distinct sizes of aggregate, namely stone, sand and filler. In the UK, where such mixes are known as hot rolled asphalt, the stone in the wearing course is generally 10 to 15 mm, (though smaller or larger sizes are sometimes used), the sand is generally a natural sand (fairly single-sized in the range 150 to 600 μm), and the filler is limestone filler (sometimes mixed with a proportion of the dust from the stone and sand, and chiefly passing a 75 μm sieve). Unless the stone content is 60 % or more there is very little stone-to-stone contact in the compacted mix; hence the mixes are made with a relatively hard bitumen (usually 40 to 60 penetration), in order that the mortar, consisting of the sand, filler and bitumen, may be as stiff as possible. However, all the constituents have an effect on the properties of the mix, as will be seen in the next section.

Similar mixes have been used in the past in other parts of the world under such names as Topeka, Stone-filled Sandsheet and Sand Asphalt, but these tended to go out of favour when asphaltic concrete as specified by the US Asphalt Institute and designed with the aid of the Marshall test became more widely known. In the UK, however, where there was a tradition and considerable expertise in the use of hot rolled asphalt, its merits of durability and tolerance to the inevitable manufacturing variations were considered to outweigh the possible benefits of asphaltic concrete. At the same time, world-wide experience with asphaltic concrete had shown that while capable of giving very stable mixes it was very sensitive to these manufacturing variations and generally needed a greater degree of control if its potential was to be fully realised. Thus other countries also began to make trials with gap-graded mixes and in several parts of the world— notably South Africa—their use is firmly established.

It is perhaps unfortunate that in the UK, hot rolled asphalt was so highly regarded that its reputation for good performance persisted and led engineers to ignore the fact that traffic loadings were by the 1970s increasing to the point where this good performance could not always be relied upon. It is only in the last five years that any serious study has been made by

U.S. Asphalt Institute.

researchers of the factors governing the behaviours of these mixes and tentative design procedures have been proposed.

The Components of Gap-graded Mixes

Before describing the effects that the properties and the proportions of the components can have on the performance of a complete mix, it is necessary to discuss briefly the test methods that can be used when investigating these effects. Obviously, test methods which are to be used in the laboratory should be correlated with road performance. However, this requires road trials that are both lengthy and expensive, and other methods have sometimes been used. Marais[1] and Brien[2] have both shown that a good correlation exists between the results of laboratory wheel tracking tests and Marshall tests made on gap-graded mixes. This is particularly so if the Marshall test results are expressed as 'Marshall quotient' (Q_m)—that is Marshall stability (S_m) divided by flow (F_m). If it is accepted that wheel tracking tests are a reasonable simulation of road performance so far as deformation is concerned, then the Marshall test can also be used to study the deformation properties of mixes. In the sections that follow therefore, evidence from Marshall tests has been used to draw the conclusions that are made. The Marshall test itself will be described in more detail in a later section.

Stone

The type, size and grading of a stone appear to have only a small effect on the properties of gap-graded asphalt. Duthie[3] has shown the effect when five different types of stone were put into an asphalt, the other materials remaining unchanged. A flint gravel gave the lowest stability and an artificial aggregate the highest. The other three stones (diabase, granite and a granite gravel) gave intermediate values. However, the range of Marshall test results obtained on these mixes was small, the highest and lowest being only plus and minus 10% respectively of the mean. Similarly, Duthie showed that the size of stone had only a small effect on the result; again there was an improvement of about 10% of the Marshall properties when the biggest size stone ($\frac{3}{4}$ to $\frac{1}{2}$ in) was used. This work was confirmed by Brien who also showed there was little or no effect on the properties when the grading of the stone was changed from completely single sized ($\frac{1}{2}$ to $\frac{3}{8}$ in) to a graded aggregate ($\frac{3}{4}$ in to No. 7 sieve).

There is, however, a fairly big effect caused by the quantity of stone in a gap-graded mix. At first sight this is perhaps surprising, since at the stone contents that are typically used, there can be no stone-to-stone contact, and

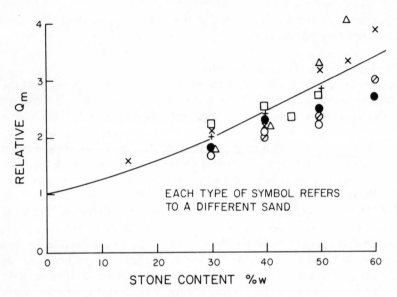

FIG. 1.   Marshall quotient and stone content.

hence no contribution from stone friction or interlock. However, the explanation is that more stone means correspondingly less mortar, and since in gap-graded mixes the deformations are in fact deformations of the mortar, a smaller quantity of mortar leads to less deformation for the same applied stress. Figure 1 shows the Q_m values obtained by the author for mixes containing different amounts of stone. Several different sands were used and, to eliminate the differences in the level of results caused by this, the results of the various mixes with each sand have been expressed as being relative to a zero stone content mix with that sand. The results show that, compared with a mix containing no stone, a 30% stone content mix has a relative Q_m of 2, a 40% mix has a relative Q_m of 2·4, and a 55% mix has a relative Q_m of about 3. As might be expected, there is more scatter of the results at higher stone contents where compaction becomes more difficult and is to some extent affected by the nature of the sand in the mortar.

Clearly then, a high stone content has advantages as regards resistance to deformation, but its use may introduce other problems. At 55% stone content there is a danger that the compacted mix will be permeable owing to the difficulty of compacting the mortar in the presence of so much stone. The limited permeability that can arise in these conditions is dangerous in that it allows rain water to soak into the mix which is then slow to dry out when the rain ceases. Under these conditions and with some aggregates it is possible for stripping of the binder from the aggregate to occur. To prevent this it is necessary to ensure that the voids in the mortar are restricted, and provisionally 9% maximum has been suggested.[2]

If the present technique used in the UK is employed to obtain a rugous surface—that is the asphalt mix has either 30 or 40% of stone incorporated in it, and is then dressed on the surface with additional chippings—there will be no difficulty in obtaining an impervious surface, and a test to check for this is not necessary. If, however, it is desired to use a higher stone content, either to obtain a rugous surface, or to provide a strong support for an anti-skid treatment such as a friction course, the voids in mortar should be checked. The method of doing this is explained in a later section.

Sand

Of all the components that go to form a gap-graded asphalt, the sand is probably the most important in controlling the performance of the finished mix. The sands can be of natural origin (that is from river, pit or dune) or they can be formed as the by-product of crushing or mining operations. Natural sands, which are probably the most commonly used, tend to be fairly single size, but depending on the weathering and transportation processes they have undergone they can vary considerably in the shape and surface texture of their particles. If they are inspected under the microscope the grains can be seen to vary from spherical and glassy in the case of dune sands, to angular and relatively rough textured in the case of pit sands. It is these shape and texture differences rather than the differences in grading that exist between natural sands that control the properties of mixes made with them.

The amount of variation caused by different natural sands has been investigated by several workers. Brien[2] has reported wheel tracking tests on hot rolled asphalts made with a number of sands, but all at the same bitumen content, in which the rut depth varied by a factor of 4 from the best mix to the worst. Duthie[3] has shown differences of the same order between mixes made with a pit sand and a dune sand. These differences can be reduced considerably however, if instead of making the mixes at a fixed recipe bitumen content they are made at a bitumen content designed to be appropriate to each sand. If this is done using optimum Marshall stability criteria to select the bitumen content, the four-fold difference can be reduced to a factor of about 1·5 for the range of sands commonly met with. This does mean that for some sands bitumen contents will be selected that are below the range of values specified by the British Standard (BS) for hot rolled asphalt. However, it appears from the limited trials that have been carried out that provided these low bitumen contents are used with discretion, and that attention is paid in design to the maintenance of durability, such mixes should be perfectly satisfactory.

The 1973 revision of BS 594[8] included a procedure for selecting an optimum bitumen content for a sand. This will be described later.

Crushed stone sands do not in fact give the large benefits that might be expected to arise from their angular shape and rough texture. This is because their continuous grading results in lower voids in the mortar at the optimum bitumen content, and this in turn results in bigger flow values in the Marshall test. Consequently, although mixes made from them have higher S_m values than mixes with natural sands, the F_m values are also increased by nearly the same amount: hence the Q_m value is practically unchanged. Since laboratory wheel tracking tests have shown that it is the quotient rather than the stability that is related to deformation, there would appear to be little advantage in using crushed rock fines. A full-scale trial to clarify this point would be welcome. One disadvantage of crushed rock fines is that mixes made with them tend to be less tolerant to variations in bitumen content than are mixes with natural sand. An excess of 1% bitumen above the optimum content will reduce the Q_m of an asphalt made with natural sand by about 25%; for an asphalt made with crushed rock fines the corresponding figure is about 40%.

One way of characterising sands is by a 'dry-viscosity test'. In this test the time taken for a known weight of sand (using the 52 to 100 mesh portion only) to flow through an orifice is recorded. An orifice of about 15 × the sand particle size has been found to give the best discrimination between different sands. Tests using a 6 mm orifice in the author's laboratory have shown that the results are very repeatable, and range from about 13 to 18 s per 100 g of sand. Sands having a dry-viscosity of 15 s or less need to be used at a designed bitumen content if a reasonable Q_m value is to be obtained. While a test of this sort cannot replace the making and testing of actual mixes, it might usefully be employed on occasions to select the better sands for further testing out of a larger number of unknown candidates.

Filler

Filler can be considered as acting in one of two ways. Firstly it can be thought of as modifying the grading of the sand, thereby giving a denser mix with more points of contact between the grains, and at the same time reducing the amount of bitumen that is required to fill the remaining voids. However, simple calculations made on this basis to estimate the bitumen requirements of a sand/filler mixture usually show that mixes which are known to perform satisfactorily in practice, are theoretically over-filled. Secondly, a better way of regarding the action of the filler, and the one that will be used here when considering the proportions of sand, filler and bitumen in the mortar, is to say that filler and bitumen together form a paste (hereafter referred to as 'the binder') that both lubricates and binds the sand to form a mortar. Clearly the properties of this mortar will depend partly on the nature of the sand as discussed in the previous section, and partly on the amount and viscosity of this paste or binder.

Heukelom,[12] Rigden[13] and others have shown that the ratio between the viscosity of a filler/bitumen mixture and the pure bitumen is a function of the effective volume concentration of the filler. The term 'effective' is important here, since different fillers have different effective volumes (even after allowing for specific gravity differences) due to their different packing characteristics. The packing characteristics can be measured by the 'voids of dry compacted filler' test originally devised by Rigden[13] and now included in BS 812.[15] Typical limestone fillers used in the UK give a void content of about 35% by this test. A filler such as slate dust that usually gives a smaller value than this will need to be used in larger amounts in order to achieve the same viscosity as is obtained with limestone filler. Although it is possible to calculate from a knowledge of the void content values what the effect of different fillers will be, it is better to regard this test as only a screening test for different fillers, and to assess the fillers by making complete mixes as was suggested in the previous section when comparing sands.

Bitumen

The function of the bitumen in an asphalt mix is to act as a lubricant when the mix is being laid in order to assist compaction, and thereafter to act as a viscoelastic binder of high viscosity under traffic. In order to have this high viscosity at service temperatures a hard grade of bitumen is required. Practice has shown that the limit here is about 30 penetration since asphalts made with harder bitumens may crack if the base is not sufficiently strong, or may fret at the surface if they are not properly compacted. In order to provide a margin of safety one grade softer—50 penetration—is usually employed. Such a bitumen will reach a viscosity of 2 to 4 P which is suitable for coating the aggregate at about 160 °C, and will be at a viscosity of 20 P which is suitable for mix compaction at about 120 °C.

The liability of mixes to deform under heavy traffic in hot weather can be estimated from a knowledge of the bitumen viscosity at a typical hot weather temperature—say 40 °C. Investigations by Hills *et al.*[4] have shown that there is a good correlation between the results of laboratory wheel tracking tests and unconfined creep compression tests. While earlier creep tests showed that over the range of interest the results of creep tests on gap-graded asphalts can be approximated to

$$S_{mix} = k(S_{bit})^{0.25}$$

where S_{mix} is the stiffness of a mix at any temperature and loading time, and S_{bit} is the stiffness of the bitumen at the same temperature and loading time. This relation can be used to compare the effect of using bitumens of different viscosities in wearing course mixes, since for any loading conditions the deformation will be proportional to $1/S_{mix}$, while S_{bit} can be calculated from the bitumen viscosity. Calculations made on this basis show that if the deformations given by a 50 penetration bitumen are regarded as unity, a mix with 40 penetration bitumen loaded in the same manner (i.e. same temperature, and same weight of traffic) will have a deformation of 0·94 units, while a mix with 30 penetration bitumen will deform 0·75 units. Conversely, if a softer bitumen is used, 60 penetration will give 1·1 units of deformation, and 100 penetration 1·5 units.

All the conventional road grades of bitumen have approximately the same temperature susceptibility. Expressed on a scale known as the 'penetration index' (*PI*) this value is between −0·5 and 0. However, it is possible to make bitumens sometimes known as 'high *PI*' bitumens that have a reduced temperature susceptibility. An example of this is 40 penetration bitumen having a *PI* of +2·0. At 40 °C this will have a viscosity of 6×10^5 Ns m^{-2}, whereas a conventional 40 penetration bitumen would have a viscosity of about 4×10^4 Ns m^{-2} at the same temperature. This gives a factor of 15 in the viscosity and hence in the stiffness of the two bitumens. Applying the 0·25 power formula quoted above, it gives a factor of approximately 2 in the stiffness of mixes made with these two bitumens. That is to say, deformations in a mix made with the bitumen *PI* + 2·0 would be only 0·5 those in a mix made with normal bitumen. Naturally, since the high *PI* bitumen has intentionally been made less temperature susceptible it will need to be handled at higher temperatures when being laid. An increase in rolling temperature of about 10 °C compared with normal bitumen is required.

In addition to having an effect on the stiffness of a mix the bitumen also affects the weathering of the asphalt surface, and hence its skidding resistance. This aspect is dealt with more fully in Chapter 6, but it may be noted that pitch-bitumen, which was originally intended to be a weathering bitumen to give good skidding resistance, generally has a low PI, and is therefore prone to deformation in hot weather.

Proportions of Sand, Filler and Bitumen

The effect that the amount of stone has upon the properties of a mix has already been described. It is possible to treat the stone in isolation in this manner since its effects appear to be largely independent of the properties of the mortar into which it is put. When the proportions of the sand, filler and bitumen are being considered, however, it is found that there is an inter-relation between these three quantities, and that some technique that allows all three quantities to be varied at the same time is desirable.

The inter-relation can be seen from a figure published by Duthie[3] and reproduced as Fig. 2. If mixes are made at a fixed filler content, then as the bitumen content increases the Q_m value also increases. This is due partly to the lubricating effect of the bitumen which leads to better compaction being obtained, and partly to the increased cohesion of the mix which contains more bitumen. However, a point comes when further increases in bitumen content cause a reduction in the Q_m value. This is due to there being too big a volume of bitumen to go into the voids of the sand and filler. Consequently the aggregate becomes dilated, and points of contact between the sand grains are lost as the grains are separated by films of bitumen.

If another set of mixes is made at a higher filler content, a similar effect is found, but this time the optimum occurs at a lower value of bitumen content, and at a higher value of Marshall quotient. This is because the added filler has reduced the void content in the sand thereby causing the over-filling with bitumen to occur at a lower bitumen content. At the same time, the added filler has increased the viscosity of the bitumen, thus giving a mix that is more resistant to deformation.

In order to investigate this inter-relation in more detail a technique has been described[2] in which the contents of sand filler and bitumen in a mortar are calculated to total 100 %. It is then only necessary to state the quantity of any two of these components to specify the composition of the complete mortar. Using this principle, the results of tests to measure any parameter of the mortar (e.g. Marshall quotient, voids content) can be portrayed as values written against the appropriate composition points on a chart such as is shown in Fig. 3. If sufficient points are available, interpolated contours can be drawn to give a better impression of the effect of changing the mortar composition.

Several sets of data from the author's investigations[2] and from the investigations of others[5] have been plotted in this manner, and a consistent

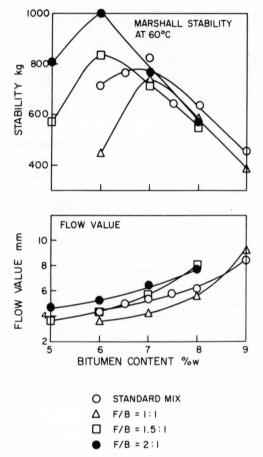

FIG. 2.   Effect of filler content on the Marshall properties of hot rolled asphalt.[3]

pattern of results is found. Tests that measure the resistance to deformation give contours as shown in Fig. 4, while measurements of void content give contours as in Fig. 5.

The Q_m contours shown in Fig. 4 are for a set of mixes made with a wide range of filler and bitumen contents, and all containing 30% stone. Contours of similar shape, but of course having lower values are obtained when mortar-only mixes are tested. The contours always show an axis or ridge coming from top left (high filler, low bitumen region) at a slope of about 5 to 1, down to the bottom right (low filler, high bitumen region).

The reason for the shape of the contours can readily be appreciated using

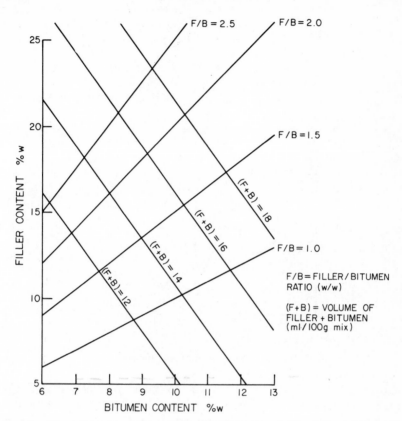

FIG. 3. Chart for presentation of the properties of sand–filler–bitumen mortars.

the concept of a paste of filler-plus-bitumen acting as a binder on the sand to form the mortar. A series of mixes made at compositions lying on a constant F/B ratio line in Fig. 3 will have in their mortar a binder of constant rheological properties; the volume of this binder will increase as the mixes go from left to right on the chart. Consequently, one finds an optimum position along this line, with weaker mixes to the right where the large volume of binder leads to big deformations and also weaker mixes to the left, where the small volume of binder leads to inadequate compaction.

Similarly, a line can be drawn on the chart representing a constant volume of binder. Mixes made to compositions on this line will have a very soft binder at one end of the line (low F/B ratios) and a very stiff binder at the other end of the line (high F/B ratios). In this case the soft binder gives low stabilities, and the stiff binder gives higher stabilities. There does not

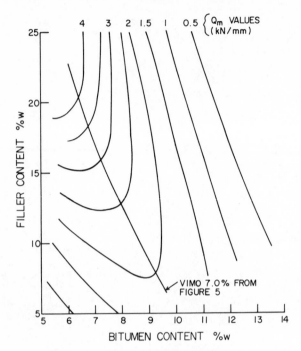

FIG. 4.   Marshall quotient contours.

appear to be an F/B ratio at which the binder becomes so stiff that undercompacted weaker mixes are produced. It will be noted that the axis of the Q_m 'ridge', and the lines of constant voids in mix do not follow exactly the slope of the constant volume of binder (i.e. filler + bitumen) lines, as might be expected. The latter have a slope of about $2\cdot7:1$, this being the ratio of the specific gravity of the two materials, whereas the ridge has a slope of about $5:1$, and the voids in mix lines are curved. This means that to obtain the best results, it is necessary to increase the volume of the binder as it gradually becomes stiffer with the addition of more filler. This $5:1$ slope appears to be valid for all mixes that the author has studied in this manner.

Most conventional gap-graded mixes have a mortar that contains 10 to 11% of bitumen and 12 to 15% of filler. Figure 6 shows that such mortars are considerably less stiff (in terms of Q_m values) than the best that can be produced, and there may therefore be scope for considering mixes with lower bitumen contents and higher filler contents than are used at present. The design problem is to determine the position of the 'ridge' in a chart such as Fig. 6 without having to make a very large number of mixes. A simple

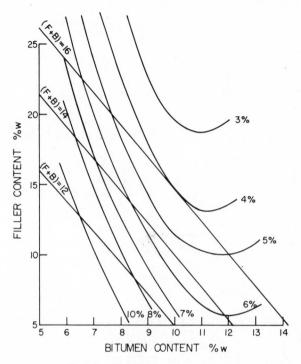

FIG. 5. Voids in mortar contours.

method would be to determine the position of one point on the ridge by making a set of mixes at a fixed filler content (say 13 %) and several bitumen contents. Since the axis of the ridge always runs at a slope of about −5, further mixes can then be made lying on a composition line that passes through the optimum composition of the first set of mixes, and changing the filler to bitumen in this ratio. More details of this are given in the next section.

The various sets of data plotted in the manner described have shown that the axis of the ridge coincides with a contour of constant voids (usually about 6 % voids in mortar). This means that that part of the mix durability that is affected by the voids (ingress of air and water) will be unaffected by changing the mix composition up and down the axis. However, that part of the durability that is affected by bitumen film thickness (chiefly fatigue life) will be worse for mixes at the high filler/low bitumen end of the axis. Just how far along the axis it is safe to go is still to be determined. Figure 6 also shows the composition of 3 mixes laid in 1960 on the Colnbrook by-pass

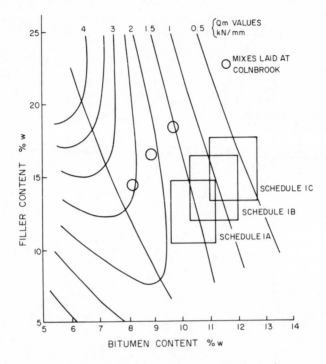

FIG. 6.   Marshall quotient contours and typical mixes.

(A4), (mixes 7, 9 and 11)[6] which are still performing satisfactorily. Using the fatigue nomograph produce by Cooper and Pell[7] indicates that a 1%(w) reduction of the bitumen content of a mix (that is a 1·3% reduction in the bitumen content of the mortar) approximately halves the fatigue life of a mix; the practical results of this depend on the stiffness of the structure carrying the asphalt wearing course. For stiff structures as are given by the use of Road Note 29,[19] fatigue does not appear to be a problem, and it could well be that a 50% reduction in fatigue life is not important.

Mix Design Procedures for Gap-graded Mixes
BS 594[8] contains a section devoted to the evaluation of sands which are to be used in hot rolled asphalt. This procedure, which is described in the next section is a partial design method only. It enables the optimum bitumen content to be selected for a sand, which is used at a fixed sand/filler ratio, but it does no more than this. It gives no guidance as to whether the

resulting optimum sand–filler–bitumen mix is sufficiently stable for the loads it will have to carry; neither does it give any guidance as to the effects of varying the stone and filler content. Brien[2] has suggested a design procedure which starts with the BS method, but continues to study other variables as well. This is described in a later section.

Since both these methods make use of the Marshall test, it is necessary at this point to give a brief description of the equipment and the procedure used for this test. More detailed information is given in the references quoted.[8-10] In this test cylindrical specimens of asphalt are produced, 102 mm diameter × 64 mm high, by the use of a standard compaction hammer in a cylindrical mould, and are then tested for their resistance to deformation at 60 °C. For this two parameters are measured, 'stability' (S_m), which is the maximum load that the specimen will carry before it fails, when deformed at a specified rate, and 'flow' (F_m) which is the amount of deformation that takes place up to the moment of the maximum load being recorded. Before the deformation test is carried out, the specimens are weighed in air and in water in order to determine the density. From a knowledge of the specific gravity of the components, the void contents can also be calculated. The test can also be carried out on cored samples cut from a compacted road surface, but in this case it must be remembered that there is always a difference in the Marshall test values of specimens produced by hammering and by rolling. It has been shown that the Q_m value of hammered specimens is about 1·6 × that of the same mix, when tested as rolled and cored specimens.

Unfortunately, the three authorities that specify the Marshall test (British Standards Institute, Ministry of Public Buildings and Works, Asphalt Institute) all use different terms and symbols for the various parameters to be calculated. Because of this an Appendix to this chapter gives the formulae needed to calculate the parameters in the different symbols.

Design Procedure—BS 594[8] Method
As already indicated, the BS method uses the Marshall test not to design a complete mix, but to determine the optimum bitumen content of a mortar consisting of the sand, filler, and bitumen that will be used in the mix. The sand and filler are then used in any of the standard rolled asphalt formulations shown in the BS at a bitumen content that can be calculated from the test results. No provision is made for varying the filler content in the mixes. In the past, conventional rolled asphalt mixes made to the BS recipe formulation contained sand and filler in approximately a 6:1 ratio by

weight. This ratio is maintained in the design procedure, which consists of the following steps:

1.   Dry all aggregates, and blend the sand(s) and filler used so as to give a ratio of 6:1 for the aggregate retained and passing a 75 μm sieve.

2.   Make two specimens for each bitumen content—twelve bitumen contents at $\frac{1}{2}\%$ increments should be used. The Marshall compaction is to be with 50 blows of the hammer to each face of the specimen. Temperatures to be used as shown in Table 1.

3.   Determine the mix density (CDM), aggregate density (CDMA), Marshall stability (S_m) and flow (F_m) for each specimen, and calculate the average for each set of two specimens. The necessary calculations are:

$$\text{CDM} = \frac{\text{weight of specimen}}{\text{volume of specimen}}$$

(obtained by weighing in air and in water)

$$\text{CDMA} = \text{CDM} \times \frac{(100 - B)}{100}$$

(B = bitumen content, ($\%$w)).

4.   Plot the average mix density, aggregate density, and stability for each bitumen content, and determine the three bitumen contents giving the maximum value on each curve. The average of these three bitumen contents is the optimum bitumen content for that sand.

5.   The optimum bitumen content obtained in this manner is used to calculate the nominal bitumen content of a mix containing $S\%$ of stone by the expression:

nominal bitumen content

$$= \frac{\text{optimum bitumen content } (100 - S)}{100} + \frac{2 \cdot 3S}{100}$$

6.   Stone contents are limited to the following percentages 15, 30, 40, 55. The BS gives no guidance in the selection of a stone content, but 55 % would not be suitable if a dressing of pre-coated chippings was to be rolled into the surface.

If the value found in step 5 lies within the range of bitumen contents that was used in the earlier recipe editions of the BS, then no problems follow; the mix is made at that bitumen content. It sometimes happens, however, that a sand gives an optimum bitumen content that is below that range of contents. In situations such as this practice is variable. Some engineers

TABLE 1
MARSHALL TEST—TEMPERATURE REQUIREMENTS

Material or operation	Test procedure		
	Asphalt Institute (°C)	British Standards Institute (°C)	Ministry of Public Buildings and Works (°C)
Aggregates	"EVT for 180 cSt plus 30 °C	165	177–191
Bitumen	"EVT for 180 cSt	160	163–177
Mixer	—	—	94–122
Aggregate at start of mixing	"EVT for 180 cSt	—	149–177
Mix at start of compaction	"EVT for 300 cSt	146–142	132–138
Compaction moulds and hammer	94–149	146–142	94–149
Stability test	60 °C ± 1	60 °C ± $\frac{1}{2}$	60 °C ± 1

[a] Equi-viscous temperatures for typical bitumens are:

Grade	Temperature (°C) for	
	180 cSt	300 cSt
60/70	155	145
80/100	150	140

claim that the sand is unsuitable for use, while others are prepared to use it at that bitumen content. It is possible that such low bitumen content mixes are lacking in durability, and this is discussed in the next section.

Mix Design—Complete Method

The following design procedure has been suggested by Brien[2] as covering most of the factors that contribute to the performance of an asphalt. In outline the procedure consists of first designing a mortar from the sand filler and bitumen that are available, and then seeing how the properties of this mortar can be increased to match some specified value, either by (a) the addition of stone, or (b) the use of different sand or bitumen, or (c) varying the proportions of the mortar. As quoted above, alternatives (a), (b) and (c) are probably in order of preference for mixes used in the UK. In parts of the world not linked to BS specifications, the order of preference might be different.

D. BRIEN

The procedure is very flexible in that it allows mixes to be produced either inside the limits of BS 594,[8] or outside the limits. It also allows the required mix properties to be achieved in a number of different ways.

The Marshall quotient is used as a parameter for comparing the resistance to deformation of mixes, and the voids in mortar as a parameter for durability. If mixes of low bitumen content result from the procedure some consideration is also given to their fatigue life. It is also suggested that the Q_m value can be used as a performance specification for mixes that are to be laid in various traffic and climatic conditions. Properly controlled field trials would be necessary to establish the levels of Q_m value required for different conditions. Indications in the UK after the hot summers of 1975 and 1976 are that about $2.5 \, kN \, mm^{-1}$ is required for the most severe sites (the up-hill slow lanes on south facing slopes of motorways), falling to $1.0 \, kN \, mm^{-1}$ for less severe sites.

The stages in design are:

1. Using the sand, filler and bitumen available, make mixes of these three components at a constant filler content ($13 \% w$) and a range of bitumen contents. Alternatively, the $1/6$ filler/sand ratio called for in BS 594[8] can be used instead; in this case the quantity of filler, although changing with changes in bitumen content, will be close to 13%. Determine the bitumen content giving the maximum Q_m; record the Q_m and the voids in mortar (VIMO) of this mix.

2. Compare the Q_m of the best mortar produced in step 1 with the specified Q_m. Typically the value found for the mortar will be in the range 0.7 to $1.2 \, kN \, mm^{-1}$, whereas the specified Q_m value might be $2.0 \, kN \, mm^{-1}$. There are four ways by which the former can be increased to match the latter, and the choice between them will be largely a matter of economics, over-ridden by BS requirements (if these apply), and the other limitations mentioned later. To increase the Q_m therefore, carry out one or more of the following steps:

   (a) Addition of stone: 40% of stone will raise the Q_m by a factor of about 2.4 times. If this ratio is sufficient, make mixes with this amount of stone in the mortar. The bitumen content of these mixes can be calculated, as in step 5, in the previous section, and check the Q_m and VIMO. If this increase is not sufficient, higher stone contents may be tried (55% stone will raise the Q_m of the mortar by a factor of about 3), but it must be remembered that it will not be possible to roll pre-coated chippings into these higher stone content mixes. High stone content mixes should be made at 50, 55 and 60% stone, and again the Q_m and VIMO noted. If the Q_m is adequate at all stone contents, the choice of mix will be governed by (i) the VIMO, which should not exceed 9%, and (ii) the texture depth produced in a rolled slab of the mix.

(b) Change of bitumen: if the addition of stone does not raise the Q_m sufficiently, a high PI ($+2\cdot0$) bitumen can be used in place of the normal bitumen or pitch-bitumen. This modification should be made after the addition of stone, and will raise the Q_m by a further factor of approximately 2. A mix should be made as in (a) at either 30 or 40% stone, but using a high PI bitumen, and the Q_m noted. For many asphalt sands the combination of 30% stone and a high PI bitumen will give a Q_m of 2·5 to 3·0.

(c) Change of sand: if alternative sands or crushed rock fines are available, the design can be repeated from step 1 using these.

(d) Change of mortar composition: the most effective improvement in Q_m values will be obtained if further mixes are made with compositions following the 'ridge' shown in Fig. 4. The optimum bitumen content established by stage 1 determines one point on this ridge, which may then be followed by making further mixes in which the bitumen is replaced by filler in a 5:1 (wt) ratio. Hence a mortar mix can be made with 0·5% less bitumen and 2·5% more filler than the optimum mix of stage 1, and its Q_m and VIMO determined. If desired, further mixes can be made continuing these changes in bitumen and filler. The limits to this procedure come when either the void content of the mortar becomes too high (more than 9%) or when the bitumen content is so low as to cause fatigue cracking or fretting. No firm evidence exists for the onset of these conditions, but it seems likely that on a reasonably stiff road foundation such as is obtained when designing with Road Note 29 in the UK, bitumen contents of the mortar can be reduced to at least 8% without endangering the mix. Mortars having less than 9·4% bitumen and/or more than 15% filler are outside the current limits of BS 594,[8] if this should be applicable.

CONTINUOUSLY GRADED MIXES

When designing a continuously graded mix (asphaltic concrete) the object is to produce a blend of aggregates so proportioned that they will compact to give a dense interlocked structure of stones. Voids between large stones will be filled by smaller stone, which in turn will be supported by finer particles still. It is of course impossible, as well as undesirable, to produce a completely voidless mix of aggregate. Experience shows that depending on the size, grading, shape and texture of the stone a void content (VMA) of about 14 % is about the minimum obtainable, but that 16 to 18 % is more usually found.

Sufficient bitumen is included with the aggregate so that the mix, when compacted, will be impervious and will have viscous and elastic properties. The bitumen also has the function of acting as a lubricant during the compaction process. Because of the large variation in void content that different types of aggregate will give (even when at the same grading) it is essential to use a design procedure to determine the optimum amount of bitumen in the mix, and it was for this purpose that the Marshall test was first introduced. The Marshall test has also been used by a number of workers to study the effect that changes in the components have on the properties. Other tests have also been used for these purposes; they include the Hveem test[9] (in the USA) and Duriez test[17] (in France).

The Components of Continuously Graded Mixes

By the nature of the grading it is not possible to regard the aggregate of an asphaltic concrete as being made up of distinct fractions, as can be done with gap-graded asphalt. Consequently, the traditional approach to the design of the mixes has been to consider the entire grading, from the largest to the smallest particle size, and having adjusted this to some optimum value, either by the use of recipes, rule-of-thumb, or more recently by more rational methods that have been produced, to select an optimum bitumen content that will give the maximum stability and satisfactory durability. Nevertheless, to aid the comments that follow, the terms 'stone', 'fines' and 'filler' have been used; stone has been taken as being larger than the BS No. 7 sieve (ASTM No. 8 sieve, or approximately 2·4 mm), and fines from this size down to the No. 200 sieve (0·075 mm).

Stone

The nature of the stone has considerably more effect on the properties of an asphaltic concrete mix than it has on a gap-graded mix. Angular crushed rock can give nearly double the stability of rounded uncrushed gravels, while the size is also of importance—larger stone giving higher stabilities. The quantity of stone is also important, the optimum amount will usually be about 55 %, but this can vary considerably depending on its shape and texture. It is generally held that the aggregate grading which gives the greatest possible aggregate density will also give the highest stability when combined with the optimum amount of bitumen, and to this end various ideal grading curves have been published by different workers. The curve commonly quoted is that due to Fuller,[16] and is of the form $p = 100(d/D)^n$ when D = maximum size of aggregate or blend, d = size of aggregate in question, p = percentage of aggregate in question, and $n = 0.5$.

Nijboer[14] made mixes with aggregate blended to grading curves of this form, but with a range of n values, and showed that the densest mixes were given when n lay between 0.4 and 0.5, there being no significant difference in the voids over this range. Using this formula with $n = 0.45$ (the mid-point of the range) gives 60 % stone content as the optimum for a 18 mm maximum size, and 52 % stone content for a 12 mm maximum size. Other workers have attempted to specify a desirable n value from the results of tests of the angularity and roughness of the aggregate, but in view of the latitude in choice of value found by Nijboer this hardly seems necessary.

Fines

As with the stone, the shape and roughness of the fines has a big effect on the properties of a mix. Although the use of crushed stone fines makes it easier to follow the smooth grading curves of the Fuller type, the presence of all crushed material (that is both crushed stone and crushed fines) will lead to harsh mixes that are difficult to compact at the time of laying. If sufficient bitumen is put into these mixes to give a suitable void content as laid, there is a likelihood of their fatting up gradually when subject to traffic. For this reason, it is usual to include at least some natural sand in with the fines of asphaltic concrete to improve its workability. This inclusion of sand will also have the effect of lowering the Marshall stability and Marshall quotient, but this is not serious, for with the use of crushed rock for the stone sizes it is fairly easy to achieve the level of stability values that are commonly specified—say 8 to 9 kN.

The use of one single size sand for the fines would make it difficult to keep within the limits of a specified grading envelope and would also lead to a higher optimum bitumen content. It is therefore usual either to select and blend two sands whose modal particle sizes are different, or to blend one natural sand with a crushed stone dust. Both of these devices will have the effect of smoothing what would otherwise be a steep grading curve.

Filler

The remarks made in the previous section concerning fillers in gap-graded asphalt apply to fillers when used in asphaltic concrete. Due to the large amount of crushed material used in asphaltic concrete, there will often be enough dust extracted by the cyclones to be used as filler. However, most specifications require that a certain amount of limestone dust or cement (usually 2 % of the mix weight) be included in the filler, because of the added resistance to the effects of water that it gives to the mix.

Because so much of the stability of asphaltic concrete comes from the interlock of the aggregate, the need for a stiff binder (that is filler plus bitumen) is not so great as it is with gap-graded mixes. Hence the filler content is not critical, and low values are even to be preferred because of the additional bitumen that they can accommodate. Also, it is found that although the stability of a mix can be increased by an increase in filler content coupled with a decrease in bitumen content, such a change causes the mix to become very sensitive to further slight changes in bitumen content. Variations in bitumen within the normal manufacturing tolerances can cause a much greater fall-off of stability when the filler content is high, than when it is low.

Bitumen

As was stated when discussing the effects of filler, asphaltic concrete is not dependant for its stability on having a stiff binder—hence the effects of changing the bitumen viscosity are less for asphaltic concrete than for gap-graded asphalts. Bitumen of either 100 or 70 penetration is used with satisfactory results over a wide range of climates, the latter giving about 10 % greater stability than the former when used in a typical mix. It is not usually necessary to use a high *PI* bitumen in order to obtain the required level of stability.

Aggregate Grading

It is generally accepted that the ideal aggregate grading is one that gives the greatest density of compacted aggregate, since a mix in this condition will have the greatest internal friction or interlock.

The theoretical grading curves for maximum density described in the previous section on stone were intended to give this condition, but do not always do so in practice because of variations caused by the roughness and shape of the aggregate particles. A more rational approach has been described by Lees,[11] who begins by measuring the compacted density (and hence void content) of the various aggregate fractions that are available for blending. The coarsest fraction is then blended with the next finer fraction in such a proportion as to give the minimum void content, and this combination is then treated as a new coarse fraction to be combined with the next finer fraction, again in such proportions as to give the minimum void content of the new blend. This process is repeated until all the fractions to be used have been brought into the calculation process. The proportions in which the fractions should be mixed, together with the resulting void contents, are determined from a series of charts, the input parameters of which are the sizes of the fractions, and their void contents when compacted separately. If the void content of the resulting aggregate blend is too low to hold an adequate amount of bitumen, the procedure allows the blend proportions to be varied to increase the void content.

Mix Design Procedures for Asphaltic Concrete

The most widely used mix design procedure is based on the Marshall test. The general details of the test have been described previously, but its method of application to asphaltic concrete varies in different countries. The following two sections describe the use as specified in the USA by the Asphalt Institute (since many local or national Marshall-type specifications are in fact closely based on this) and in the UK by the Ministry of Public Buildings and Works (since this is significantly different from the Asphalt Institute procedure).

Marshall test—Asphalt Institute Method

Aggregate preparation: the first stage in the design is to dry and grade samples of the aggregates that are available, or which it is proposed to use. (Here the importance of a proper sampling technique cannot be too strongly emphasised; see ASTM D75[18] or BS 812[15] for further information on this point).

Having determined the gradings of the available aggregates a blend should be designed which approaches the specified or desired grading curve as nearly as possible. The specific gravity of the mixed aggregate in the blend should be found either by determining separately the specific gravity of each aggregate in the blend and combining them according to the following formula:

$$SGMA = \frac{100}{\dfrac{P_1}{G_1} + \dfrac{P_2}{G_2} + \dfrac{P_3}{G_3} + \cdots}$$

(where P_1, P_2 and P_3 are the percentages by weight of the aggregates 1, 2 and 3 forming the blend and G_1, G_2 and G_3 are their specific gravities); or by determining directly the specific gravity of the mixed aggregate. In either

TABLE 2
ASPHALT INSTITUTE DESIGN CRITERIA—ROADS AND AIRFIELDS

| | Roads | | | Airfields | | |
| | Traffic | | | Airport type | | |
	Heavy	Medium	Light	Small	General aviation	Air carrier
No. of blows, compaction	2×75	2×50	2×35	2×50	2×75	2×75
Stability (minimum)						
(lb)	750	500	500	500	1 000	1 500
(N)	3 340	2 220	2 220	2 220	4 450	6 670
Flow (maximum)						
(0·01 in)	8–16	8–18	8–20	8–20	8–16	8–14
(mm)	2·0–4·1	2·0–4·6	2·0–5·1	2·0–5·1	2·0–4·1	2·0–3·6
Voids in mix (VIM) (%)						
Surface	3–5	3–5	3–5	3–5	3–5	3–5
Base course	3–8	3–8	3–8	3–8	3–8	3–8
Voids in aggregate (VMA) (%)	See Fig. 7			See Fig. 7		

case the ASTM (American Society for Testing and Materials) 'Bulk Specific Gravity' (equivalent to the BS 'Relative Density on an oven-dried basis') should be adopted.

Preparation of test specimens: the object when designing a mix is to put sufficient bitumen into the voids of the mixed aggregate as will nearly, but not quite, fill them. If too much bitumen is put into them, sooner or later with the gradual degradation of the aggregate and with the further compaction that takes place under traffic, excess bitumen will be squeezed up to the surface of the carpet, making it slippery. It may also lead to hydrostatic pressures developing in the body of the carpet, thus reducing its stability. If too little bitumen is put in then rainwater and air can move about through the voids of the carpet leading to early failure through insufficient durability. Experience has shown that to avoid these two extremes of behaviour sufficient bitumen should be added to reduce the voids in the mix (VIM) to 3 to 5 %. The higher figure should be aimed at with hot climates, friable stones and intense 'channelised' traffic, while the lower figure should be aimed at with cold climates and traffic that is scattered or of low intensity.

Six mixes are usually made, with binder contents at increments of 0·5 %w, from 5·0 to 7·5 %. Four specimens should be made of each mix, and each specimen should be made from an individual batch, the weight of which has been determined to produce a block of the required dimensions (4 in diameter, 2 in high $\pm$ 1/20 in).

Mixing should be carried out with the mixer, the binder and the aggregate all at the temperatures given in Table 1.

Compaction is carried out with the standard hammer, giving 35, 50 or 75 blows to each side of the specimen, according to the specification (see Table 2). It is important to adhere to the specified form of compaction pedestal, since differences can result in less compaction being obtained. If hand compaction is used it is preferable to keep the same operator throughout any one job.

Testing specimens: when the specimens have been compacted and cooled they should be weighed in air and in water. From the two weighings the density of compacted mix (CDM), can be calculated. Four specimens will normally have been made of each mix. The CDM of each specimen is calculated, and the average CDM of each mix is used in the subsequent calculations.

Following the measurement of the average CDM the following should be calculated: specific gravity of mix (SGM), voids in mixed aggregate (VMA), voids in mix (VIM). The formulae for these are given in the Appendix to this

CDM: Density of the Compacted Mix
SGM: Specific Gravity of the Mix.
VMA: Voids in Mixed Aggregate

chapter. While these calculations are being made the specimen can be put into the water bath at 60 °C, and then tested for stability and flow.

The VIM calculated in the manner given in the previous paragraph assumes that there is no absorption of bitumen into the stone; for some stones a correction to the VIM will be needed. The most accurate method of correcting the calculated values to allow for absorption is based on Rice's method.[9] This is the basis of the Asphalt Institute procedure for calculating VIM, but the following procedure while giving the same results is easier and more logically laid out than that described in the Asphalt Institute manuals.

Rice's method consists of measuring the specific gravity of a coated mix by a water displacement method—that is, either by using a pyknometer or by weighing the mix suspended in water. The mix should be warmed and broken up into loose particles so that all entrapped air can escape. It should be inspected to ensure there are no uncoated surfaces present (since an uncoated stone might absorb water, thus invalidating the results), and weighed. The weighed sample should then be covered with water, a vacuum being applied to assist the removal of air, and weighed whilst suspended in water. The actual specific gravity of the mix is then calculated as:

$$\text{SGM actual} = \frac{\text{weight of coated mix in air}}{\text{weight of coated mix in air} - \text{ditto in water}}$$

The difference between this value and the theoretical SGM is a measure of the amount of bitumen absorbed by the aggregate. The volume of bitumen absorbed (VBA) is given by

$$\text{VBA} = \text{CDM}\left(\frac{1}{\text{SGM}_{\text{theo}}} - \frac{1}{\text{SGM}_{\text{actual}}}\right) \times 100$$

This amount may be different at different bitumen contents; for this reason it is suggested that $\text{SGM}_{\text{actual}}$ should be determined for at least two mixes, namely those mixes immediately above and below the optimum bitumen contents.

Selection of bitumen content: from the results obtained, five graphs should be plotted. These are stability, flow, CDM, VIM and VMA, each plotted against bitumen content. (For this purpose the VIM values are calculated without any correction for absorption.) From these, the three bitumen contents corresponding to maximum stability, maximum CDM, and a desired value of VIM (usually 4 %, but see Table 2) are read off—the optimum bitumen content is taken as the average of these three values.

The increase in the VIM caused by bitumen absorption should then be determined by applying Rice's method to the two mixes whose bitumen contents are nearest to the optimum just calculated. If necessary the optimum bitumen content should be altered to maintain the corrected VIM at 4%. Finally, the stability, flow and VMA that correspond to the optimum bitumen contents should be checked for compliance with the specification.

Design criteria: Table 2 gives the design criteria recommended by the Asphalt Institute. In addition Fig. 7 specifies the minimum VMA value

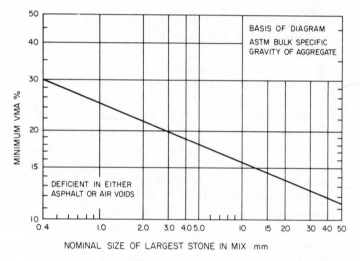

FIG. 7.   Minimum VMA (voids in mixed aggregate) in mixes.

which will enable sufficient bitumen to be included in the mix to give adequate durability.

Marshall Test—Ministry of Public Buildings and Works (MPBW) Method

Preparation of aggregate and specimens: when using the Ministry of Public Buildings and Works method[10] for mix design, the first stages in the Marshall test are the same as for the Asphalt Institute method. That is to say, the aggregates should be dried and graded, and a blend designed that meets the grading specification. The specific gravity of this mix should be determined, and here the first difference arises between the two methods. In the Ministry of Public Buildings and Works' method a less precise method is used to allow for the absorption of bitumen by the aggregate. The water absorption of the aggregate is determined by the BS method (BS 812[15]); if the value obtained is less than 1 %w the specific gravity of the aggregate is taken as being the BS Apparent Relative Density thus assuming that the bitumen absorption is equal to the water absorption. If the value is greater than 1 %, then the average of the Apparent Relative Density and the Relative Density on an oven-dried basis is used, thus assuming that the bitumen absorption is half the water absorption.

Mixes are then made as before at 0·5 % increments of bitumen content. Four specimens should be made at each bitumen content, each from an individual mix; mixing should be carried out with the mixer, the bitumen and the aggregate all at the temperatures given in Table 1. Compaction is carried out with the standard hammer, giving 75 blows to each side of the specimen.

Testing specimens: when the specimens have been compacted and cooled they should be weighed in air and in water, and the average compacted density (S_A) for each mix calculated as in the Asphalt Institute method. The following should then be calculated; theoretical specific gravity of mix (S_T), voids in mixed aggregate (VMA), voids in the mixture (V_T), and voids filled with bitumen (VF). The specimens are then tested for stability and flow at 60 °C as before.

Selection of bitumen content: from these results obtained, five graphs should be plotted. These are stability, flow, S_A, V_T and VF all plotted against bitumen content. From these, the contents corresponding to maximum stability, maximum S_A, and the desired value of V_T and VF are read off; the optimum content is taken as the average of these values. The five test values that correspond to this optimum content should be checked to see that they comply with the specification.

Design criteria: Table 3 gives the design criteria specified by the MPBW.

Suitability of the Design Criteria

It will be seen that the Marshall procedures for both the Asphalt Institute and the Ministry of Public Buildings and Works use the maximum stability as one of the criteria for determining the optimum bitumen content. While there is some justification for the use of this criterion when designing hot rolled asphalts, its use with asphaltic concretes which usually contain a preponderance of crushed aggregate, can give unnecessarily high S_m (and hence Q_m) values. Such mixes could well have their bitumen contents increased. This would reduce the S_m and Q_m values to a level that, although lower, was still acceptable. At the same time it would increase the durability of the asphalt, particularly its resistance to fretting and to cracking.

TABLE 3
MPBW DESIGN CRITERIA FOR AIRFIELDS

These are values to be achieved in the laboratory design mixture; some relaxation is allowed in the 'Job Standard Mixture', for which reference should be made to the specification.[10]

No. of blows, compaction	2×75
Stability (minimum)	
(lb)	1 800
(N)	8 020
Flow (maximum)	
(0·01 in)	16
(mm)	4·1
Voids in mix (V_T) %	3–4 (wearing course)
	3–5 (base course)
Voids filled with bitumen (VF) %	76–82 (wearing course)
	67–77 (base course)

CONCLUSIONS

It must be realised that all the procedures described in this chapter are not complete design procedures. They design principally for adequate resistance to deformation, and rely on a control of void contents to ensure adequate resistance to other forms of distress such as abrasion of the surface, or fatigue cracking. Nevertheless, there seems to be a general trend towards the adoption of these design procedures for asphalt in lieu of the recipe specifications used in the past. In the UK this received some impetus as a result of the two hot summers in 1975 and 1976 which served to magnify the amounts of deformation already taking place. While fuller and more detailed design procedures may be desirable, even the use of the simple procedures described in this chapter should enable many of the past troubles to be avoided.

APPENDIX

Formulae for Marshall Test Calculations
Some difficulty will be found when comparing the various methods of applying the Marshall test because they all use different names and symbols for the parameters that have to be calculated. The following notes list all the

formulae that are used in Asphalt Institute terms and gives their equivalents, where appropriate, for other test methods.

1.   Compacted density of mix CDM

$$= \frac{\text{weight in air}}{\text{weight in air} - \text{weight in water}}$$

(also known as relative density of specimen (S_M), apparent specific gravity of specimen (S_A) and density of compacted mix (γ_m)).

2.   Compacted density of mixed aggregate CDMA

$$= \text{CDM} \times \left(\frac{100 - B}{100}\right)$$

where B = bitumen content ($\%$w)
(also known as compacted aggregate density (S_A) and mass of aggregate/unit volume (M_a)).

3.   Specific gravity of mixed aggregate $\text{SGMA} = \dfrac{100}{\dfrac{P_1}{G_1} + \dfrac{P_2}{G_2} + \dfrac{P_3}{G_3} + \cdots}$

where P_1 is the $\%$ of aggregate having specific gravity G_1, etc. (also known as G_a)
(See previous sections on the Marshall test for details of specific gravity to be used.)

4.   Specific gravity of mix $\text{SGM} = \dfrac{100}{\dfrac{100 - B}{\text{SGMA}} + \dfrac{B}{G_B}}$

where G_B = specific gravity of bitumen
(also known as theoretical specific gravity (S_T) and theoretical maximum density (γ_{max})).

5.   Voids in mix $\text{VIM} = \dfrac{(\text{SGM} - \text{CDM})}{\text{SGM}} \times 100$

(also known as voids in the mixture (V_T) and (V_V)).

6.   Voids in mixed aggregate $\text{VMA} = \dfrac{(\text{SGMA} - \text{CDMA})}{\text{SGMA}} \times 100$

$$\left(\text{also calculated as VMA} = \text{VIM} + \left(\frac{B \times \text{CDM}}{G_B}\right)\right).$$

7.   Voids filled with bitumen $VFB = \dfrac{(VMA - VIM)}{VMA} \times 100$

$$\left(\text{also known as VF, and calculated as } VF = \dfrac{B \times CDM}{G_B \times VMA} \times 100 \right)$$

8.   Voids in mortar $VIMO = VIM \times \dfrac{100}{(100 - S)}$

where S = stone content (%w). This is an approximation only, to be more accurate S should be % vol.

9.   Correction to VIM using Rice's[9] method. The theoretical specific gravity (that is assuming no absorption of bitumen into the aggregate) is determined as in 4 above, and is designated SGM_{theo}. The actual specific gravity (SGM_{actual}) is determined as described in the previous section on the Marshall test. Then the increase in VIM must equal the volume of bitumen absorbed (VBA), and

$$VBA = CDM \left(\dfrac{1}{SGM_{theo}} - \dfrac{1}{SGM_{actual}} \right) 100$$

REFERENCES

1. MARAIS, C. P. Proc. Conf. asphalt pavements for Southern Africa, Durban, 1974.
2. BRIEN, D. The design of improved asphalt road mixtures, paper presented to the Society of Chemical Industry, London, October 1976.
3. Duthie, J. L. The Marshall Test in the design of hot rolled asphalt wearing courses, paper presented to the Society of Chemical Industry, London, January 1974.
4. HILLS, J. F., BRIEN, D. and VAN DE LOO, P. J. *J. Inst. Pet.*, Paper IP 74-001, January 1974.
5. WATERWAYS EXPERIMENTAL STATION. Tech. Memo 3-254, Vicksburg, 1948.
6. PLEASE, A. and LAMB, D. R. TRRL Report LR 319, Crowthorne, 1970.
7. COOPER, K. E. and PELL, P. S. TRRL Report LR 633, Crowthorne, 1974.
8. BS 594. Specification for rolled asphalt (hot process) for roads and other paved areas, British Standards Institution, London, 1973.
9. THE ASPHALT INSTITUTE. *Mix design methods for asphalt concrete*, Manual Series MS-2, Maryland, USA, 1974.
10. MINISTRY OF PUBLIC BUILDINGS and WORKS. General Specification No. 201, Airfield pavements, London, 1965.
11. LEES, G. Proc. Ass. of Asphalt Paving Technol. **39**, 1970.
12. HEUKELOM, W. Proc. Ass. of Asphalt Paving Technol. **34**, 1965.

13. RIGDEN, P. J. *J. Soc. Chem. Ind.*, 66, 299, 1947.
14. NIJBOER, L. W. *Plasticity as a factor on the design of dense bituminous road carpets*, Elsevier Publishing Co., London, 1948.
15. BS 812. Methods for sampling and testing mineral aggregates, sands and fillers, British Standards Institution, London, 1975.
16. FULLER, W. B. and THOMPSON, S. E. *Trans. Amer. Soc. Civ. Engrs*, 59, 67–172, 1907.
17. LABORATOIRE CENTRAL DES PONTS ET CHAUSSÉES. Method REE/1.
18. ASTM D75-71. *Standard methods of sampling aggregates*, American Society for Testing and Materials, Philadelphia, USA.
19. TRANSPORT AND ROAD RESEARCH LABORATORY. Road Note No. 29—A guide to the structural design of pavements for new roads, 3rd ed., HMSO, London, 1970.

Chapter 4

COMPACTION OF BITUMINOUS MATERIALS†

W. D. POWELL and N. W. LISTER

Transport and Road Research Laboratory, Crowthorne, UK

SUMMARY

In general, compaction of bituminous materials has been considered satisfactory in the UK and poor performance of pavements has rarely been ascribed to inadequate compaction. Recently however, an appraisal of the state of compaction of dense roadbase and basecourse macadams being achieved in current practice has revealed a considerable variation of compaction at different sites and has indicated there is considerable scope for improving compaction in the critical wheel path zones whose behaviour largely determines the structural performance of the road.

This chapter considers the important factors determining the level of compaction on the road and describes recent developments directed towards improving the compaction of dense roadbase and basecourse macadam. The relationship between compaction and parameters related to pavement performance enables an assessment to be made of the benefits to be derived from improving compaction. Finally, brief mention is made of the development of new materials, in which studies of their compactibility plays an important role.

INTRODUCTION

All road materials need to be well compacted if they are to give good performance under traffic and bituminous materials are no exception. A

---

† Any views expressed in this chapter are not necessarily those of the Department of the Environment.

high degree of compaction improves their stiffness and hence their ability to distribute the loads imposed by traffic more effectively over the lower pavement layers and the foundation soil. Good compaction also increases the resistance of bituminous layers themselves to deformation and improves their durability. However, until recently the relationships between compaction and these properties, which are important in determining road performance, have not been studied in quantitative terms for materials in common use in the UK.

In many countries end-result specifications in terms of density are used to ensure that good compaction is achieved. The density required after rolling is usually determined in the laboratory as part of the design of the bituminous mixture and field densities required for compliance are quoted as percentages of this laboratory density. Alternatively the required level of field density is specified as a percentage of the theoretical maximum density, i.e. the density corresponding to the voidless mass. Specification of the method by which the layer is to be constructed is another approach to ensuring adequate compaction and is the one used in the UK.

Compaction procedures vary widely from country to country. In the USA the compaction process is frequently a three-phase activity: breakdown rolling, intermediate rolling, and finish rolling.[1] Different types of roller are often specified for the separate phases of compaction. In contrast, guidance in the current British Specification[2] is limited to definition of the type and overall weight of the roller to be used for the whole compaction process. The maximum permitted thickness of bituminous layers and limiting values of temperature of the materials delivered on site and at the start of rolling are specified. The type of roller permitted for the compaction of all bituminous layers is an 8–10 Mg smooth wheeled roller having a width of roll not less than 450 mm or a multi-wheeled pneumatic tyred roller of equal weight. Surfacing courses must however be finished with a smooth wheeled roller.

In practice the three-wheel type is most widely used for compaction of roadbases and basecourses in the UK. The material is rolled in a longitudinal direction from the sides to the centre of the laid width, overlapping on successive passes by at least half the width of the rear roll. Although neither the number of rollers nor the number of passes is specified, materials must be compacted to meet other clauses in the Specification concerned with the levels of pavement layers in relation to the nominal finished road surface and, in the case of surfacing courses, to clauses regarding surface irregularity. The normal procedure therefore is for compaction to commence as soon as it is possible to do so without causing undue displacement of the material and to continue until all roller marks have disappeared.

British contractors have had little difficulty in meeting these Specifications, either for the traditional surfacing materials, or for the dense bituminous bases, the use of which has become widespread generally in the last few years. The performance of bases and surfacings has been considered to be generally satisfactory and poor performance of pavements has rarely been ascribed to inadequate compaction of the bituminous layers. In consequence little was known until recently about the actual state of compaction being achieved, particularly in roadbases. This is in contrast to the situation in countries where 'end-product' specifications focus attention on the state of compaction and appear to provide incentive for contractors to use more sophisticated and expensive laying and compacting equipment than normally used in the UK.

Recent developments in the UK have been directed towards establishing the scope for improving the compaction of bituminous roadbase and basecourse materials and the performance benefits thus derived. Improvements have been identified primarily as a result of altered rolling procedures and the use of thicker layers. Because the continuously graded macadams are more difficult to compact there is likely to be more scope for improving their compaction. Dense macadams are also being used increasingly as roadbase and basecourse materials because they contain less bitumen than rolled asphalt. Emphasis has therefore been placed on dense coated macadams rather than rolled asphalt. Developments concerning wearing courses, which have functions additional to those of the roadbase or basecourse, are considered in Chapter 3.

DEFINITION OF THE COMPACTED STATE

The state of compaction cannot be uniquely characterised by a single parameter; the simplest, that of the density of the layer, is affected by the density of the constituent materials. More useful parameters are those which take into account the effect of density of aggregates and binder. These are mixture density γ_M, expressed as a percentage of the theoretical maximum density γ_{max}, or void content V_v. They are related to one another by the following formula:

$$V_v = \frac{100(\gamma_{max} - \gamma_M)}{\gamma_{max}}$$

The percentage of voids in the mineral aggregate, VMA, is an alternative measure of compaction describing the degree of packing of the aggregate matrix. An expression relating VMA and void content is given by

Per centage of Voids in the Mineral Aggregate → $$VMA = V_v + V_B$$ *← Binder content by volume of total mixture*

where V_B is the binder content by volume of total mixture. This, in turn, is related to binder content by weight, M_B, and the specific gravity of the binder, G_B, by the relation

$$V_B = \frac{M_B \gamma_M}{G_B \gamma_W}$$

where γ_W is the density of water.

When comparing materials which have been compacted by different methods or to take account of anisotropy, it may also be necessary to consider properties of internal structure, such as particle orientation, to describe fully the state of compaction.

To evaluate the void content or VMA, it is first necessary to determine the density of the mixture. The conventional method involves cutting a specimen of appropriate size and weighing in air and water. The method may be inaccurate if there are large voids or interstices at the surface of the specimen even though it is coated in paraffin wax.

A gamma-ray core scanner has been developed[3] which is much faster and at least as accurate as the conventional method and has the added advantage of providing the variation of density with depth. Figure 1 is a

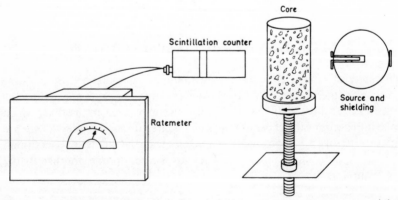

FIG. 1. Schematic view of gamma-ray core scanner. (Crown copyright, reproduced by permission of the Controller of HM Stationery Office.)

schematic view of the apparatus. Cylindrical cores are placed in a vertical position on a platform which rotates as it descends through a gamma-ray beam emanating from a 1 mCi source of caesium 137. Changes in density produce changes in absorption of gamma-rays. The beam is detected by a scintillation counter after passing through the core and the transmitted count rate, which is recorded on punched tape, and is analysed using a computer program to calculate mean densities for core layers approximately 4 mm thick.

Considerable effort has been directed towards the development of a rapid, non-destructive test to measure compaction on site for both control and acceptance; the most common techniques used are the nuclear backscatter method[4] and the air-permeability test.[5] There are many possible sources of error involved in these techniques including the effects of surface texture and the variation of density with depth; material near the surface has greater influence on the results than deeper layers. Results obtained with the air-permeability test are also affected by the degree of interconnection of voids in the material. Although many of the gauges that are commercially available are inaccurate for measuring density on an absolute basis they have potential for measuring variations in density on a comparative basis. The most promising technique is the nuclear method; the gauge is compact, easily handled and rapid reading. It consists of a low strength gamma-ray source horizontally separated from a detector by lead shielding and when placed on a road surface detects gamma-rays that are back-scattered in the upper road layers. More recently, mobile nuclear density gauges[6] have been developed to provide a continuous record of density variations along the road. As a research tool the nuclear gauge is particularly useful for extending the information obtained from cores on a comparative basis.

PRESENT STANDARDS OF COMPACTION OF DENSE COATED MACADAMS

The common practice of roller drivers leads to a characteristic initial variation in density across the laid width; it has been shown[7] that, in practice, less roller passes are made towards the edges, and compaction is therefore not uniformly distributed across the laid material. Figure 2 shows typical distributions of roller passes and the resulting compaction obtained at 2 sites. Passes at the edge are 3 and 5 compared with 20 and 27

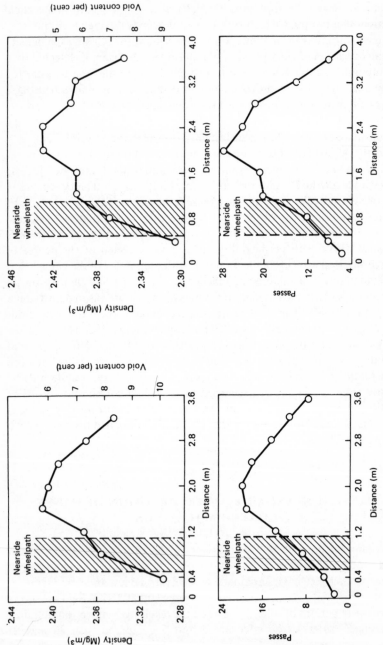

FIG. 2.   Variation of density and roller passes (three-wheel roller) across the laid width of dense bitumen macadam roadbase at two sites. (Crown copyright, reproduced by permission of the Controller of HM Stationery Office.)

respectively at the centre, resulting in differential void contents of about 5 % in both cases. Passes have been defined as being half the sum of the number of coverages of the front and rear rolls of the compaction machine; this has been shown to be reasonable even though in the case of three-wheel rollers, the front and rear rolls are of different diameter and have different masses per unit width.

Because the wheel-paths are critical in determining pavement performance, the definition of the zone constituting the wheel-path must be related to performance considerations. For this purpose it is not the relatively narrow width carrying the majority of the commercial vehicles but a rather wider zone that is most severely stressed by traffic. Its position on the road at any particular location will depend on the road's curvature and super-elevation there. On Fig. 2 it is shown as lying between 0·5 and 1·1 m from the edge of the road, assuming that the edge of the road coincides with the edge of the laid width. On left-hand bends the severely stressed areas will certainly extend considerably closer to the edge of the road. It is therefore reasonable to assume that the pavement 0·5 m from the edge of the road plays an important role in determining the performance of the road. The void content at this point is typically 3 or 4 % greater than the minimum value between the wheel-paths and there is clearly scope for improving compaction in this critical wheel-path zone.

Little or no densification occurs in dense roadbase macadam under traffic and the performance of the material is therefore determined by its initial properties at the time of construction.[8] To establish the typical compaction levels of these materials in the critical wheel-path zone, cores were removed 0·9 m from the nearside edge of the left-hand lane on 12 newly constructed roads. Although at a few sites, granite, basalt and slag aggregates were used, most of the layers contained limestone; this reflects the extensive use made of this aggregate in coated macadams. Figure 3 summarises the compaction results in terms of VMA. Excluding slag, approximately 90 % of the values of VMA lie within the range 13 to 16 %. At 0·5 m distance from the edge of the road the corresponding range would be 14·5 to 17·5 %.

From the limited data available, the values of VMA for dense coated macadams produced from slag are significantly higher than the overall average value. The void contents for slag mixtures are also generally higher than those for other aggregates even though higher binder contents are specified for slag mixtures.

The relatively narrow range of VMA values indicates that the compaction of the aggregate structure achieved was similar on most sites. A much wider range of void contents was found;[7] most values were in the

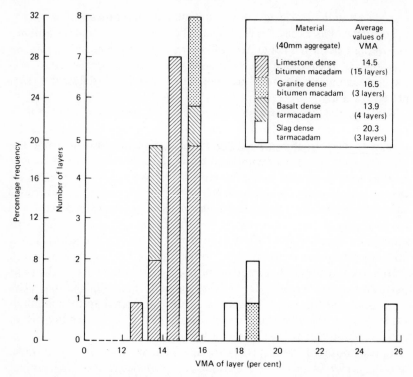

FIG. 3. Frequency distribution of values of VMA in dense coated macadam. (Crown copyright, reproduced by permission of the Controller of HM Stationery Office.)

VMA: voids in mixed aggregate,

range 2 to 8 %. This is a consequence of the wide range of binder contents in the mixes studied; these mixes were to roadbase and basecourse specifications and there were 2 distinct distributions corresponding to the two mixes. Most basecourse layers contain less than 5 % voids, whereas the void contents of most roadbases were greater than this value. The effect of binder content is considered later.

In countries where compaction levels are specified in terms of void content, the maximum permitted value of void content is generally in the range 7 to 10 % for continuously graded mixtures.[1] In the UK, mean values of void content in the wheel-path are only occasionally higher than the highest maximum permitted abroad but there is scope for increasing the compaction in the critical wheel-path zone by at least 3 %, to equal maximum levels currently achieved between the wheel-paths.

FACTORS AFFECTING COMPACTION

In order to improve compaction it is necessary first to identify the important factors determining the level of compaction obtained on the road. Several approaches can be used to investigate these factors. Field work is one, but is costly and conditions are difficult to control, whereas laboratory work is less time consuming and is relatively easy to control. However, if laboratory methods of compaction are used, these should simulate compaction in the field, not only in terms of density but also in terms of aggregate structure, e.g. particle orientation. Most methods that have been used are either unable to duplicate field compaction or have not been properly examined in this respect and there is a possibility that the results obtained using these methods may not be valid for full-scale construction work. The preferred approach is to conduct pilot-scale experiments using normal compaction equipment which provides a means of good control of experimental variables combined with realism.

To investigate the effect of several factors on compaction, trials have been carried out at the Transport and Road Research Laboratory (TRRL) in a pilot-scale test facility on a foundation of realistic stiffness.

Material Temperature and Associated Factors

The viscosity of a bituminous binder changes rapidly with temperature and has an important effect on the compactability of a bituminous material. Figure 4 confirms the importance of temperature in determining the level of compaction achieved with a given number of roller passes.[9] Dense bitumen-macadam on which rolling commenced with the material at a mid-depth temperature of 85 °C is far more difficult to compact than material on which rolling commenced at 130 °C; after 20 roller passes the VMA of the cooler material is approximately 5% higher than that of the hotter material. Evidence from many experiments shows that, over the permitted range of rolling temperature, the compaction of dense coated macadam containing crushed rock or slag is facilitated if its temperature at commencement of rolling is increased.

The thickness of the laid material also effects its compactability. Practice has been to lay bituminous materials in relatively thin layers of 75 mm or less; this facilitated control of the level and regularity of the rolled surface and hence that of the finished road surface. It was also generally believed that better compaction was achieved by the use of thin layers because of the higher stresses applied to the materials. In limited trials some years ago

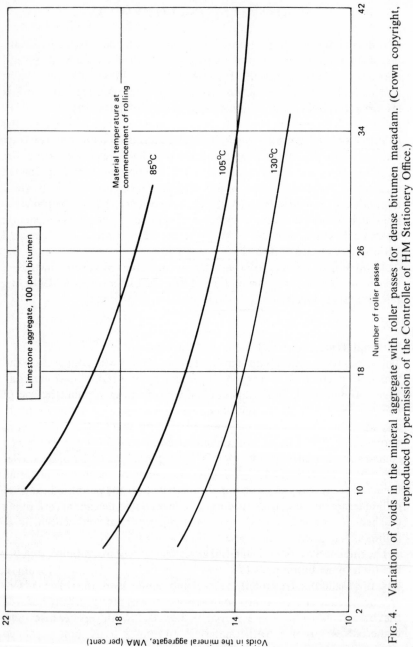

FIG. 4. Variation of voids in the mineral aggregate with roller passes for dense bitumen macadam. (Crown copyright, reproduced by permission of the Controller of HM Stationery Office.)

both dense bitumen-macadam and tarmacadam were, however, compacted satisfactorily in layers up to 130 mm thick, the thicker layers being shown to retain heat longer,[10] and this prompted an increase in the maximum permitted thickness of layer to the current value of 105 mm.

Weather conditions also influence the rate at which cooling takes place; the interaction of thickness, weather and material temperature has been studied using computer programs.[11,12] The distribution of temperature through a thick layer and one of normal thickness 30 min after laying, when rolling is normally still in progress, is predicted in Fig. 5. Comparison of curves 1 and 2 and of 3 and 4 illustrate the superior heat retaining ability of thick layer construction under different conditions. Curve 5 will be considered later. The importance of weather conditions and initial laying temperature is also illustrated in Fig. 5; the two curves corresponding to the 90 mm layer show that the mid-depth temperature 30 min after laying under normal conditions would be 95 °C whereas that of material laid cold in wintry conditions would be 35 °C lower. Factors which have greatest effect on cooling of roadbase and basecourse layers have been shown[9] to be the thickness and initial temperature of the material. Ambient temperature has less effect and wind speed is least important.

Binder Content

Over a wide range of practical binder contents, a change in binder content, although reflected by a corresponding change of void content, does not affect the final achieved values of VMA. Results are shown in Fig. 6 for a range of binder contents wider than that permitted by the present UK specification and for widely differing compactive efforts. The materials, dense coated macadams containing crushed Croft granite of 40 mm maximum size mixed with 100 pen bitumen, were compacted with an 8·5 Mg tandem roller at temperatures between 100 and 105 °C. The binder fills the interstices in the aggregate matrix and affects the void content of the mix but does not influence the compacted state of the aggregate, i.e. the VMA.

Other Factors

Other factors known to influence compaction are the type and grading of the aggregate,[13] the type of binder and the stiffness of the working platform.[7,14] For conditions in the UK they are however generally of less importance.

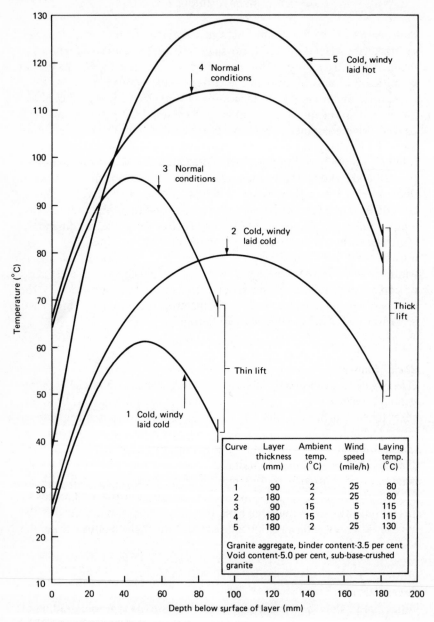

Curve	Layer thickness (mm)	Ambient temp. (°C)	Wind speed (mile/h)	Laying temp. (°C)
1	90	2	25	80
2	180	2	25	80
3	90	15	5	115
4	180	15	5	115
5	180	2	25	130

Granite aggregate, binder content-3.5 per cent
Void content-5.0 per cent, sub-base-crushed granite

FIG. 5. Variation of temperature with depth of bituminous layer 30 min after laying. (Crown copyright, reproduced by permission of the Controller of HM Stationery Office.)

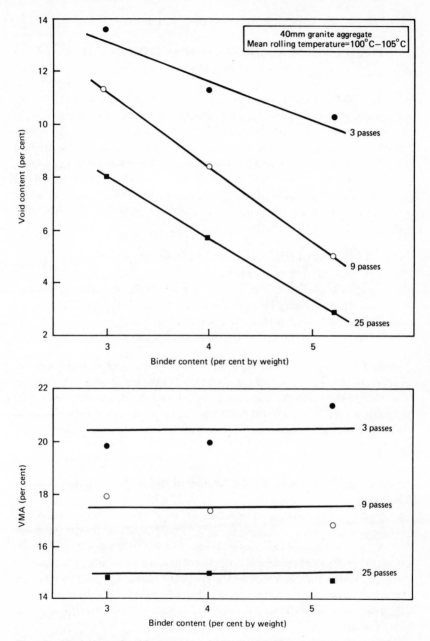

FIG. 6.   Variation of void content and VMA with bitumen content at different stages of compaction of dense bitumen macadam. (Crown copyright, reproduced by permission of the Controller of HM Stationery Office.)

expedite: help or hurry the progress of

METHODS OF INCREASING COMPACTION IN THE WHEEL-PATHS

It has been shown that in typical road construction the final density of dense roadbase and basecourse macadam achieved in the nearside wheel-path is about 3% less than that at the centre of the laid width. The cost of compaction in the UK is only a few per cent of the total cost of laid material[15] and there is considerable scope for improving compaction at little or no extra cost by modifying the compaction procedures. Given the prospect of cost savings arising from improved performance of better compacted materials, it is worthwhile considering the following methods of achieving improved compaction in the field:

(a) modify the pattern of rolling to increase the number of roller passes in the nearside wheel-paths;
(b) expedite the rolling process to ensure that adequate compactive effort is applied before the material has cooled excessively;
(c) construct the roadbase in a single thick layer;
(d) employ more powerful compaction machines.

In the following, roller passages have been used as a convenient general measure of rolling; a roller passage is defined as the longitudinal movement of a roller past a reference line across the laid width. However, to quantify the compactive effort at a given point, the lateral position and dimensions of the roller have been taken into account to calculate roller passes as defined earlier.

screed: tiresomely long list or letter etc.

Patterns of Rolling to Increase the Number of Roller Passes in the Nearside Wheel-path

One method of increasing compaction in the nearside wheel-path, (only possible where a hard shoulder is being constructed), is to lay the hard shoulder and left-hand lane in a single pass of a paver equipped with a wide screed; the position of the nearside wheel-path would then be near the middle of the laid width and thus receive the greatest number of roller passes. An alternative approach capable of more general application is to modify the rolling pattern so that the rolling effort is concentrated towards the edges of the laid width.

Using a computer technique to simulate roller-pass distributions across a laid width, it has been shown that if one of the two rollers normally on site was used solely to roll the edges this would improve compaction in the wheel-path zones. It was also evident that a tandem roller used for this purpose would give the most improvement.

The normal rolling procedure using two three-wheel rollers has been compared with a method in which one three-wheel roller, used normally, was followed by an 8–10 Mg tandem deadweight roller concentrating on the edges of the laid material. Figure 7 shows the distributions of compaction and passes obtained. The edge rolling method increased the number of passes in the critical wheel-path zones at the expense of the passes between the wheel paths; lower values of VMA were achieved in the wheel-path and the minimum value of VMA did not occur at the centre of the laid width. Conventional rolling using a three-wheel roller has also been compared with a method in which the laid material is first rolled normally and then rolled solely at the edges with the three-wheel roller. A small increase in number of passes was achieved in the nearside wheel-path zone with the modified procedure but the improvement was considerably less marked than that obtained with a tandem roller; the peak density remained at the centre of the laid width. There was no detrimental effect on the surface finish obtained and no other practical difficulties were encountered.

Rolling Requirements to Expedite the Rolling Process

Compaction is most effective when the maximum compactive effort, directed on the lines indicated in the previous section into the material in the wheel-path zones, is applied when material temperatures are such as to allow compaction to take place easily, i.e. at temperatures well above the threshold temperature below which significant further compaction is not possible. Before developing improved compaction procedures it is important to establish the time available after the laying of the bituminous material for its effective compaction. This is determined by the rate at which compaction is applied by rollers and the threshold temperature.

Time Available for Effective Compaction

The minimum temperature for the completion of rolling has generally been taken[16,17] to be that mid-depth temperature corresponding to a binder viscosity of 10^3 P. The grade of binder will of course determine the minimum compaction temperature; for 100 pen bitumen, the most common binder in dense roadbase and basecourse macadams used in the construction of heavily trafficked roads, the temperature corresponding to a binder viscosity of 10^3 P is 60 °C. The time taken for the temperature of a bituminous layer to fall to this minimum level will vary considerably with ambient temperature, layer thickness and its temperature when laid.

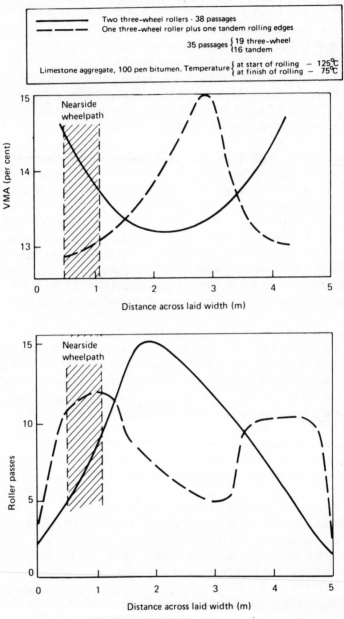

FIG. 7. Comparison between modified rolling using a tandem and normal rolling using three-wheel rollers. (Crown copyright, reproduced by permission of the Controller of HM Stationery Office.)

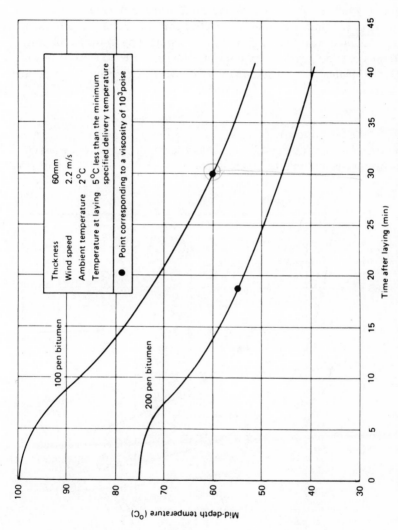

Fig. 8. Rates of cooling of dense roadbase macadam containing different grades of binder, under adverse site conditions. (Crown copyright, reproduced by permission of the Controller of HM Stationery Office.)

A computer program has been used to predict the rates of cooling over a wide range of conditions. Figure 8 shows that under adverse conditions when poor compaction is most likely to occur the time taken for material containing 100 pen bitumen to cool to 60 °C is 30 min. This period is a good estimate of the time available for effective compaction of dense roadbase and basecourse macadams except those containing 200 pen bitumen; material containing 200 pen bitumen must be delivered at temperatures at least 10 °C higher than the minimum 80 °C specified to ensure that a period of 30 min is available for compaction.

The Rolling Operation

A model of the rolling operation enables the important factors governing the coverage achievable to be identified.[9] Figure 9 shows the number of

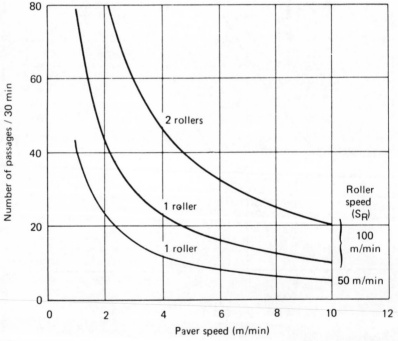

FIG. 9.   Effect of paver speed on number of roller passages completed in 30 min. (Crown copyright, reproduced by permission of the Controller of HM Stationery Office.)

roller passages calculated for different speeds of both roller and paver and a rolling period of 30 min. The mean paver speed at sites is normally less than $6 \, m \, min^{-1}$, typically 2 or $3 \, m \, min^{-1}$, whereas the roller speed is about $100 \, m \, min^{-1}$. These values of roller and paver speed enable more than 30 passages to be completed in 30 min using the 2 rollers that are normally available on site; indeed in many practical situations, one roller would be sufficient to complete 30 passages in this period. The number of passages can be increased by increasing the speed or number of rollers and by reducing the roller-passage length or the speed of the paver.

The number of roller passages actually completed varies considerably, not only from day to day on a given contract, but continuously during each day's work. The typical number of passages completed in 30 min at locations regularly spaced along the carriageway and the contribution made by each of the two three-wheel rollers is shown in Fig. 10. Rolling begins within 6 min of laying and the speed of rolling is sufficient for the completion, on the average, of over 30 passages in 30 min. There is, however, considerable variation in the number of passages completed in the first 30 min. The furthermost reference point along the carriageway represents the end of one section of paving and it is a common feature that fewer passes are made by the second roller as it approaches this point. This is a consequence of the second roller working far back from the paver initially and gradually moving closer to the paver during the period of paving.

In general, best use is not being made of the compaction plant available at sites and there is considerable variation in the rolling procedures adopted. There is therefore a need to ensure that compaction procedures in general are brought up to the best standards being achieved at the present time.

Proposed Compaction Requirements
The analytical and site evidence indicated that proper control of rolling operations should enable the completion of 30 roller passages in 30 min. With conventional rolling, 30 passages over a laid width of 4 m should result in about 7 roller passes in the wheel-path zones. Modified rolling, in which half the total number of roller passages are made by one roller concentrating on rolling the edges, would increase the number of passes made in the wheel-path. If this second roller were a tandem, about 11 passes would be completed in the wheel-paths after a total of 30 passages had been made, whereas 8 or possibly 9 passes would be achieved if a three-wheel roller were used for this purpose. Of course, the rolling capacity on site frequently enables considerably more than 30 passages to be completed

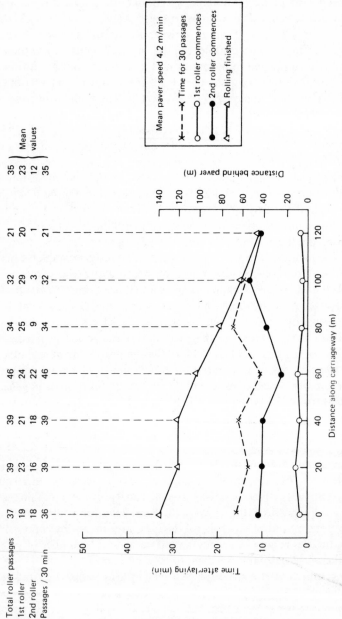

Fig. 10. Time taken to complete the different stages of rolling—typical result. (Crown copyright, reproduced by permission of the Controller of HM Stationery Office.)

within 30 min of laying. Consideration of the foregoing has led to the following proposals:

(a) For a laid width of 4 m a minimum of 30 roller passages should be completed within 30 min of the material being laid. The number of passages made are not of course limited to 30; if the rolling capacity available at a site is more than adequate, additional passes should be made within the 30 min period or later. When the laid width is other than 4 m the minimum number of roller passages should be adjusted in direct proportion with the laid width.

(b) Half of the roller passages should be carried out with the nearest edge of the roller within about 300 mm of the edge of the laid material. This could usually be achieved by using one of the two rollers normally available at sites, to concentrate on rolling the edges. Greater improvements in compaction at the wheel-path zones can be realised if this second roller is a tandem.

(c) The minimum delivery temperature should be increased from 80 °C to at least 90 °C when 200 pen bitumen is used.

The compaction time of 30 min specified in (a) is the time available for effective compaction under adverse conditions when poor compaction is most likely to occur. Effective compaction can of course still continue for longer than 30 min when conditions are more favourable and the requirements could be adjusted to take account of such conditions.

With the above procedure and keeping existing delivery temperatures unaltered except for 200 pen bitumen, the specification of a minimum compaction temperature becomes unnecessary. Rolling temperatures can be controlled by the specified delivery temperature and the required rate at which rolling is carried out. Accurate measurement of the temperature of the laid material is difficult because of the large variation of temperature with depth and it would be a distinct advantage if this measurement were not necessary in a modified specification.

An improved compaction specification which incorporates the proposed requirements is now being implemented in a number of contracts to observe its operation.

Thick Layer Construction

The superior heat retaining ability of thick layer construction noted earlier indicates the potential of this form of construction for improving compaction. However, the ability of thick layer construction to provide sufficiently well regulated roadbase and basecourse levels to allow the

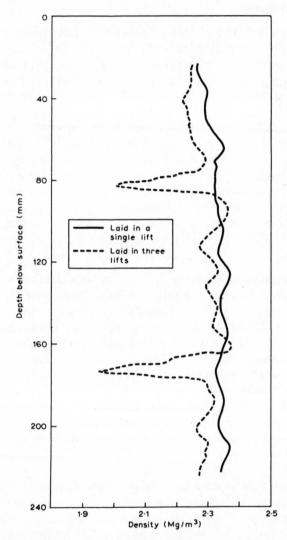

FIG. 11. Typical density depth profiles. (Crown copyright, reproduced by permission of the Controller of HM Stationery Office.)

construction of a wearing course to meet the requirements of current specifications relating to the riding quality of the finished surface has been questioned. An experiment was therefore constructed by the TRRL at Sevenoaks By-pass on the A21[10] to investigate the performance of a fully flexible road, the roadbase and basecourse of which were constructed in four different configurations of thickness of gravel asphalt. The performance was assessed in terms of degree of compaction achieved, surface irregularity and the accuracy of surface levels of the bituminous pavement layers. During compaction, heat losses to the atmosphere and underlayer resulted in low densities at the upper and lower boundary regions of the layer. The variations of density with depth for a single thick layer and the same total thickness compacted in three thinner layers are given in Fig. 11. Thick layer construction reduces the number of interfaces between layers and therefore the number of zones of low density. The overall rate of cooling is also slower in thick layers as shown in Fig. 5 and effective rolling can be carried out for a longer period of time than on thin layers. There may, however, be associated disadvantages; curve 5 of Fig. 5 represents the condition of a thick layer laid hot to counteract the adverse wintry conditions. A skin of relatively cold and stiff material on the upper surface rests on an extremely hot mass, the centre temperature having only dropped by 2 °C over a 30 min period. There is the danger of cracking the surface material and of lack of stability of the mix under the roller.

Lack of stability was in fact encountered in precisely these circumstances in the thicker layers of the experiment. Good compaction was achieved in all thicknesses of asphalt employed. The specifications regarding surface irregularity and level could not be met on the thickest layer, a combined base and basecourse 240 mm thick. The laying of the wearing course improved the final surface finish to within specification but under traffic the riding quality deteriorated more rapidly than that of the pavement containing base layers of conventional thickness. The most successful form of thick layer construction was the single layer of roadbase 175 mm thick. The irregularities at its surface were reduced by the laying of conventional surfacing courses to give a final surface of acceptable regularity whose deterioration under traffic has been no worse than the pavement laid to a conventional thickness. Specified levels were also achieved without difficulty.

Although the results of experiments in thick layer construction are encouraging, certain aspects of this type of construction using conventional equipment require further investigation before its general use can be advocated with confidence. In particular the ability to compact thick layers at rolling temperatures closer to the minimum specified, needs study.

More Powerful Compaction Machines

Figure 4 shows that the VMA can still be decreasing with increasing number of passes beyond the 30 pass level. It is difficult or impossible to complete this number of passes in the nearside wheel-path in the time available for effective compaction and there is clearly a need for a more efficient compaction machine if compaction close to refusal is to be obtained.

Vibrating rollers are not currently permitted in the Specification for compaction of bituminous road layers largely because of lack of experience in this country. They are increasingly used abroad where it has been claimed[18,19] that productivity is increased by the use of these rollers because of the reduction in number of roller passes required to achieve specified levels of compaction. This could enable the number of rollers employed at a site to be reduced or, alternatively, a higher overall density to be achieved with the same number of rollers. Further advantages claimed, include the ability of vibrating rollers to compact materials at lower temperatures and, to achieve a more uniform density across the laid width of material than that obtained with deadweight rollers. However, there is, as yet, no conclusive evidence which demonstrates that the vibrating rollers currently available in the UK will consistently provide greater compaction of dense coated macadams than that currently achieved with conventional deadweight machines; optimum vibrational characteristics, such as amplitude, frequency and centrifugal force, have not been established for their use on bituminous materials.

An alternative approach would be to use heavier deadweight machines. Trials in Ontario[20,21] have shown that a 30 Mg pneumatic-tyred roller provided considerably improved compaction of material on which difficulty had been experienced with conventional 9 Mg machines. The most effective rolling sequence found was to use initially a relatively light steel-wheeled roller close to the paving machine, followed by the pneumatic-tyred roller and, finally, by a steel roller for finishing. A heavy steel-wheeled deadweight roller may therefore have potential for improving compaction of dense coated macadams, possibly as a second roller following a conventional deadweight machine.

THE RELATIONSHIP BETWEEN COMPACTION AND PAVEMENT PERFORMANCE

Improved compaction is of benefit only if improved pavement performance results. An understanding of the way in which compaction influences structural performance is necessary in order to be able to assess whether obtaining improved compaction in the wheel-path zones are sufficient to justify significant reductions in pavement thickness or extensions of design life.

The role of a bituminous roadbase and basecourse, acting as the main structural elements of a fully flexible road, is to reduce stresses and strains generated in the road foundation by traffic to an acceptable level. At the same time the roadbase and basecourse must be resistant to internal deformation and cracking under repeated traffic loading.

Full-scale road experiments have not included the state of compaction of bituminous materials as an explicit variable. However, information is now becoming available on the influence of compaction on several parameters related to pavement performance.

The conclusions regarding the relation between performance and the compacted state drawn from the study of any one parameter are not, by themselves, convincing for reasons which will be discussed. By considering the results as a whole, broader based conclusions emerge.

Dynamic Stiffness Modulus

As described in Chapters 1 and 2 the dynamic stiffness moduli of bituminous materials define their load spreading capacity and are also related to their resistance to fatigue cracking. Moduli of bitumen macadam roadbases and basecourses laid in pilot-scale trials have been measured *in situ* using a wave propagation technique.[22] Low level sinusoidal loading was used to generate flexural waves in the roadbase over a range of frequencies between 4 and 22 kHz and their velocity of propagation measured. The relation between velocity and wavelength depends on the density and modulus of the roadbase; for the purposes of comparison the modulus was evaluated in terms of the velocity approaching zero wavelength.

The common relation obtained between dynamic stiffness modulus and void content for the four materials studied is given in the top half of Fig. 12; a substantial increase in material stiffness results from better compaction, a 3 % reduction in voids bringing about a 26 % increase in the modulus of an initially well compacted (5 % voids) macadam.

Because of the unrealistically high frequency employed in the test method, values of moduli obtained are much larger than those relevant to the road situation. Cores taken from the experimental pavements were also tested in the laboratory using more realistic stress levels and loading frequency.[23] The results are given in the lower half of Fig. 12 and confirm the rate of

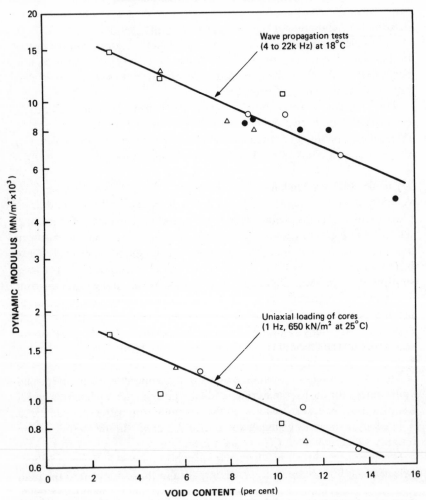

FIG. 12.   Variation of dynamic modulus with void content. (Crown copyright, reproduced by permission of the Controller of HM Stationery Office.)

change of stiffness with void content, the actual values of moduli being about one decade smaller.

At TRRL a more complete picture of the stiffness of bitumen-macadams over the whole practical range of frequency and temperature is now being obtained by testing specimens in three-point bending in a computer controlled facility. Results are in general agreement with those of Fig. 12.

The possible consequences of stiffer base materials on road performance are considered below.

Load Spreading Capacity

An indication of the effect of changing dynamic moduli of the roadbase and basecourse layers is obtained by considering the road as a simple two-layer elastic system. The relation between the vertical component of stress (σ_z) transmitted to the road foundation of modulus (E_2) and the modulus (E_1) and thickness (h) of the pavement can be approximated to by[24]

$$\sigma_z \propto \left(\frac{1}{h}\right)^{1 \cdot 85} \left(\frac{E_2}{E_1}\right)^{0 \cdot 64} \tag{1}$$

In the UK, deterioration of pavements with bituminous roadbases is manifested by the development of deformation in the wheel-paths with cracking taking place only at a later stage. Deformation is seasonal, taking place primarily in warm weather when E_1 is low. All pavement layers and the subgrade contribute to the developing deformation; the stresses transmitted to the sub-base and subgrade are therefore sufficiently large for any improvement in the load spreading capacity of the roadbase and basecourse to be beneficial to pavement performance.

Increasing the modulus of the macadam by 26 % reduces σ_z by 15 % and, from eqn. (1), a reduction in pavement thickness of about 8 % will give the same value of stress σ_z under the stiffer pavement. There is little evidence as to which subgrade parameter is most directly related to the deformability of the subgrade; using vertical subgrade strain as an alternative a similar conclusion is reached.

Practical road pavements contain more layers than the simple model considered above and their dynamic behaviour is also affected by such factors as the distribution of temperature with depth through the bituminous layers. However, more sophisticated analysis which takes these factors into account yields substantially similar reductions in design thickness.

Resistance to Cracking

The review of bituminous materials given in Chapter 2 indicates that in laboratory fatigue tests of a particular bituminous material at a given temperature, the prime factor controlling the onset of cracking is the maximum dynamic tensile strain in the specimen at the start of the test. The laboratory fatigue performance of a particular material may be characterised by the relationship between the tensile strain, ε, and the number of load cycles to failure, N_f which is of the form

$$N_f = C\left(\frac{1}{\varepsilon}\right)^m \qquad (2)$$

where C and m are constants for a particular material and test condition: m is typically between 4 and 5 for dense bitumen-macadam.

An increase in compactive effort, results in a small increase in percentage volume of binder and it has been predicted[25, 26] that this will indirectly influence fatigue performance in laboratory tests. However, the maximum change in binder volume resulting from the variation in compactive effort is less than 1 % and its possible effect on the strain–life relationship of eqn. (2) was not observed in recent fatigue tests at TRRL in which the dynamic stress amplitude was kept constant throughout each test. Results obtained at Nottingham University,[25] at TRRL and by Kirk[26] indicate that in practice the primary influence of compaction is an indirect one; the increase in dynamic modulus brought about by better compaction decreases the tensile strain produced by a given load in the laboratory test. This point has been considered in more detail in Chapter 2.

The simple two-layer pavement model can be used to illustrate the way in which fatigue behaviour is affected by dynamic strains generated in the pavement. In the road it has been postulated[27] that the strain at the bottom of the roadbase layer ε is the critical parameter which determines fatigue life. Using the same nomenclature as before

$$\varepsilon \propto \left(\frac{1}{h}\right)^{1\cdot 8} \log\left(\frac{E_1}{E_2}\right)\frac{1}{E_1} \qquad (3)$$

The tensile strain in the roadbase therefore decreases almost linearly with increasing pavement stiffness for most practical road conditions. As the form of eqn. (2) indicates that small increases in the modulus of the bituminous roadbase will result in considerable increases in fatigue life, improved compaction should have a marked effect on fatigue performance. The percentage increase brought about by better compacted and therefore stiffer materials would depend greatly on temperature used to characterise the pavement in the analysis.

Equation (3) indicates that the highest strain levels are obtained with low values of pavement modulus and this has been confirmed in strain measurements made on experimental pavements; warm and hot weather conditions would control fatigue behaviour. Under these conditions eqn. (3) indicates that a reduction in the thickness of a pavement made of the stiffer material to give the same value of tensile strain as that of a material of lower stiffness (with 3 % greater voids) is in the range 3 to 8 %.

The apparent promise of greatly improved fatigue performance in the road from better compacted materials has however to be considered in relation to the fact that there is virtually no evidence in the UK of failure by fatigue cracking of bituminous roadbase materials to present specifications. In order to develop a better understanding of fatigue behaviour in practice, predictions made from laboratory fatigue results need to be compared with the performance of flexible pavements tested under controlled conditions of temperature and wheel load.

Resistance to Internal Deformation

Up to half the surface deformation of a pavement incorporating a bituminous roadbase and surfacing takes place in these two layers; their deformation characteristics are therefore important in determining pavement performance.

The resistance to deformation of 150 mm cores cut from experimentally compacted sections has been studied in the wheel tracking test.[16] The standard test temperature of 45 °C adopted is approximately the highest temperature ever reached at the top of the basecourse in the UK; a limited number of tests were therefore also made on base material at 32 °C, more typical of the highest temperatures recorded in the middle of the roadbase layer. Results expressed in terms of the depth of track at the centre of the specimen after 40 min operation are given in Fig. 13. The few measurements made on base material at 32 °C gave a similar trend and absolute values for the better compacted material lower than values obtained at 45 °C.

These results indicate the desirability of attaining the maximum possible level of compaction. However the tracking test, although valuable from the point of view of its convenience and speed, is far removed from the reality of the road.

In an attempt to overcome this, more realistic tracking tests[28] have been carried out on slabs of macadam roadbase material mounted on a rigid table and trafficked at 31 °C by a pneumatic tyre loaded to 20 kN at an inflation pressure of $690 \, \text{kN m}^{-2}$. The slab is moved to-and-fro under the wheel and at the end of each to-and-fro cycle the wheel moves sideways to simulate the distribution of actual traffic in the wheel-path zone. The results confirmed the dependence of deformation resistance on the compacted state, the slope of the relation being greater than that shown on Fig. 13.

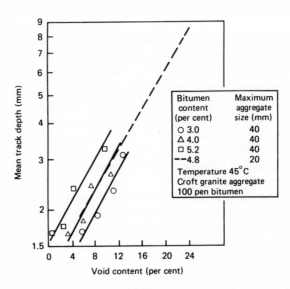

FIG. 13.   Effect of void content and binder content on mean values of track depth. (Crown copyright, reproduced by permission of the Controller of HM Stationery Office.)

Deflection

Deflection of the complete road pavement is a more general indicator of structural performance as discussed elsewhere.[31] When measured in a standard manner it has been shown to correlate well with pavement performance expressed in terms of life up to the stage when strengthening by overlaying is advisable.[29] Deflection criteria were established primarily in relation to the development of surface deformation; as already noted this is the main mode of deterioration of flexible pavements in the UK.

The inclusion of a sub-base and subgrade of realistic strength in the pilot-scale facility at TRRL enabled deflection of experimental pavements to be used to examine the relation between performance and the compacted state. Deflection measurements were taken on the top of a crushed stone sub-base and on compacted bitumen-macadam roadbases, the latter results corrected for the effects of temperature to an equivalent standard temperature of 20 °C. Variations in foundation stiffness between experimental sections as reflected by deflections measured on the top of the sub-base were also allowed for. The considerably greater stiffness of the better compacted material is reflected in the relation between deflection and void content shown in Fig. 14; the trend is readily distinguishable for individual binder contents.

Because it is the deflection of the finished road surface which has been correlated with pavement performance under traffic, the deflections in Fig. 14 have been adjusted to allow for the effect of typical rolled asphalt surfacings, 40 and 100 mm thick, again using ref. 29; the results are given on the same diagram. A decrease in void content from 13 to 3 % results in a decrease in deflection from 64 to 48×10^{-2} mm. The relation between deflection and performance in ref. 29 indicates that this change would more than double the critical life of the pavement up to the point where overlaying is necessary.

The decrease in deflection brought about by reducing the void content of the roadbase in the wheel-paths by 3 % to that of the peak value is between 7·5 and 9·5 % for a pavement with a 40 mm rolled asphalt surfacing, the actual percentage depending on the initial state of the compacted material. The corresponding increases in pavement life are 30 and 35 % equivalent to reductions in the combined thickness of the bituminous surfacing and roadbase of about 5 %. With the thicker 100 mm surfacing the reductions in deflection are rather smaller but correspond to reductions in thickness of the order of 6 %.

The above analysis has been carried out on results obtained on experimental areas in which the same weight of material per unit area was laid and compacted. The quantified improved behaviour is therefore not attributable to the presence of more material in a better compacted layer.

The deflection approach can be criticised on the grounds that the stiffness of the foundation varied considerably between the test sections, and that the relation between deflection and performance used was not explicitly derived for pavements with bituminous bases of different compacted states. However, a second analytical approach ignoring the effects of foundation stiffness yielded a similar relation to that shown on Fig. 14 and examination of limited data from pavements with rolled asphalt roadbases at a full-scale experiment indicated that the state of compaction did not appear to affect the deflection–performance relationship.

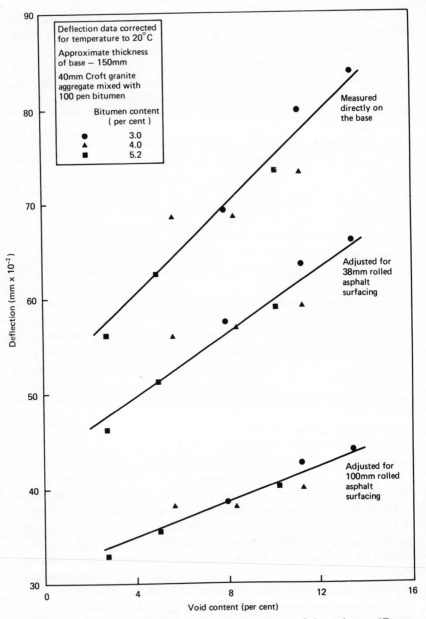

FIG. 14. Variation of deflection with void content of base layer. (Crown copyright, reproduced by permission of the Controller of HM Stationery Office.)

Relation of Compaction to Performance

There is at present a lack of authoritative and quantitative information describing the mechanism which governs the deterioration and failure of flexible pavements but research currently in progress at various centres should improve our ability to interpret measurements of dynamic modulus and fatigue in terms of the real stress–strain behaviour of pavements and therefore of their performance. However, all the studies reported show that improving the state of compaction of dense coated macadam is beneficial to pavement performance. Significant benefit would be obtained if densities in the wheel-paths were increased to the peak values currently achieved between the wheel-paths.

NEW MATERIALS

Because the properties of bituminous materials are dependent on their compaction it is essential when developing new materials to study their compactability at an early stage.

Low Binder Content Macadams

It is now commonly believed that the current composition specification for dense coated macadams could be improved; equal performance from materials of lower binder content, better compacted in the wheel-path areas, may be possible. This approach is particularly attractive in view of the recent large increases in the price of bitumen, about 400 % since 1973.

Figure 6 shows that for granite macadam and bitumen contents in the range 3·0 to 5·2 %, a change of binder content, although reflected by a corresponding change of void content does not affect VMA. More recently it has been found that this conclusion holds for macadams with bitumen contents as low as 2·5 %. However, below this value there is insufficient binder present to provide material of adequate integrity, the material is difficult to compact and the values of VMA are considerably higher than those of Fig. 6. Preliminary performance data for low binder content materials are promising. The trends indicated in Figs. 12, 13 and 14 for dynamic modulus, resistance to deformation and deflection can be extended to bitumen contents as low as 2·5 %, that is, to materials with a binder content 1 % less than the target value currently specified. Changes in modulus and deflection brought about by reducing binder content are potentially adverse in relation to structural performance, but may be offset by better compaction in the wheel-paths. On the other hand the resistance to deformation of these low binder content materials is at least as good as currently specified materials. There is, however, a marked reduction in resistance to fatigue cracking if the binder content is reduced and this may be only partly compensated for by achieving better compaction. This reduced fatigue performance must be considered in relation to the lack of evidence in the UK, already noted, of fatigue cracking of bituminous roadbases complying with current specifications. Further work is in progress to establish the fatigue lives of these materials in the road situation and to investigate the compaction characteristics and performance of low binder content macadams over a wider range of aggregate types.

Grave-bitume

Grave-bitume, a dense-graded bituminous material similar in some respects to the dense coated macadams used in the UK, but incorporating a stiffer binder, has been developed in France primarily to give high resistance to permanent deformation under traffic.[30] The structural performance of dense coated macadam incorporating the essential features of grave-bitume is under investigation but careful consideration must again be given to compaction of these materials; considerable emphasis is placed in France on the high level of compaction necessary to obtain satisfactory performance from grave-bitume and the required compaction plant is considerably more powerful and expensive than the 8–10 Mg smooth wheeled deadweight rollers normally used in the UK.

SUMMARY

In the UK the Specification for compaction of dense roadbase and basecourse macadams does not stipulate the number or distribution of roller passes or the degree of compaction to be obtained. There is therefore no direct incentive to achieve the high degree of compaction, particularly in the wheel-path zones, necessary to obtain optimum performance from these materials. The common practice of roller drivers leads to densities in the wheel-paths typically 3 % less than those achieved between the wheel-paths. Because little or no densification under traffic occurs in dense roadbase macadam the performance of this material is determined by its properties at the time of construction and there is therefore scope for improving performance by improving compaction in the wheel-paths. Compaction is relatively cheap and such improvements could be obtained at little or no extra cost.

The results of studies of the factors affecting compaction and of field trials in which a tandem roller operated specifically in the wheel-path zones have been combined to formulate improved compaction procedures which should expedite the rolling process and ensure that greater compactive effort is applied before the material has cooled excessively. Construction in thick layers is a further possible means of improving compaction but this may be achieved at the expense of some loss of riding quality. The superior heat-retaining ability of thick layers, in many ways advantageous, can also present construction problems under certain circumstances and further work is necessary before advocating the general use of thick-layer construction. Finally, there is clearly a need for a more efficient compaction machine if optimum compaction in the wheel-paths in all practical conditions is to be obtained.

Investigations of dynamic stiffness modulus, resistance to deformation and fatigue cracking, of coated macadams in various stages of compaction and deflection of the total pavement containing these materials all show that improving the state of compaction is beneficial to pavement performance. Worthwhile extensions of pavement life or, alternatively, reduction in pavement thickness can be obtained if compaction in the wheel-paths is increased to the peak values now being obtained in the centre of the laid width.

New materials, such as low binder content macadams and grave-bitume, have promise as roadbases and basecourses for use in the UK. The importance of compaction in determining performance makes compaction studies an essential part of their development.

REFERENCES

1. HIGHWAY RESEARCH BOARD. Special Report 131, 1972.
2. DEPARTMENT OF TRANSPORT. Specification for road and bridge works, HMSO, London, 1976.
3. HARLAND, D. G. Magazine of Concrete Research, 18, 95–101, 1966.
4. HUGHES, C. S. and RALSTON, H. H. Proc. Ass. of Asphalt Paving Technol., 32, 106–42, 1963.
5. HEIN, T. C. and SCHMIDT, R. J. ASTM No. 309, 49–62, American Society for Testing and Materials, Philadelphia, 1961.
6. HOFSTRA, A. Shell Bitumen Review, 52, 11–14, 1975.
7. LEECH, D. and POWELL, W. D. Department of the Enviornment, TRRL Laboratory Report LR 619, Transport and Road Research Laboratory, Crowthorne, 1974.
8. LEECH, D. and SELVES, N. W. Department of the Environment, TRRL Laboratory Report LR 724. Transport and Road Research Laboratory, Crowthorne, 1976.
9. POWELL, W. D. and LEECH, D. Department of the Environment, TRRL Laboratory Report LR 727, Transport and Road Research Laboratory, Crowthorne, 1976.

10. GAUNT, J. and POWELL, W. D. Department of the Environment, TRRL Report LR 596, Transport and Road Research Laboratory, Crowthorne, 1973.
11. JORDAN, P. G. and THOMAS, M. E. Department of the Environment, TRRL Report LR 729, Transport and Road Research Laboratory, Crowthorne, 1976.
12. CORLEW, J. S. and DICKSON, P. F. Proc. Ass. of Asphalt Paving Technol., **37**, 101–40, 1968.
13. LEFEBVRE, J. A. and ROBERTSON, W. D. Proc. 14th Annual Conf. Can. tech. Asph. Ass., **14**, 193, 1969.
14. EPPS, J. A., GALLAWAY, B. M., HARPER, W. J., SCOTT, W. W. and SEAY, J. W. Texas Transportation Institute, Res. Report 90-2F, Texas A & M Univ.,|1970.
15. HILLS, J. F. and FINEY, J. T. Practical aspects of the compaction of bituminous materials, Asphalt and Coated Macadam Association Annual Seminar, London 1974.
16. ROAD RESEARCH LABORATORY. Department of Scientific and Industrial Research, Bituminous materials in road construction, HMSO, London, 1962.
17. McLEOD, N. W. Highway Research Record No. 158, 76–115, 1967.
18. FORSSBLAD, L. Vibration of asphalt surfacings, Research Bulletin Ref. No. 8016, AB Vibroverken, Sweden, 1968.
19. WELDIN, F. *Muck Shifter*, 40–2, January 1968.
20. FROMM, H. J. Proc. Ass. Asphalt Paving Technol., **33**, 241–84, 1964.
21. FROMM, H. J. and PHANG, W. A. Proc. Ass. of Asphalt Paving Technol., **35**, 529–47, 1966.
22. JONES, R., THROWER, E. N. and GATFIELD, E. N. Proc. 2nd Int. Conf. on the struct. design of asphalt pavements, Ann Arbor, 1967, Univ. of Michigan, 1968, p. 404.
23. SNAITH, M. Deformation characteristics of dense bitumen macadam subjected to dynamic loading, Ph.D. thesis, Department of Civil Engineering, Univ. of Nottingham, 1973.
24. LISTER, N. W. and JONES, R. Proc. 2nd Int. Conf. on the struct. design of asphalt pavements, Ann Arbor 1967, Univ. of Michigan, 1968, p. 1021.
25. COOPER, K. E. and PELL, P. S. Department of the Environment, TRRL Report LR 633, Transport and Road Research Laboratory, Crowthorne, 1974.
26. KIRK, J. M. Proc. 3rd Int. Conf. on the struct. design of asphalt pavements, London 1972, Univ. of Michigan, 1972, p. 241.
27. DEACON, J. A. Fatigue life prediction, Hwy Res. Brd, Special Report 140, 78, 1973.
28. RAITHBY, K. D. and RAMSHAW, J. T. Department of the Environment, TRRL Report LR 471, Transport and Road Research Laboratory, Crowthorne, 1972.
29. LISTER, N. W. Proc. 3rd Int. Conf. on the struct. design of asphalt pavements, London 1972, Univ. of Michigan, 1972, p. 1206.
30. HINGLEY, C. E., PEATTIE, K. R. and POWELL, W. D. Department of the Environment, TRRL Supplementary Report 242. Transport and Road Research Laboratory, Crowthorne, 1976.
31. LISTER, N. W. and KENNEDY, C.´ K. Assessment of performance and overlay design of flexible pavements, Chapter 4, in *Developments in Highway Pavement Engineering—2*, P. S. Pell (ed.), Applied Science Publishers, London, 1978.

Chapter 5

CEMENT STABILISED MATERIALS

R. I. T. WILLIAMS

University of Surrey, Guildford, UK

SUMMARY

Current practice in Great Britain regarding the use of cement stabilised materials in highway pavements is reviewed with respect to material selection, thickness design and pavement construction.

In the text, emphasis is placed on the inherent crack susceptibility of materials of this type since this characteristic has had a major influence on both mix design and pavement design. Test procedures, and their limitations, are considered in some detail and an attempt is made to comment in a constructive manner on specification matters which the author regards as unsatisfactory. Attention is also drawn to the need to conserve high quality materials and at the same time to improve the environment by giving consideration to the use of cement treated industrial waste materials.

INTRODUCTION

The original concept of stabilising soils with cement is attributed[1] to the trials by H. E. Brooke-Bradley on Salisbury Plain in 1917, but it was not until 1935 in South Carolina that the technique was used on a substantial scale. Since then, cement stabilised materials have been extensively used in many countries and a considerable amount of information is now available regarding the properties and field performance of materials of this type.

In Great Britain, the urgent need for airfields during the second world war followed by the pressing demands for highway construction during the post war years provided a stimulus for research and for innovation by practicing engineers. During this era, a particular type of cement stabilised material known as lean concrete, or more descriptively as rolled dry lean concrete, gained widespread acceptance for roadbase construction. It involves the use of washed aggregate of concreting quality, a low cement content and a low water content, thereby producing a relatively uniform material of modest strength at an extremely low workability. This is laid without joints other than construction joints, compacted by rolling, cured by the application of bitumen emulsion and, in flexible pavements, surfaced with bituminous material. It suffers from a disadvantage, so far as construction is concerned, in that a maturing period of at least 7 days must be observed before use by site traffic and this is particularly inconvenient in reconstruction schemes. Nevertheless, the material has been used in many parts of the country over the full spectrum from motorways to minor housing estate roads. Its popularity is attributable to the ease with which it can be produced and laid using plant which is readily available and to its favourable record as an all-weather working platform for site traffic. So far as performance is concerned, the most common defect in pavements incorporating lean concrete roadbases is the incidence of transverse cracks and, over the years, this has influenced practice in favour of using progressively leaner mixes and progressively greater thicknesses of bituminous cover.

Although lean concrete is often used as a sub-base under concrete paving, it is essentially a roadbase material for flexible pavements and, as such, it is widely used. A quantitative indication was given in 1972 by James[2] who analysed 60 successful tenders for new road construction started in 1969. The analysis related to a length of 422 km and, of the 60 schemes, lean concrete was used in 26 instances. Further information is given by Brooks[3] who stated in 1972 that lean concrete roadbases had been the most common form of construction in recent years in most parts of the country. His remarks were based on a cost study of the lowest three tender prices on eight motorway contracts in the Midlands. He concluded that there was economic justification for its use since the alternatives of concrete paving, dense bituminous roadbase and rolled asphalt were 2 to 4, 5 and 8 % dearer respectively. However, it was suggested that many engineers have technical reservations about this form of construction.

Two other forms of cement stabilised material are defined[4] in British practice and, whilst they may be used in roadbases for light to moderate traffic conditions, they are essentially sub-base materials. Yet, even in this restricted role, their use appears to be limited as illustrated by the fact that James[2] found that 56 of the 60 contracts analysed used unbound granular material. It may well be that the specification,[4] although attempting to encourage the use of a wide range of local materials, imposes too heavy a testing burden on contractors during the tender preparation period if a realistic cement content is to be selected. Furthermore, in comparison with the method specification followed with Type 1 or Type 2 granular sub-base materials, the successful contractor is faced with an end-product specification in which large areas of sub-base will be at risk until the compliance test results become available after 7 days. This state of affairs is especially disappointing in view of the need today to conserve high quality materials and, whenever practicable, to use non-traditional material such as industrial waste.

It would seem appropriate, therefore, to concentrate the text of the chapter on lean concrete and, in particular, to review the background of research and experience which forms the basis of current practice.

EARLY HISTORY

Papers published during the formative years in the development of cement stabilised materials are especially interesting since they reveal the philosophy underlying the original work. From a number of these papers, it would seem that the principal aim was to achieve and maintain a level of stability rather than to produce a material with pronounced structural strength. Thus, for example, Sparkes and Smith[5] stated in 1945 that 'the purpose of stabilisation is to maintain the moisture content and the mechanical properties of the soil at a satisfactory level so that it will retain its originally compacted state indefinitely under traffic and weather conditions. This is achieved to an appreciable extent by compacting soil to an adequate density. The same object can also be secured by adjusting the grading of the soil, by adding certain cementitious binders such as cement, or by waterproofing the soil with bitumen or resin'. It follows that cement stabilisation was regarded merely as one means of achieving and retaining the desired state.

This approach was extended in 1953 by Maclean and Robinson[6] who suggested that a stabilised soil should be regarded as forming part of a flexible pavement. They presented theoretical evidence and examples of crack patterns to show that soil–cement with a 7 day compressive strength of $1.75 \, \mathrm{MN \, m^{-2}}$ and a flexural strength of $0.35 \, \mathrm{MN \, m^{-2}}$ would develop closely spaced fine cracks which divide the material into pieces the size of hardcore, interlock between the two sides of a crack being relied upon to maintain stability under load. Furthermore, the authors recommended that compressive strengths in excess of 3.5 MN m^{-2} at 7 days should be avoided and suggested methods for reducing the rigidity of stabilised granular soils.

A somewhat different emphasis, however, is found in a paper by Markwick and Keep[7] in 1942 on the use of low grade aggregates and soils in the construction of roads and airfields. The paper gives details of American practice at the time—especially regarding the use of durability tests to determine the suitability of a mix. They suggested that a preliminary indication of the suitability of a soil for treatment with cement could be obtained by determining the crushing strength of the mixed material. Experience at the Road Research Laboratory indicated that soils suitable for stabilisation harden satisfactorily and give 7 day strengths of at least 1.75 MN m^{-2}—a value which was to become associated with materials of this type for many years. The authors also drew attention to the 'rigid' rather than 'flexible' nature of stabilised materials, quoting the tendency to cracking and for the cracks to be reflected into the superimposed surfacing. The paper mentions the increasing use of 'lean mix rolled concrete', described as a material 'intermediate in character between soil–cement and ordinary concrete, the aggregate being in general more like a normal concrete aggregate' and mentions core strengths of over 14 MN m^{-2} on a two-year-old airfield pavement in Massachusetts. Another interesting aspect of this comprehensive paper is that it prompted a contribution by G. H. Hodgson who gave details of the use in North Wales in 1936 of lean mix concrete, using crushed stone and quarry fines and an aggregate/cement ratio of 10, which was compacted by a heavy steam roller. On the following day, a 25 mm bituminous surfacing was applied and the road opened to traffic in the evening. Crushing strengths of some 35 MN m^{-2} were measured on samples cut from the road after 5 years and Mr Hodgson concluded that 'the use of lean-mix, semi-dry, rolled concrete made for quicker construction and also had the advantage that the materials could be mixed at a central plant and might be transported considerable distances in ordinary tipping lorries', thereby predicting today's widespread use of ready-mixed lean concrete.

In summary, a study of the early literature reveals some uncertainty regarding the mode of behaviour of cement stabilised materials and it is largely against this background that subsequent developments are discussed with attention being paid in particular to the implications of the inherent crack susceptibility of materials of this type.

TYPES OF STABILISED MATERIAL

Traditionally, the term 'soil–cement' has been widely accepted in most countries for describing all forms of road construction which involve stabilising a soil or soil-like material with cement and, in general, it is associated by many engineers with *in situ* processing. This concept has always had immense appeal in practice, partly because of the greatly reduced volume of material to be conveyed to a site and partly because of the very rapid rate of construction normally achieved by this method.

Experience has shown, however, that this concept is too generalised and that, for example, there are distinct merits in many instances in adopting plant mixing rather than *in situ* processing. Furthermore, the word 'soil' requires elaboration since the nature of the material processed has a major effect on the properties of the finished product. Thus, so far as this country is concerned, by far the greatest emphasis in recent years has been on plant mixed granular material and, in consequence, terms have been adopted which aim at describing the types of material in use in Great Britain.

When generalising, therefore, it is more appropriate to use the description 'cement stabilised materials' for defining a family in which a common feature is that the addition of cement makes a material suitable for use in road construction or enhances its suitability. This definition clearly covers a wide spectrum of materials since increasing the cement content from zero up to a fairly substantial value would produce a range of materials with the properties of soil at one extreme and Portland cement concrete at the other extreme. It follows from this observation that materials processed with a modest amount of cement will be intermediate in character between unbound material and conventional concrete, so that is not possible to assign values which will adequately characterise the range of values of strength and of stiffness likely to be encountered. It also follows that the testing philosophies and procedures developed by individual research workers have often been influenced by their earlier involvement either with soils or with concrete, so that immense care must be exercised when interpreting data reported by various sources or specified by different authorities. The importance of this latter aspect cannot be over-emphasised since, for example, the strength levels specified in various countries cannot be compared unless account is taken of factors such as the specimen shape used and the degree of compaction aimed at.

In this country, the current highways specification[4] makes separate provision for three classes of cement stabilised material referred to as soil–cement, cement bound granular material and lean concrete. The 'raw'

TABLE 1
MATERIALS ALLOWED FOR STABILISATION[4]

Cement stabilised material	Material for processing
Soil–cement	Soil, chalk or pulverised fuel ash, a washed or processed granular material, crushed rock or slag, well burnt shale or spent oil shale or any combination of these Liquid limit and plastic limit not to exceed 45 and 20 % respectively.
Cement bound granular material	Naturally occurring gravel–sand, a washed or processed granular material, crushed rock or slag or any combination of these
Lean concrete	Either separate coarse and fine aggregate or an all-in aggregate, the quality and cleanliness complying with the requirements of aggregate for conventional concrete

materials and the corresponding grading limits are set out in Tables 1 and 2. From these it may be seen that the specification allows a very wide range of materials to be used in soil–cement, restricts the choice to essentially granular materials for the intermediate category and, finally, further restricts the granular materials to aggregate of concreting quality when the term lean concrete is used. Whilst this approach appears to be logical at first sight, a closer examination reveals that there are limitations relating

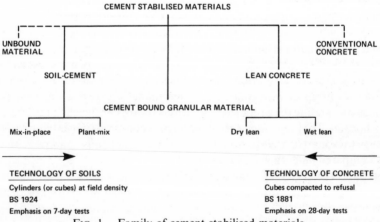

FIG. 1.   Family of cement stabilised materials.

TABLE 2
GRADING REQUIREMENTS FOR CEMENT STABILISED MATERIAL[4]
(Cumulative percentage passing)

BS Sieve size	[a]Soil–cement	Cement bound granular material	Lean concrete 37·5 mm nominal max. size	20 mm nominal max. size
75 mm	—	—	100	—
50 mm	100	100	—	—
37·5 mm	95	95–100	95–100	100
20 mm	45	45–100	45–80	80–100
10 mm	35	35–100	—	—
4·75 mm	25	25–100	30–40	35–45
600 μm	8	8–65	8–30	10–35
300 μm	5	5–40	—	—
150 μm	—	—	0–6	0–6
75 μm	0	0–10	—	—

[a] Grading to be finer than the values listed, and to have a coefficient of uniformity of not less than five.

principally to the prediction of crack susceptibility since, for example, soil–cements based on a sandy gravel or a light clay behave very differently even when their compressive strength is similar.

Nevertheless, when account is also taken of the specification clauses relating to construction and to testing, the approach allows broad generalisations to be made regarding the use of cement stabilised materials in both flexible and rigid pavements and, in Fig. 1, the descriptions are summarised in chart form. The chart also shows a subdivision of lean concrete into dry lean and wet lean, the former being the commonly used form in which compaction is by rolling whilst the latter relates to the occasional use of lean mixes in which the workability is increased to suit compaction by vibration.

It is interesting to note at this point that the definitions adopted in other countries differ quite appreciably from those used in this country as indeed does the approach to testing. The dominant influence is undoubtedly American practice and this has recently been comprehensively reviewed by Norling.[8] In America, the evaluation of materials of this type has traditionally centred around durability as the principal criterion with strength tests being used largely for providing supplementary data. The emphasis on durability is made clear in the definition of soil–cement as a 'mixture of pulverised soil, Portland cement, and water, which upon compaction at optimum moisture content to a standard density forms a hard, durable structural material meeting brushing loss and strength criteria or other acceptable criteria'. The brushing loss criteria evaluate the performance of test specimens subjected to cycles of freezing and thawing and of wetting and drying and, whilst these establish a threshold level of durability, they can also be regarded as testing the integrity of materials subjected to internally generated stress. If insufficient cement is added to meet the criteria for soil–cement, the resulting material is described as cement modified soil or, when the soil processed is granular, as cement treated aggregate.

TERMS USED IN RELATION TO CEMENT STABILISED MATERIALS

Cement Content
In the case of soil–cement and cement bound granular material, it is usual to express the cement content as a percentage of the mass of dry soil processed.

Where lean concrete is concerned however, the concrete technology approach is followed and the term aggregate/cement ratio is used to relate the mass of aggregate to the mass of cement, the specification[4] requiring the aggregate to be considered in the saturated but surface dry condition of BS 812.[9]

A more meaningful method is to express the cement content as the mass per m³, a practice followed for many years in the technology of concrete overseas and more recently so in this country. In this way, the cement requirements for a given amount of construction are directly calculable and, more importantly where soil–cement is concerned, it avoids a possible misunderstanding when comparing for example the use of 8 to 10% cement on a relatively low density material such as pulverised fuel ash with only 5 to 6% cement on a sandy gravel since, in fact, the absolute cement requirements in the two instances are not notably different.

Water Content
On most contracts involving cement stabilised materials, compaction is by rolling using either dead weight or vibrating rollers. Thus, invoking a Proctor analogy, there is an optimum moisture content at which maximum density is achieved for a given level of compactive effort. The bulk density, defined as the mass of material per unit volume, is a useful parameter but it is more usual to calculate the dry density, defined as the mass of solid

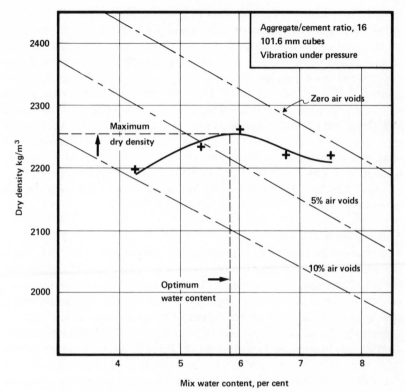

FIG. 2.   Compaction curve for lean concrete.

material per unit volume. The form of a typical compaction curve is shown in Fig. 2 with lines superimposed to indicate the theoretical density at 0, 5 and 10 % of air. The selection of the optimum water content in this way is explicitly required for soil–cement and cement bound granular material and is implicit for lean concrete since compaction by rolling is specified.

Therefore, for all cement stabilised materials, the water content is quoted by expressing the mass of water as a percentage by mass of solid material, i.e. cement plus aggregate or soil. Again, it is more meaningful to express the water content as the mass per m^3.

The water content normally considered is the total value and thereby includes the free water and the water absorbed by the soil or aggregate particles. In this chapter, therefore, mention of the water content of a material implies the total value unless the free value is explicitly stated. The total water content is amenable to determination by drying to constant weight, either in an oven operating at 105 °C† over a period of about 24 h or, when the information is needed for quality control purposes, by rapid drying over a primus stove. Concern is sometimes expressed on sites regarding the introduction of serious error in such determinations due to the possibility of part of the water being rendered non-evaporable by hydration of the cement but the mixes are relatively lean and very little hydration occurs in the first 2 h. Therefore, providing that a representative sample is carefully taken shortly after mixing and rapidly dried when spread out thinly on a tray and stirred, an acceptable measure of the mix water content is obtained. In contrast, low estimates will be obtained if sampling is delayed, if a large sample is dried or if the oven or heater is overloaded. Comparisons have been reported by Sherwood[10] and information is also given in BS 1924[11] and in the 'Notes for guidance'.[12]

Compaction to Refusal
Test cubes of lean concrete are prepared in accordance with BS 1881[13] with the additional proviso that Clause 2705 of the specification[4] requires the cubes to be 'compacted to refusal'. This term was introduced as a result of a study[14] of methods of compacting test cubes of lean concrete from which it was concluded that the more usual state of 'full compaction' aimed at with conventional concrete was not realistic with mixes lacking sufficient paste to fill the voids in the aggregate framework. Prior to this work, cube making on various sites was largely left to the discretion of individuals and, in consequence, cube strengths were prone to considerable variation. This was often erroneously interpreted as a measure of the inherent variability of lean mixes.

The current approach therefore involves applying, under pressure, the foot of a vibrating hammer directly on to the material in the mould and the technique is described in detail elsewhere.[11] Nevertheless, even though the procedures have been standardised, care must still be exercised since the technique remains operator dependent in terms of the pressure applied and the duration of vibration. There is merit therefore in planing the top surface flush with the mould and in noting the weight of the specimen on removal from the mould so that the bulk density can be estimated and taken into account when the strength result is obtained. Furthermore, in a central laboratory, it is worth mounting the hammer in a frame and surcharging the system so as to consistently reproduce the pressure normally applied when compacting with a hand held hammer.

† A closer estimate is obtained by operating the oven at 210 °C.

Field Density

The degree of compaction achieved in the field is a critical factor in determining the subsequent performance of cement stabilised materials and it is for this reason that specifications place so much emphasis on this aspect. Under laboratory conditions, for example, a 5% shortfall in compaction reduces the cube strength of lean concrete by as much as 50%.[14,15] Furthermore, the stress induced in the field is governed by the modulus of elasticity of the material. It so happens that this parameter is less critically influenced[16] by compaction so that high stresses would still be generated and, therefore, partially compacted material is especially vulnerable to cracking.

The importance of compaction is acknowledged for soil–cement and cement bound granular material by requiring[4] test specimens to satisfy strength criteria when compacted to a density within $30 \, \text{kg m}^{-3}$ of the average density being achieved in the pavement. Yet this is not satisfactory because errors in field density measurement would thus directly influence the strength tests results. In any case, the approach cannot be fully implemented because measurement of the field density must be made 'at least 4 h after the completion of the compaction work and preferably within a period of 24 h', a requirement which highlights the problem of determining field density by the sand replacement test. Whilst errors in field density measurement are reduced by allowing the compacted material to stiffen but not harden excessively, such a delay cannot be allowed in making strength test specimens. A density level therefore has to be selected and, ideally, this should be the value achieved in the preliminary site trial.

A different approach is followed in the case of lean concrete for which strength and density are separately specified.[4] However, the compliance level for density is stringent since the average of three determinations for each $800 \, \text{m}^2$ or part thereof laid each day is to be not less than 95% of the theoretical dry density at zero air voids. The theoretical value is readily calculable from the simple but quite fundamental equations

$$V_{con} = \sum (V_c' + V_{fa} + V_{ca} + V_w + V_a) \tag{1}$$

where V_{con} = volume of concrete, V_c = volume of cement, V_{fa} = volume of fine aggregate, V_{ca} = volume of coarse aggregate, V_w = volume of water, V_a = volume of air, taken as zero when calculating the value used for judging compliance, and

$$S = \frac{M}{V} \tag{2}$$

where S = relative density, M = mass, and V = volume.

However, the accuracy of the value so determined is greatly dependent upon the accuracy of the constituent parameters and, in particular, the relative density of the various aggregate fractions must be measured on a basis appropriate to the concept of eqn. (1). Thus when considering total water, made up of free water and absorbed water, it is the 'apparent' value of BS 812[9] which should be used. Furthermore, it is not necessary to consider hydration effects when calculating theoretical density for use in connection with field density tests on material less than 24 h old.

Mix Proportions

It is perhaps fortunate that the term 'water/cement ratio' is rarely used in connection with cement stabilised materials. Being a ratio of two variables, it has distinct limitations and, whilst it allows strength to be roughly predicted under given conditions, it cannot be directly related to workability. In contrast, regarding water content and cement content as separate entities has much in its favour since, for a given material, the water content determines the workability and, for a given material at a given

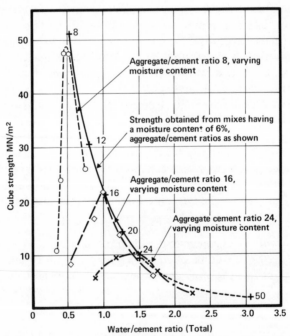

FIG. 3. Effect of water/cement ratio on 28-day cube strength, after Williams.[15]

water content, the cement content determines the strength. This forms a sound basis for mix design and is implicit in current practice.

Nevertheless, it is of interest to note that the strength of cement stabilised materials is governed by their water/cement ratio;[15] this being the case for flexural and cylinder splitting tests as well as for compression tests, in spite of the high values of water/cement ratio appropriate to mixes of this type. For example, a typical lean concrete mix with an aggregate/cement ratio of 20 using river gravel and sand would usually respond well to a vibrating roller when the mix water content is about 6%, so that the water/cement ratio on a total basis would be 1·26. Figure 3 illustrates the effect of water/cement ratio on strength, based on a series of mixes produced at a constant water content of 6% but with a progressive reduction in cement content over an aggregate/cement ratio range of 8 to 50. Figure 3 also shows the effect of varying the water content at a given cement content and thereby draws attention to the importance of strict control over the water content of mixes on site. The water/cement ratio values in Fig. 3 are on a total basis, and allowance would need to be made for aggregate absorption in order to permit direct comparison with conventional concrete mixes since the latter are normally based on free water/cement ratio.

THE NATURE OF CEMENT STABILISED MATERIALS

Flexible versus Rigid

A widely held view is that the strength of cement stabilised materials is low enough for extensive cracking to occur in-service and that the roadbase will thereby be divided into interlocking blocks of hardcore size which will allow the pavement to behave in an essentially flexible manner. This concept is not unreasonable for a fine-grained soil–cement and, should it occur, one would expect the load spreading behaviour to be no better than that of stone bases and that failure would ultimately manifest itself as crazing and pronounced deformation in the wheel paths.

However, this response is certainly not consistent with the observed behaviour of roads incorporating lean concrete roadbases which, instead, are characterised by the incidence of fairly regularly spaced transverse cracks more in keeping with the crack patterns associated with conventional concrete paving. The cracks in the lean concrete usually develop during the curing period, before the length is opened to site traffic, and their occurrence sometimes causes concern, but it must be accepted that they are a natural feature of all cemented materials laid without joints.

Fig. 5. A pronounced reflection crack through an 80 mm surfacing.

Fig. 4. A typical transverse crack in a lean concrete roadbase.

FIG. 6.   Local failure of lean concrete under site traffic. (Reproduced through the courtesy of *Highways and Road Construction International*.[34])

Indeed, it has been suggested elsewhere[17] that the presence of cracks of this type provides confirmation that a reasonable tensile strength has been achieved.

This type of cracking is believed[18] to be the result of restrained thermal effects which induce tension when the layer attempts to warp under a temperature gradient and when shortening under a temperature fall is opposed by friction. The cracks may also be due to restrained drying shrinkage effects in the case of cement stabilised fine-grained soils but this is less likely to be the case with granular materials such as lean concrete since they contain a high volume fraction of stiff and inert aggregate particles.

A fairly typical transverse crack in a recently laid lean concrete roadbase is shown in Fig. 4 and the form of reflection crack one might expect through 80 mm of bituminous cover is shown in Fig. 5. Very occasionally, crazing complying with the 'pre-packed' hardcore philosophy occurs in lean concrete but this is usually a localised failure under site traffic. An example is shown in Fig. 6.

Roadbases of this type possess considerable stiffness and, as a penalty for their favourable load spreading behaviour which reduces the magnitude of the vertical stresses transmitted to the subgrade, radial tensile stresses of substantial magnitude are generated at their underside. A number of papers, notably those by Whiffin and Lister[19] and by Lister and Jones,[20] include useful information relating to cement stabilised materials and, more recently, Lister[21] has dealt comprehensively with the analysis of pavements incorporating cement stabilised materials.

However, some confusion has arisen over the years regarding a paper by Jones[22] in which details are given of surface wave propagation tests on road pavements. The data showed that the effective modulus of weak or thin cemented bases reduces to that of a stone base when extensive cracking occurs but the operative words here are 'weak' and 'thin' so that it must not be inferred that all cemented bases deteriorate in this manner.

The extent to which cracking modifies the stiffness of a cemented layer is not well understood and, in consequence, it is not surprising that the descriptions 'semi-rigid' or 'semi-flexible' are sometimes used. Whilst they have the merit of emphasising that materials of this type do not fall conveniently into either of the traditional categories, they do not advance the understanding of the behaviour of these materials and they do little to simplify the problem of selecting the appropriate value of modulus of elasticity to be used in pavement analysis.

Perhaps a more rewarding approach so far as analysis is concerned would be to acknowledge that cement stabilised materials, and especially those involving the use of relatively clean granular soils, are effectively a form of concrete and will therefore possess a very substantial modulus of elasticity and a significant tensile strength. Therefore, by definition, they are rigid materials and will in consequence develop tensile stress when, for example, thermal contraction is restrained by friction. These stresses will ultimately exceed the strength of the material and will be relieved by cracking. If the resulting crack width becomes excessive, a concrete pavement approach[23] based on Westergaard's analysis of wheel load stresses in slabs would indicate that the 'edge' stress developed at the discontinuity would appreciably exceed the 'interior' stress at locations remote from discontinuities. It follows that bases which had been underdesigned in terms either of thickness or of strength would be critically stressed at the discontinuity first of all and that local failure in the form of breakdown of the material would then occur. This must clearly be indicative that a terminal condition is being reached and, in this context, it is interesting to note that Lister[21] concluded that general cracking will be avoided only in stronger materials and, in recommending that pavements carrying the heaviest traffic should be designed against general cracking, stated that the current design recommendations[24] conform to this requirement.

In summary, it would appear that cement stabilised materials such as lean concrete are rigid in nature and will develop 'primary' cracks before being subjected to wheel loading. At a later stage in the life of pavements incorporating roadbases of this type, 'secondary' local cracks may occur largely as a result of repeated wheel loading and the onset of such cracking indicates that the pavement is approaching failure. In the case of fine-grained soil–cement, the issue is less critical since they will normally be used as roadbases only for lightly trafficked roads. It may then be appropriate to assume that extensive cracking will occur, or may be induced by rolling, so that a flexible action can be relied upon in analysis and especially in selecting the thickness of bituminous cover.

The Effect of Cracking in Practice

The principal concern is that a crack in a cemented base will in due course be reflected into the bituminous surfacing, thereby providing a passage for water to reach the subgrade and, by reducing the strength and therefore the support provided by the subgrade, allow excessive deflection and possibly mud-pumping to occur so that failure would soon follow under heavy traffic.

Yet, as early as 1942, Markwick and Keep[7] reported that the American attitude to cracking was that it was 'quite normal and not deleterious' and, over 30 years later, Norling[8] reviewed American experience with soil–cement and concluded that cracks are not a problem from an engineering point of view except in some very localised instances. Broadly similar views have frequently been expressed in this country and yet the evidence is that concern has been felt and especially so in relation to heavily trafficked roads. Indeed, the Notes for Guidance[12] to the 1976 edition of the specification state that 'In order to prevent regular cracking which inevitably reflects through the surfacing, the strength of lean concrete should lie between 10 and 20 MN m^{-2}'. Unfortunately, no evidence is given in support of this statement and it is unlikely that meeting this requirement will in itself eliminate the problem of reflection cracking.

So far as this country is concerned, the manner in which the inherent crack susceptibility of cemented materials has influenced current practice is most clearly evidenced by tracing the history of lean concrete roadbases and considering the way in which this characteristic has influenced both the choice of mix proportions and the selection of pavement thickness.

As a general background, it is interesting to note that whilst mixes with an aggregate/cement ratio of 14 were in general use in airfield construction in the early post war years, this did not immediately influence practice on road construction where, instead, mixes with an aggregate/cement ratio of 8 were used largely on a local trial basis in minor road schemes. By the early 1950s, when road systems were being built for new towns, there had been a progressive reduction in cement content prompted principally by the need to conserve cement and justified by the satisfactory results of the earlier trials. Aggregate/cement ratio values of 12 and 14 were then the norm and, under a bituminous surfacing thickness of some 80 mm, many of the roads developed cracks, some being longitudinal but the majority being transverse, the latter occurring both over and remote from construction joints. The crack spacings encountered prior to surfacing varied between wide limits but a spacing of some 6 m was reasonably typical.

The impact of the cracking tendency was very evident in the next phase in the development of the material when progressively leaner mixes were adopted on the premise that, under the action of restrained thermal contraction, lower strength material would crack more frequently and thus yield finer cracks which would be less likely to propagate into the surfacing. Mixes with aggregate/cement ratios of 15, 16, 18 and 20 were then used on various sites and, in some instances, comparisons were undertaken by local authority engineers of the relative performance on individual sites of, for example, mixes with an aggregate/cement ratio of 15 and mixes with an aggregate/cement ratio of 20.

Much of this activity related to the use of gravel aggregate in areas lacking supplies of good quality roadstone. A very different view was taken when crushed rock aggregate was available and an aggregate/cement ratio of 24 was then favoured since it was considered that the angular shape and rough texture of crushed rock particles would ensure favourable load transfer across cracks.

The 1957 edition of the specification[4] gave support to these trends by requiring the use of 15:1 to 20:1 mixes for gravel aggregate in comparison with 18:1 to 24:1 for crushed rock aggregate. Yet the problem of cracking remained and even leaner mixes were used in some schemes. The need to obtain information regarding the desirability of using very lean mixes was recognised when a 35:1 mix was included in a TRRL experimental road at Whitchurch, Glamorgan, in 1959.

Clearly, a progressive reduction in cement content would, if taken to the limit, overcome the problem of cracking, but at the cost of sacrificing the potential benefits associated with the use of a cemented material. Other solutions were therefore considered during the 1950s, much of the development work being undertaken by the engineering staff of the new towns and notable at Crawley.[25] The approaches displayed considerable ingenuity and, in addition to the obvious answer of providing a greater thickness of bituminous cover, included reinforcing the lean concrete, reinforcing the surfacing over construction joints in the lean concrete, forming wide construction joints and filling the gap with coated stone, using rubberised asphalt surfacing and, finally, replacing part of the mixing water in the lean concrete with bitumen emulsion. With the exception of the use of thicker surfacings, the degree of success of the various solutions was often marginal and rarely justified in terms of cost.

Crack surveys were frequently undertaken, many engineers locating the cracks in the roadbase and tracing their subsequent propagation into the surfacing, but it was extremely difficult to obtain meaningful information in this way because of the large number of factors influencing the incidence and propagation of cracks. This was highlighted in 1963 by Wright,[26] reporting details of a survey of 35 roads in England and Wales, from which it was not possible to relate cracking to factors such as the strength and thickness of the lean concrete or to the type and thickness of the surfacing because of the large number of variables involved. The survey revealed, however, that the majority of the roads were performing satisfactorily with 11 being completely sound, 12 sound except for transverse cracking and 12 with other defects which were often minor. Less cracking was also detected when limestone aggregate was used, presumably because of its lower thermal coefficient. In 1965, Wright[27] reported that the proportion of roads showing cracks had remained similar but the amount of cracking had increased. There was also more evidence of deformation and of crazing, especially in heavily trafficked roads with thin lean concrete roadbases, and remedial measures had been necessary in some instances.

By the early 1960s, when the motorway programme was well under way, opinion had moved away from the use of extremely lean mixes on the grounds that a roadbase failure would be difficult to rectify and, in 1963, the use of an aggregate/cement ratio of 15 to 20 was specified for all types of aggregate. It was also decided that the problem of reflected cracking was best resolved for heavily trafficked roads by providing a substantial thickness of bituminous cover and the term 'composite roadbase' was introduced. Thus, the earlier thickness design for heavily trafficked roads of 100 mm of rolled asphalt on 250 mm of lean concrete was altered to 100 mm of rolled asphalt on an upper roadbase of 75 mm of dense bituminous material above a lower roadbase of 175 mm of lean concrete. The 175 mm thickness of lean concrete also had the advantage that single layer compaction could be satisfactorily undertaken without undue difficulty.

This was a major step in the official attitude to lean concrete and one that made available a form of construction that subsequently contributed in no small way to the success of the major roadbuilding programme undertaken in the 1960s and 1970s. With this in mind, an attempt was made[28] in 1968 to evaluate the overall performance of lean concrete roadbases by a questionnaire survey to all county highway authorities and this revealed that the great majority were satisfied. Surprisingly, the presence of cracks was not regarded as a serious defect but the incidence of local failure had a decisive and unfavourable influence on the assessment of performance. A further but less extensive questionnaire survey was reported[29] in 1976 and this also allowed the conclusion to be drawn that lean concrete roadbases are in general continuing to perform well, thereby implying that, over the years, the recommendations for thickness design and for specifying the material and method of construction have not been seriously in error.

Morris,[30] commenting in 1968 on the very extensive use of lean concrete in major road schemes, regarded the decision to restrict lean concrete to the lower part of a composite roadbase as an indication of progressive disenchantment with lean concrete founded to some extent on its unsatisfactory behaviour in a number of early motorways, but he drew attention to the presence of contributory factors such as poor drainage. The latter observation prompts the need to bear in mind when judging the performance of the lean concrete used in some of the earlier major road schemes that practice varied regarding the quality of the aggregate used. In some instances, as-raised material of near hoggin quality was used and, more recently, aggregate of this type is allowed only for use in cement bound granular material and would thereby be restricted to roads designed for only moderate traffic.

In the case of cement bound granular material and soil–cement, restrictions on their use in roadbases for heavily trafficked roads has effectively designated them as sub-base materials in either flexible or rigid pavements. Nevertheless, a comprehensive survey of roads with cement stabilised bases was reported by McLaren[31] in 1963 and, in 1969, Lewis and Broad[32] published further details for nine of the major roads originally surveyed, all having roadbases of cement bound granular material. This showed that the roads, with an average age then of $5\frac{1}{2}$ years, had all performed well despite being under-designed for thickness. So far as soil–cement bases to lightly trafficked roads are concerned, Wright[33] gave details in 1969 of a survey of 164 roads which were 8 to 23 years old. The survey gave data which suggested that simple cracking in the surfacing was a defect not likely to worsen with time and that the load spreading ability of soil–cement was no better than that of unbound materials. The latter finding is of interest since the view was often expressed in the late 1950s that a reduction in design thickness in comparison with unbound material would be appropriate for stabilised bases, a reduction of some 30 % being suggested at various times.

To conclude the review, a study of the 1976 edition of the specification[4] provides the opportunity to observe the manner in which the evidence accumulated in recent years has been interpreted by the Department of Transport. So far as soil–cement and cement bound granular material are concerned, the requirements remain essentially unchanged but the Notes for Guidance[12] include a clarification of the way in which the strength clause is to be interpreted with regard to variability.

However, in the case of lean concrete, a major change has been introduced and it is worth briefly summarising the historical background of the specification[4] over the past 20 years before discussing this. The 1957 edition was a method specification which listed the permissible aggregate/cement ratio range, the aggregate grading limits and the free water content to be used in mixes. There was no strength requirement but cubes were nevertheless made on many sites, presumably on the initiative of individual engineers who wished to monitor the uniformity of the mixes. In contrast, the 1963 edition introduced a rigorous set of minimum strength criteria and field density requirements which jointly defined the end product whilst, at the same time, the aggregate/cement ratio range and aggregate grading were specified. This approach was continued in the 1969 edition.

However, the aggregate/cement ratio is omitted from the 1976 edition of the specification[4] although the Notes for Guidance[12] state that the aggregate/cement ratio should normally be between 15 and 20. Instead, the specification requires that a value be selected to meet the average strength specified. Regarding strength, the key stipulation already referred to is that the 28-day cube strength should be between 10 and 20 $MN\,m^{-2}$ so that, in future, mixes will have to satisfy both lower and upper criteria. In this context, the Notes for Guidance makes reference to the high strengths obtained as a result of the cementitious action of the fines in some limestones and, in such cases, allows the use of mixes leaner than 20:1 providing a homogeneous material is produced but suggests that mixes leaner than 24:1 are unlikely to be acceptable.

This is a major change in thinking and it remains to be seen whether or not mixes can be produced economically on site to meet the stringent limitations imposed regarding variability. More fundamentally, the important issue is the decision to abandon the limiting aggregate/cement ratio of 20 and to rely instead on achieving a selected level of cube strength as the means of dealing with the cracking problem. It has been argued elsewhere[29,34] that this could well be a retrograde step partly because of the generally favourable performance record of lean concrete laid to the earlier editions of the specification and partly because of lack of evidence to support the premise that limiting the strength will ensure freedom from major maintenance in the future.

A more desirable approach would be to accept an aggregate/cement ratio of 20 as the leanest mix to be used and to consider other methods, possibly along the lines suggested later in the chapter, for dealing with the problem of cracking.

Experimental Roads
The most comprehensive TRRL experiment involving roadbases was at Alconbury Hill[35] and the findings from this study have greatly influenced current pavement design recommendations. So far as lean concrete is concerned, excellent use has subsequently been made[36] of computerised structural analysis techniques by calculating the likely stress level in various test sections and judging the values against the flexural strength of test specimens and against the observed behaviour of the sections over a period of up to 15 years. A particularly enlightening illustration is the effect of lean concrete roadbase thickness (75, 150 and 230 mm) under 100 mm of rolled asphalt and it is shown that the high stresses calculated for the 75 mm sections are consistent with their early failure, the 150 mm sections are shown to be critically stressed whilst the 230 mm sections develop stresses likely to be acceptable and which is confirmed by their excellent performance. A reassuring feature of the comparison, and one that suggests a very appropriate use for structural analysis techniques at the present state of knowledge, is that the pavement design recommendations in force at the time of construction of the road called for a thickness of 250 mm lean concrete under 100 mm of surfacing.

When, however, a 150 mm thickness of lean concrete was surfaced with either 40 or 75 mm of asphalt, the performance was poor and the authors, in commenting on the rigid nature of lean concrete, emphasised that the long potential life was only realised when the asphalt surfacing was thick enough to keep the stresses to an acceptable level. Further information on the

Alconbury Hill experiment in terms of deflection beam data is given by Lister[37] and, once again, attention is drawn to the poor performance of lean concrete under thin surfacings.

The soil–cement used at Alconbury Hill was a single-sized fine sand mixed with 8 % of cement and a moisture content of 14 %, preliminary tests having indicated that this would give the 7 day cylinder crushing strength of 1.75 MN m^{-2} associated with soil–cement at that time. Due to difficulty in compacting the soil–cement on site, the mean 7 day strength achieved was only 0.95 MN m^{-2}. During the first 6 years in the life of the road, 6 of the 7 soil–cement sections failed in the slow lane whereas, by contrast, none of the sections with either tarmacadam or asphalt bases required replacing. Croney and Loe[35] emphasised that the poor performance of the particular soil–cement did not necessarily apply to stronger soil–cements or to soil–cements made from better graded materials. In this context, Thompson et al.[36] have stated that low strength soil–cements employing well graded aggregates are performing well in other experimental roads. Nevertheless, it is likely that the attitude of practising engineers towards soil–cement has been unfavourably influenced by the Alconbury Hill experiment.

Other TRRL experimental roads include provision for studying cement stabilised materials. At Whitchurch, Glamorgan, lean concrete sections were laid in 1959 with 28-day cube strengths ranging from 4·5 to 23.8 MN m^{-2}, at aggregate/cement ratios of 14, 17·5, 23 and 35, and with two types of aggregate. No detailed information has yet been published regarding this road, nor regarding the major experiments on the Alconbury bypass and the Wheatley bypass which included cemented roadbases with gradings ranging from that of lean concrete to that of sand–cement at 28 day strengths of 3·8, 7·6 and 13.8 MN m^{-2}. The conclusions from these experiments could be especially useful since they may give guidance on the effect of strength level on cracking and on performance in general.

Structural Properties

Modulus of elasticity and Poisson's ratio are vital properties for pavement analysis using the approaches described in Chapter 1 and, in American terminology, they are aptly referred to as material descriptors. They are part of the essential input data for pavement analysis which, for materials such as lean concrete, enable the critical stresses to be estimated[21] and compared with strength in the traditional manner of engineering design. Also of importance is a knowledge of the thermal and shrinkage properties

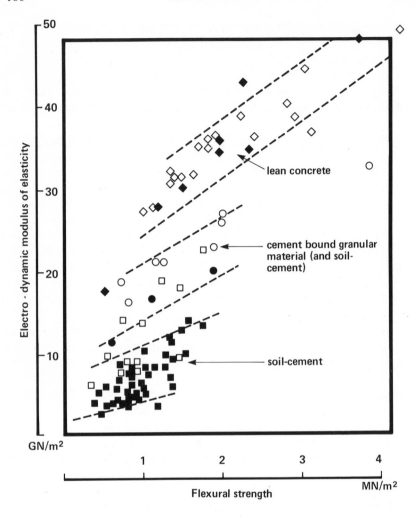

FIG. 7.   Modulus of elasticity plotted against flexural strength for lean concrete,
cement bound granular material and soil–cement (after Williams[38]).

of cemented materials since they play a major role in determining the spacing of primary cracks and their width.

An attempt was made in 1971 to review[38] the state of knowledge concerning the properties of the full range of cement stabilised materials. Regarding strength, it was found that flexural strength was broadly related to cube strength such that, for lean concrete and cement bound granular material, the flexural strength was approximately one-tenth of the cube strength with gravel aggregate and rather higher for a given cube strength with crushed rock and especially with limestone. Published information in relation to soil–cement was more limited in extent and more difficult to interpret but it appeared likely that a flexural strength of about one-fifth of the uni-axial compressive strength, measured on cylinders or prisms, could be relied upon in most cases.

Where modulus values are concerned, it was found that modulus and strength were not uniquely related when a range of materials was considered. Instead, it was found that the 'cleaner' the aggregate, the lower was the cement content to attain a given strength and the higher the modulus at that strength. In particular, it was found that the use of washed and processed aggregate resulted in lean concrete being a high modulus material with a value approaching that of conventional concrete. At the other extreme, soil–cement involving a fine grained soil has a low modulus even if the cement content is increased so as to raise the strength very substantially. Between these two extremes, materials that might be described as cement bound granular material were found to have intermediate values of modulus. This is illustrated in Fig. 7 and emphasises the severe limitations of classifying materials solely in terms of strength when the projected use is in an application in which the stress generated within the material is a function of the modulus of the material. A predictive equation can be formulated only for lean concrete and, in 1968, Williams and Patankar[39] suggested that a very approximate indication of the modulus is given by the expression

$$E_D = 16 \cdot 8 f_c^{1/4}$$

where E_D is the electrodynamic modulus, $GN\,m^{-2}$, and f_c is the cube strength, $MN\,m^{-2}$. This expression applied only to cube strengths in excess of $7\,MN\,m^{-2}$. For strengths below this value

$$E_D = 4 f_c$$

For lean concrete, the static modulus determined from loading tests was

FIG. 8.   Direct tension testing system used by Kolias.[16]

found to be approximately related to the electrodynamic value by the expression

$$E_s = \frac{6}{7} E_D$$

The flexural test partly simulates the manner in which a layer is deflected by wheel loading, but the calculation of the modulus of rupture involves the assumption of elastic behaviour up to failure and this detracts from the merit of the values other than on a comparative basis. More fundamental information can be obtained from uni-axial tension tests and developments during recent years make such tests feasible. This approach has been used by Bofinger[40] in his work on soil–cement and was adopted by Kolias[16] in a study of a wide range of stabilised materials in which load was applied using a double scissor grip of the type developed by Johnston and Sidwell[41] in their work on conventional concrete. Strains were measured using linear variable differential transformers located in small steel blocks glued to the specimens, the arrangement being illustrated in Fig. 8. The principal findings were that the moduli in tension and in compression were essentially equal; that the uni-axial tensile strength was approximately one-tenth of the uni-axial compressive strength and approximately 0·6 times the flexural strength; and that the behaviour under repeated uni-axial tensile loading was similar to the form established by Galloway and Raithby[42] who carried out flexural fatigue tests on conventional concrete and on lean concrete. The literature on fatigue research on concrete has been comprehensively reviewed by Raithby and Whiffin[43] and results relating to cement stabilised materials ranging from silty clay to crushed rock have also been published.[38] Further work is necessary on this topic but the information currently available suggests that a life of 1×10^6 applications is generally obtained at a stress level of about 50 % of the static strength.

Kolias[16] measured Poisson's ratio in compression on lean concrete and on cement bound granular material and obtained in all tests a value of about 0·15. The corresponding dynamic value for these materials was 0·20 and, in tests on a fine-grained soil–cement, a value of 0·33 was obtained.

The coefficient of thermal expansion of a cement stabilised material is largely governed by the coefficient of the raw material processed. Thus, with lean concrete, since some 80 % of the volume of the compacted material is made up of aggregate particles, it follows that published data[44] quantifying the effect of aggregate type on the thermal response of conventional concrete provide a useful guide and generally the values range from about 13×10^{-6} °C^{-1} for flint gravel concrete to about 6×10^{-6} °C^{-1} for limestone concrete. With soil–cement, it is not possible to suggest even notional values and, unless the type of soil accords with a type of material for which data exist, the coefficient must be determined experimentally.

Consideration of the shrinkage behaviour of cement stabilised materials draws attention to a number of important and indeed interesting concepts. A very useful qualitative understanding can be obtained by regarding the stabilised product as a two-phase material so that the laws of mixtures can be invoked as a basis for predicting the characteristics of the composite. In the case of lean concrete, for example, the tendency towards shrinkage will be low because the paste content is low and it is the paste that motivates this particular dimensional change. In addition, the high volume fraction of inert aggregate particles will further restrain shrinkage. However, should it be decided to increase the cement content, the shrinking component will be increased and, as a consequence, the volume fraction of aggregate will be decreased so that on both counts the shrinkage will be increased. In contrast, when a material such as clay is processed with cement, the susceptibility of some clays to pronounced shrinkage will in fact be reduced by the inclusion of the hydrated cement framework since, in comparison with the clay, this is relatively rigid.

It therefore follows that it is quite inappropriate to suggest values for the likely shrinkage of cement stabilised materials without defining the particular soil or aggregate processed. Values have been published, notably by Nakayama and Handy[45] who quote strains ranging from 280×10^{-6} (for a pure silica sand stabilised with 10 % cement at the Proctor optimum water content of 10·4%) to $10\,000 \times 10^{-6}$ (for a clay containing 30 % kaolinitic clay stabilised with 12 % of cement at a water content of 20 % when the Proctor optimum value was 17 %).

Factors Influencing Cracking

It is extremely difficult to predict the likely spacing of cracks in a cement stabilised roadbase and to be certain that the measures to be taken will prevent reflection into the surfacing. This is because of the very large number of factors that play a part in the problem and, since these include environmental and traffic effects, it is often impossible to derive meaningful conclusions even from a carefully controlled full scale experiment. However, by considering each variable in turn, it is possible to obtain a broad understanding of its contribution providing that other variables can be regarded as constant.

The Stabilised Material

In essence, cracking will occur when the stress induced in the material exceeds its tensile strength (f_t) and, since the stress is directly influenced by the elastic modulus (E) of the material, consideration of the ratio E/f_t provides a convenient basis[16,38] for predicting crack susceptibility, at least on a comparative basis. The modulus of elasticity of a stabilised material is largely governed by the modulus of the aggregate or soil particles so that it is relatively insensitive to age and to the cement content of the mix. In contrast, strength is heavily dependent upon the extent of cement hydration so that it increases with time and with cement content. Therefore, materials such as lean concrete are especially prone to cracking during the first day or two after laying, when the strength is low but the modulus is relatively high. It also follows that low cement content mixes will develop more cracks and, if this were the only criterion to be considered, there would be theoretical justification for favouring the use of weak mixes.

External Restraint

A particular feature of cement stabilised construction is that considerable lengths are laid without joints so that when contraction occurs under a falling temperature, tension will be developed when the shortening of the 'slab' is opposed, for example, by friction at the underside. It is likely that a well compacted, carefully levelled and well sealed sub-base will allow relatively free movement so that a superimposed roadbase would develop only occasional but wide cracks.

Standard of Construction

For reasons already given, the modulus of elasticity of a stabilised layer is less dependent upon the degree of compaction achieved than is the strength so that poorly compacted material is especially vulnerable to cracking as will be areas lacking in thickness, uniformity and in which curing has been delayed.

Temperature Regime

Material laid in the summer months will be subjected to the maximum seasonal contraction and will therefore be more likely to crack. Such material will also be subjected to severe warping stresses due to temperature differences between the upper and lower surfaces.

The Surfacing Material

This has a major effect in terms of its nature and its thickness. Thus, for example, the favourable ductility of a low stone content rolled asphalt wearing course would be expected to delay the propagation of cracks from the stabilised layer below. The propagation of cracks will also be delayed if a substantial thickness of bituminous cover is provided since this will partially insulate the roadbase and, furthermore, it will for the same reason reduce the incidence of additional cracks in the roadbase.

Time of Surfacing

Less reflection cracking would be expected if laying the bituminous material is delayed so as to allow the natural cracking pattern of the stabilised layer to occur. Otherwise, the bituminous cover would be subjected to a very considerable local strain when a crack formed in the cemented layer.

Wheel Loading

Whilst both site traffic and in-service traffic may induce some additional transverse cracks by adding a critical tensile component to the restraint or warping stresses, their dominant effect is to subject the layer to substantial tensile stress by causing flexure of the pavement as a whole. In this critical context so far as design life is concerned, the advantage rests very firmly with higher strength material. High strength is also desirable if consideration is given to the ability of the layer to transfer load across a crack by aggregate interlock since weak material is more likely to break down.

Repeated wheel loading is also likely to contribute to crack propagation by inducing vertical displacement in the bituminous material immediately adjacent to the location of cracks in the stabilised layer. This effect will be very marked when the cracks are infrequent, and therefore of appreciable width, because resistance by aggregate interlock will then be minimal.

Overall Comment

Whilst many of the factors considered above are self-evident, a study of the problem as a whole reveals its immense complexity. It is also clear that the policy of limiting the strength of the material as the sole means of controlling the spacing of cracks is questionable since the roadbase is then more likely to fail under the action of wheel loading. So far as crack propagation is concerned, reliance on the insulating action of a thick bituminous cover may become unacceptable economically in view of the dramatic increase in the cost of petroleum based products in 1973.

MIX DESIGN

The principal requirements of the current specification[4] are summarised in Table 3 and, as indicated earlier, there are two distinct philosophies in operation. In particular, the strength of soil–cement and of cement bound granular material is specified at the field density achieved whilst, for lean concrete, the strength is specified on cubes compacted to refusal and the field density must separately comply. There are also further differences to note such as the use of cylinders for soil–cement in some cases, the number of specimens within a group, the curing regime imposed and the age at which strength compliance is judged. It follows that direct comparison of the strength levels for the two approaches is misleading and is dealt with in detail elsewhere[38] with the conclusion that the *in situ* strength of lean concrete is higher than that of soil–cement and of cement bound granular material but the difference is rather less than the specified values suggest.

Frost Action
Both the specification[4] and Road Note No. 29[24] require that all materials within 450 mm of the running surface should be frost resistant as defined by the TRRL frost heave test.[46] The problems involved in evaluating frost susceptibility, and the particular factors to consider when dealing with cement stabilised materials,[47] are dealt with by Jones.[62]

Laboratory Tests
Preliminary tests aimed at obtaining a reasonably good estimate of the cement content and the mix water content to be used initially in construction can readily be undertaken in a moderately well equipped site laboratory. Essential requirements are a laboratory type mixer of about 15 litre capacity, which should be the open pan type for clean materials but may need to have an even more positive action with very cohesive soils, and a vibrating hammer.

Representative samples of the material to be processed must be prepared in advance and it is preferable that separate quantities should be batched for individual mixes at each condition to be studied partly because removing some of the mix for specimen making may introduce error and partly because degradation occurs with some materials with prolonged mixing. The prepared material should be at a known moisture content, usually after oven drying in the case of aggregate and air drying in the case of soils. The water necessary to bring the mix to the required total value should then be added and the batch stored in a sealed polythene container,

TABLE 3
COMPLIANCE TESTS[4] FOR CEMENT STABILISED MATERIALS

Criterion	Soil-cement	Cement bound granular material	Lean concrete
Standards	BS 1924[11] BS 1377[48]	BS 1924[11] BS 1377[48]	BS 1881[13] BS 1377[48]
Clauses	805 & 2706	806 & 2706	807 & 2705
Field trial	Mandatory		Only if sand grading within Zone 1 or Zone 4 of BS 882[49]
Strength specimen	Cylinder (2:1) or cube	Cube	Cube (150 mm)
Curing mode	Sealed container		Water
Testing rate	5 random samples per 800 m² of each layer		3 pairs (one for testing at 7 days and one at 28 days), each pair from a separate batch, per 800 m² or part thereof laid each day, initially, reducing to 3 pairs per 1600 m² if satisfactory
Specimen density	Within 30 kg m^{-3} of the average density being achieved in the compacted stabilised layer		Compacted to refusal
Testing age	7 days		28 days with 7 day values also specified as basis for increasing the cement if necessary
Target mix water content	Vibrating hammer test value, BS 1924[11], plus up to 2%, subject to modification in field trial	As for soil-cement but only cube strength (3·5 MN m^{-2}) specified	Not specified
'Minimum' strength	7 day average crushing strength of each batch of 5 specimens not less than 2·8 MN m^{-2} for cylinders or 3·5 MN m^{-2} for cubes		Average 28 day strength of groups of 3 cubes such that not more than one average in any consecutive 5 averages is less than 10 MN m^{-2} or more than 20 MN m^{-2}. If overall average of any consecutive 5

	groups of 3 cubes (i.e. 15 cube strengths) falls below 11 MN m⁻² or exceeds 20.5 MN m⁻² at 28 days, the engineer shall require the use of different materials or mix proportions. Also, the cement content should be altered if more than one of the 7 day average strength of groups of 3 cubes in any consecutive 5 such averages is less than 7 MN m⁻² or more than 14 MN m⁻². When a preliminary site trial is undertaken, the average 7 day strength of 3 cubes is to be not less than 8 MN m⁻² or more than 13 MN m⁻²	If the average range of 5 consecutive groups exceeds 50% of the overall average strength of the 15 cubes, the engineer shall require the use of different materials or mix proportions
Uniformity of strength	The root mean square value of the coefficient of variation of crushing strength of 5 successive batches of 5 test specimens shall not exceed 40%	As for soil-cement but RMS value not to exceed 25%
Field density	Implicit in strength compliance	Three determinations of the dry density of the compacted material per 800 m² or part thereof laid each day, initially, reducing to 3 per 1 600 m² if satisfactory. Average calculated for each successive group of 3 and not more than one average in any consecutive 5 such averages to be less than 95% of the theoretical dry density at zero air voids

overnight in the case of clean aggregate, and for 7 days in the case of cohesive soils. The likely cement content, 5 % for lean concrete and possibly 10 % for a fine-grained soil, is then added and the mix produced.

If cubes are made, the dry density can be estimated from the weight on removal from the mould, the batched or measured mix water content and, providing care has been taken to plane the top surface flush with the mould, the nominal volume of the mould. Subsequently, and after the appropriate curing, the strength can be determined.

Following this approach, the optimum mix water content can be identified by testing mixes at the likely value and at two values above and two values below this. Both dry density and strength can in due course be plotted against total water content and taken into account in selecting the optimum value. In the case of lean concrete involving gravel aggregate, only the strength results give meaningful data[14] since the relatively open structure of the clean aggregate allows the thin paste of the wetter mixes to be pumped out of the material during compaction. Often therefore, the density results fail to indicate an optimum whereas the strength values, being determined by the water/cement ratio of the paste, usually present a well defined peak. In fact, careful observation during cube making reveals the stage at which excess paste is forced on to the foot of the hammer or through joints in the mould assembly and there is little point in producing mixes at higher values of mix water content. This is a subjective approach but one that can be very valuable, since the established concrete workability tests, such as slump and compacting factor, are totally inappropriate for cement stabilised materials.

Cement content can also be varied and it is usually sufficiently accurate to use the optimum water percentage established on the mixes with the cement content originally assumed. Degree of compaction can also be taken into account for soil–cement and cement bound granular material by varying the effort applied when making cubes, so as to cover a range from the 'refusal' density down to some 90 % of this value since, in the field, the density achieved under favourable conditions is likely to be perhaps 95 to 97 % of the refusal density.

It is not necessary to consider the effect of incomplete compaction in the case of lean concrete but it is vitally important to carefully estimate the air voids remaining in cubes compacted to refusal under the favourable conditions of the laboratory. The confinement of the mix within the mould whilst it is being vigorously compacted is particularly helpful in achieving high density in the laboratory. Since only 5 % air voids are allowed in the compacted roadbase, the test specimens must therefore have lower air voids if there is subsequently to be a reasonable chance of complying with the field density clause. It is at this stage that thought must be given to using different aggregates by, for example, rejecting the use of crushed rock fines or, at least, partially replacing them with a fine sand so as to reduce the harshness of the mix. Paradoxically, certain crushed rock aggregates result in excellent lean concrete but only if their resistance to compaction, a manifestation of the excellent interlock of the angular and rough textured particles, can be overcome.

Finally, reverting to soil–cement, a short-cut evaluation of the justification for carrying out the above tests is sometimes undertaken. In this, 10% cement is added to a sample of the soil in question and water progressively added during mixing until a sample can be squeezed in the hand so as to 'ball up' without displacing water and without falling apart when the pressure is released. A cube is then compacted to refusal and, as a very rough guide, a 7 day strength of at least $7\,\mathrm{MN\,m^{-2}}$ is probably necessary if the material is at all likely to satisfy the specified cube strength level of $3\cdot5\,\mathrm{MN\,m^{-2}}$ at field density, using an economic amount of cement.

PAVEMENT DESIGN

Current recommendations relating to the structural design of pavements for new roads, including pavements incorporating cement stabilised materials, are presented in Road Note No. 29.[24] The design charts are still essentially based on the California Bearing Ratio method (CBR) but have been updated to take account of more recent research and experience. In essence, so far as flexible pavements are concerned, the CBR value of the subgrade and the estimated cumulative number of standard axles jointly determine the thickness of the sub-base whereas the thickness of the roadbase and of the surfacing are governed by the nature of the roadbase and the number of standard axles.

Sub-base
Either soil–cement or cement bound granular material may be used for all traffic values. They can be assumed to fulfil the stipulated minimum CBR value of 30%, for traffic in excess of $0\cdot5 \times 10^6$ standard axles, without the need for testing. Lean concrete is not normally regarded as a sub-base material in flexible pavements, but it is often used under concrete paving.

It is unfortunate that cement stabilised materials are not more widely

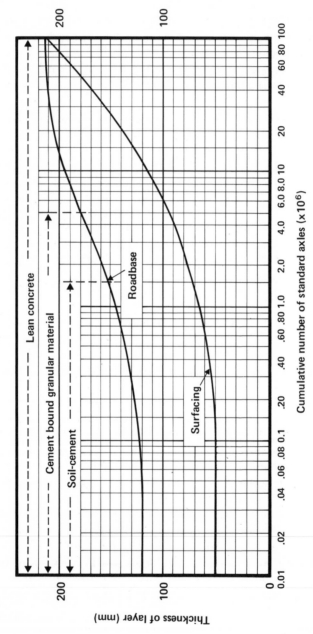

Fig. 9.   Minimum thickness of surfacing and of cement stabilised base in terms of cumulative number of standard axles (Road Note No. 29[24]).

used in this way since they are particularly well suited for use in the upper 150 mm of the sub-base as they form an excellent all-weather working platform and provide a good sub-stratum for the compaction of superimposed layers.

Roadbase

All three forms of cement stabilised materials are recognised in the design recommendations and the relevant chart is reproduced as Fig. 9. From this, it may be seen that soil–cement and cement bound granular material are restricted to 1.5×10^6 and 5×10^6 axles respectively, whereas lean concrete is permitted for the full range of traffic. This differentiation in favour of lean concrete acknowledges the extensive experience built up over the years and especially so under heavy traffic conditions.

Lean concrete is compared with other materials in Table 4 in terms of thickness of roadbase and of surfacing.

TABLE 4
RECOMMENDED THICKNESS OF ROADBASE AND OF SURFACING

	Roadbase			Surfacing			Combined thickness		
Cumulative no. of standard axles $\times 10^6$	1	10	100	1	10	100	1	10	100
Roadbase material									
Rolled asphalt	90	130	220	70	100	100	160	230	320
Dense coated macadam	100	150	270	70	100	100	170	250	370
Lean concrete	150	200	220	70	120	220	220	320	440
Wet-mix or dry bound stone	150	220	260	70	120	220	220	340	480

With regard to the combined thickness of roadbase and of surfacing, the advantage clearly lies with bituminous materials and especially with rolled asphalt, whilst lean concrete offers a marginal advantage relative to stone bases for heavy traffic. The penalty for lean concrete is the thickness of surfacing judged necessary to reduce the risk of crack propagation and this is particularly so for heavy traffic. Conversely, the thickness of surfacing recommended for lightly trafficked roads is insufficient to provide thermal insulation and reflection cracking is likely to be a feature in such roads.

CONSTRUCTION

The specification[4] provides detailed guidance regarding the construction procedures to be followed and further comprehensive information is available in the literature.[50] However, some aspects justify comment and, whilst these relate mainly to lean concrete, they also apply to some extent to cement bound granular material and to plant-mixed soil–cement.

Both batch and continuous mixers have been successfully used in the past and the essential criteria to be met are a good output coupled with an action which deals thoroughly with mixes which are simultaneously lean and of extremely low workability. The mixed material must obviously be protected from the weather, either through drying out or wetting up, during transportation and is usually and indeed preferably spread in a single layer. This is commonly undertaken with a modified bituminous paver or, on small jobs, by hand spreading. Spreading by blading the material is not good practice and, equally, the use of concrete paving type slip form pavers is not appropriate unless the workability of the mixes is appreciably increased.

Longitudinal joints must be kept to a minimum, either by restricting the length laid by a single paver so that the adjacent material can be laid within an hour or, less frequently, by using more than one paver and operating them so that there is little delay at the longitudinal joint. In all cases, however, particular care must be taken to ensure that the material at the joint is thoroughly compacted and it is sometimes necessary to handplace additional material to make up for the deficiencies in spreading. The entire operation of mixing, transporting and spreading must be effected with minimum segregation. Should this become evident, usually as clusters of coarse aggregate in the compacted surface, the techniques used should be re-examined as should the control exercised at the batcher. An increase of 5% in the sand content of the mix often improves the cohesiveness sufficiently to reduce this problem.

In the past, both dead weight and vibrating rollers have been used for compacting lean concrete but the specification subsequently allowed the use only of vibrating rollers or plates. The recent edition, however, allows a wide choice in Clause 802 of roller type, providing that a closed surface is obtained, that the density requirement is met and that compaction is completed within 2 h. It is good practice to give one 'bedding down' pass, either with a light roller or with a vibrating roller operated with the vibrator off, followed by the necessary number of compacting passes, and a final pass without vibration to remove the roller marks.

A tolerance of ± 15 mm is allowed in the level of roadbases and, in the past, the maximum depression under a 3 m straightedge has often been limited to 10 mm. The stringent density requirements sometimes concentrate attention on compaction at the expense of surface accuracy and, since the minimum strength levels specified in the past have normally been attained with relative ease, this has encouraged some contractors to use rather wetter mixes because a low air voids content is easier to achieve.

FIG. 10. Minor expansion failure at construction joint in lean concrete. (Reproduced through the courtesy of *Highways and Road Construction International*.[34])

Neither contraction nor expansion joints are provided in cement stabilised materials but considerable care needs to be taken with end of day joints to ensure that the material at the discontinuity is thoroughly compacted and that the face is vertical. A choice exists between providing a stop-end or ramping-off the roller and subsequently cutting back to a vertical face, opinion[28] seemingly being equally divided on the relative merit of the two methods. If the joints are not well constructed, minor expansion failures of the type shown in Fig. 10 may occur and the risk is high with gravel lean concrete laid in cool weather and not surfaced before the summer. Allowance must be made for the expansion of lean concrete if

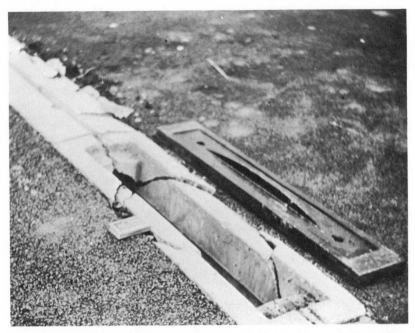

Fig. 11. Precast concrete drainage units damaged by expansion of adjacent lean concrete base. (Reproduced through the courtesy of *Highways and Road Construction International.*[34])

there is a discontinuity such as, for example, a pre-cast drainage unit laid within the base, to avoid failure in the form shown in Fig. 11.

Curing is almost invariably by the application of bitumen emulsion applied at the rate of 0·9 litre m^{-2} and this should be done without delay. It is also good practice to blind the emulsion with sand so as to lighten the colour and thereby reduce heat absorption. Site traffic, including that required for laying the surfacing material, must on no account be allowed to travel on lean concrete for 7 days and this must be extended in cold weather. This is an unfortunate but absolutely essential requirement if premature cracking and surface damage are to be avoided. In this context, there is merit in laying the basecourse of the surfacing immediately after the 7 day maturing period so as to provide some insulation for the lean concrete and to form a running surface for site traffic but, obviously, this will involve a thorough cleaning operation before the wearing course is laid. Figs. 12 and 13 illustrate construction of lean concrete roadbases in the 1960s.

FIG. 12. An excellent example of a lean concrete lower roadbase being laid on a soil–cement sub-base. (Reproduced through the courtesy of *The Surveyor*.[29])

Moving away from dry lean concrete, a modified form referred to as wet lean concrete has been used in which the mix water content has been increased, typically from 6 to 9%, in order to suit spreading and compaction using slip form pavers. Its use has recently been approved[51] and it must satisfy the grading and strength requirements for cement bound granular material. As yet, it has been used only under concrete paving[52] but, bearing in mind the ready availability of slip form pavers, an interesting possibility would be to increase also the cement content so as to comply with the strength requirements for (dry) lean concrete and then to consider the material for use in roadbases in flexible pavements.

Cement bound granular material differs from lean concrete where construction is concerned owing to the use of 'as-dug' aggregate containing up to 10 % in the silt/clay particle size range so that forced action mixers of the paddle or pan type are essential. This observation also applies to plant-mixed soil–cement. A definitive feature of soil–cement, however, is that mix-in-place methods may be used in layers of 75 to 200 mm thickness but,

FIG. 13. View showing lean concrete being delivered in a sheeted tipper, spread through a bituminous paver and compacted by vibrating roller. (Reproduced through the courtesy of *Highways and Road Construction International.*[34])

if the total depth is made up of more than one layer, *in situ* processing is allowed only for the bottom layer. This is presumably because of the danger of non-processed material being sandwiched between the layers. As an example of the use of non-traditional material such as industrial waste in soil–cement, Fig. 14 shows a field compaction trial undertaken jointly by Kent County Council, the National Coal Board and the University of Surrey in 1971. Unburnt colliery shale was plant mixed with 10 % of cement and, at the field density achieved of 95 % of the value attainable in cubes compacted to refusal, the corresponding 7 day cube strength of $6·9 \, MN \, m^{-2}$ obtained indicated that a cement content of some 7 % would have ensured compliance with the specification in this particular case.

FIG. 14.   Cement stabilised unburnt colliery shale being compacted by a vibrating roller. View shows nuclear apparatus being used to monitor density.

USE IN AIRFIELD PAVEMENTS

Lean concrete is extensively used as a working course under all types of airfield pavement, following its introduction on a major scale at Heathrow[53] in 1946. Airfield pavement design experience over the past 30 years has recently been reviewed[54] and this, together with the Specification[55] and Notes for guidance, forms a valuable and interesting source of information which has been briefly summarised elsewhere.[34] Of particular relevance to the use of lean concrete in road construction is the emphasis on thorough compaction and yet, so far as compliance is concerned, a realistic attitude is taken by requiring the contractor to consistently exceed 95% of the density established in a trial area. This comparative approach has a great deal in its favour, bearing in mind the inherent problems in field density measurement.

CONCRETE PAVING

A detailed account of cement stabilised materials would be incomplete without making brief reference to recent developments in the technology of concrete paving since there are useful parallels to be drawn. This is especially so in connection with the rigid nature of the lean concrete roadbases that are widely used in the so-called flexible type of pavement.

Concrete roads involve the use of slabs which act as the structural layer and simultaneously provide the running surface. According to Croney,[56] the first known example in the UK was built in Inverness in 1865 and there are examples of concrete roads built in the 1920s and the 1930s which are still giving good service today. Yet the form of construction has been the subject of controversy for many years.

A commonly held view some 25 years ago was that, in comparison with flexible roads, concrete roads were more expensive in terms of initial cost, their riding quality was inferior and their maintenance costs were negligible. Currently, the position has changed to the extent that the difference in first cost is often minimal and sometimes in favour of concrete roads, their riding quality can be of a high standard, but maintenance has been necessary to deal with surface defects and to restore resistance to skidding.

The design procedure,[24] comprehensively reviewed by Croney[56] in 1967, is based on pointers from theoretical considerations, on information obtained from experimental roads and on experience, and allows the use of either unreinforced or reinforced concrete. In the case of unreinforced construction, the need to avoid random cracking is taken into account by ensuring that the slabs are thick enough to resist traffic induced stresses and short enough so that thermal stresses do not greatly increase the magnitude of the traffic stresses. In the alternative approach, the slab length is greater so that transverse cracks will form but sufficient steel mesh reinforcement is provided to control the width of the cracks to hair cracks and, as such, they are regarded as a characteristic feature of reinforced paving. The spacing of the joints is one of the variables in the design procedure and is typically 5 m for unreinforced paving and 20 to 25 m when reinforcement is provided but the design recommendations also make provision for the use of continuously reinforced paving under a bituminous surfacing for city streets.

However, although the recommendations cover reinforced concrete, the preference for this form of construction in the 1950s and 1960s has given way to the much more general use in the 1970s of unreinforced concrete, largely due to the development of slip form pavers.

During construction, the aim is to produce carefully designed and closely controlled concrete which is spread with the minimum of segregation, thoroughly compacted, cured and protected from inclement weather and from site traffic during its maturing period. Since the slabs behave structurally and develop tensile or flexural stresses, compliance[4] is based on a pseudo-tension test known as the cylinder splitting test.[13]

The need for resistance to de-icing treatment is taken into account by specifying that at least the top 50 mm is air-entrained, that the cement content of the concrete is not less than $280 \, \text{kg m}^{-3}$ and that the free water/cement ratio is not more than 0·55.

The skidding problem is acknowledged by limiting the calcium carbonate content of the fine aggregate, by allowing the use of limestone coarse aggregate only if the proposed stone satisfies an accelerated wear test requirement, and by specifying that the finished surface is grooved or wire brushed at right angles to the centre line of the pavement. Grooving, however, is not allowed on roads which pass through areas deemed to be noise sensitive. So far as remedial work is concerned, grooving is regarded as the primary method of restoring texture on unsatisfactory concrete surfaces.

A 40-year life is currently envisaged for concrete roads in this country and, whilst techniques are available which allow a high standard of construction to be achieved, this will only be attained if meticulous attention is paid to all aspects of construction. This is axiomatic with concrete roads and may be viewed in perspective by comparing the typical daily outputs of 300 m of two lane carriageway some twenty years ago with the record laying[57] of 1010 m of three lane carriageway on the M69 in one day in 1976.

Finally, it is important to mention a striking development in the field of concrete materials technology where, during the past 10 years, intensive research[58,59] in many countries has produced convincing evidence that the inclusion of short lengths of steel fibre in concrete leads to a composite with some improved engineering properties. In particular, there is general agreement that the load carrying capacity in flexure is increased and that the favourable post-cracking properties of the material enable it to behave with marked pseudo-ductility. Additionally, the resistance to impact loading, to repeated loading and, in some respects, to spalling is improved. Equally, there is ample evidence[58] that small diameter wires will rapidly rust under unfavourable exposure conditions such as those which may occur across cracks in a highway pavement.

The fibres may be plain round or, more usually, deformed in various ways to improve bond with the matrix. The fibre dimensions and volume concentration in the mix are all variables but a typical mix might well incorporate $1\frac{1}{2}\%$ by volume, equivalent to 5 % by weight, of fibres which are 0·50 mm diameter and 50 mm long. The matrix used differs from conventional concrete in a number of respects which are dictated by the need to provide a high proportion of mortar so that the fibres can be satisfactorily dispersed uniformly. The proportion of sand is therefore higher than for normal concrete and the maximum aggregate size is smaller so that, in consequence, the cement content is higher.

The improved properties are highly relevant to pavement applications and small-scale field trials were undertaken around 1970 partly to gain construction experience with the new material and partly to obtain data regarding behaviour under load. The considerable degree of success recorded in many of these trials has justified more comprehensive field trials and has already led to the material being used in a number of quite substantial schemes.

So far as the construction of new roads is concerned, the prospect of laying concrete which contains its own reinforcement is very appealing and especially so since, after some initial difficulty in introducing fibres without causing 'balling-up', a common observation is that fibre concrete can be mixed, placed and finished in much the same way as plain concrete and with the same plant. However, the unit cost of fibres is high, the figure in 1977 being some 35 to 50 p per kg, so that a fibre content of $1\frac{1}{2}\%$ by volume would add £42 to £60 to a concrete mix costing £20 m^{-3}. Cheaper rust resistant fibres are in prospect using a melt extract process instead of wire drawing and, in any case, the use of fibres allows savings to be made in some aspects of construction. Nevertheless, the new material is unlikely to compete with conventional concrete paving unless the performance of experimental roads justifies a substantial reduction in thickness or increase in joint spacing.

However, the main interest is in the use of the material as an overlay for restoring existing pavements and the prospects here are more encouraging. In the case of existing concrete roads, overlaying with bituminous material has not always been satisfactory and the dramatic increase in the price of

FIG. 15.   Fibre reinforced concrete being extruded by slip form paver in overlay trial on the M10 in 1974.

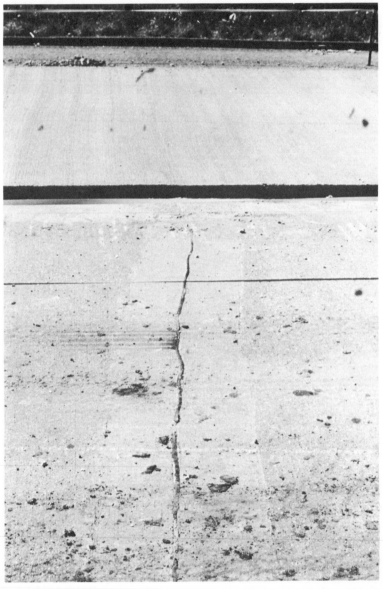

FIG. 16.   Overlay trial on the M10. In the foreground, an existing crack which has been repaired in the past may be seen. The 60 mm overlay to the slow lane has been completed.

petroleum products has underlined the need to develop alternative materials. The finding that steel fibre concrete overlays are in general performing well in trial sections is, therefore, timely and it is interesting to note that overlays of this type have also been laid on existing flexible pavements. They have been tried as a promising means of strengthening airfield pavements to meet the stringent demands of the new generation of jumbo jet aircraft. Figures 15 and 16 illustrate an overlay trial on the M10 in 1974.

The present position is quite promising, but it must be emphasised that the developments referred to have taken place largely since 1970 and there are major gaps in knowledge which are at present dealt with principally by exercising engineering judgement. It therefore remains to be seen whether or not the long term performance is acceptable but this limitation is inherent when new materials or new concepts are introduced.

THE FUTURE FOR CEMENT STABILISED MATERIALS

The current practice of relying on a considerable thickness of bituminous cover as the principal method of overcoming the problem of cracking in lean concrete roadbases is unlikely to be a viable solution in the long term. Consideration must therefore be given to finding alternative solutions which are technically feasible and which exploit indigenous materials to the full so that petroleum based products can be reserved for use in applications which demand their unique properties. This has been considered in some detail elsewhere[34] and a number of possibilities, based in part on research studies and in part on trends in other countries, have been suggested as a basis for discussion and possibly for further investigation. The suggestions are briefly summarised below.

Use of Reinforcement
The use of steel fabric reinforcement in lean concrete has been tried on a small scale on several sites in this country, on the premise that the cracks would be held tight as with conventional reinforced concrete roads. Whilst this can give good results in terms of crack control, it complicates construction by requiring two layer placing of the lean concrete and the cost is high. A small scale trial is shown in Fig. 17.

Research in progress includes the incorporation of low proportions of steel fibres in wet lean concrete and the results obtained are encouraging.[34] Adding $2\frac{1}{2}\%$ of fibres by weight increases the flexural strength by 30 to 40%

and, more importantly, results in a material with pronounced post-cracking ductility. The work has been extended so as to examine meltex fibres and also chopped polypropylene strand which, in comparison, is very much cheaper. The underlying philosophy is that, whilst the unit cost of the material will be increased in comparison with traditional lean concrete, the

FIG. 17.   An experimental road to examine the use of fabric reinforcement in a lean concrete roadbase. (Reproduced through the courtesy of *Highways and Road Construction International*.[34])

modified material could be spread and compacted by slip form paver, probably to a lesser thickness, and possibly with a substantial reduction in the thickness of bituminous surfacing.

Deliberate Pre-Cracking
Trials have been undertaken in Japan, in Sweden and at the TRRL[60] in which extensive cracking is deliberately induced in soil–cement by applying a heavy roller to recently laid material or by early opening to traffic. In this way, the problem of reflection cracking will be dealt with but it does not appear to be at all suitable for lean concrete since the favourable load spreading properties would automatically be sacrificed.

It prompts the suggestion, however, that the desired spacing of transverse cracks could be achieved by positioning crack inducers on the sub-base. Since it would then no longer be necessary to favour very lean mixes, marginally stronger mixes could be used which would better resist the wheel load stresses and which would enhance load transfer by aggregate interlock at the induced cracks. It might also be possible to treat the surface of the lean concrete immediately adjacent to the known position of cracks so as to break bond locally with the surfacing and thereby further reduce the risk of crack propagation.

Upside-down Construction

This description applies to the practice in some countries of using cement stabilised materials in the sub-base to protect the subgrade and to form a firm layer to receive a stone base and bituminous surfacing.

The upside-down concept could perhaps be applied to composite roadbases by using stone or lightly coated stone instead of dense bituminous material for the upper roadbase. Care would have to be taken to avoid trapping water between the surfacing and the lean concrete and, in addition, the radial tensile strains at the underside of the surfacing would have to be analysed in some detail using the techniques discussed in Chapter 1. As a concept however, it merits consideration because the intermediate stone layer would not only provide thermal insulation but it would isolate the surfacing from horizontal movement in the lean concrete.

Modifying the Lean Concrete

Trials were undertaken in the 1950s in which part of the mixing water in lean concrete was replaced with bitumen emulsion in an attempt to produce a more ductile material. A laboratory study[61] in which up to 20% of the water was replaced by emulsion showed little advantage but marked changes were found when, instead, the coarse aggregate particles were pre-coated with bitumen partly to break bond internally and partly to form a cushion layer between the coarse aggregate and the matrix. This approach, which is currently under investigation in France, is similar in some respects to filling the voids in an open textured coated macadam with cement grout.

Other Methods

Various other methods have been suggested, notably by Norling,[8] and they include delaying surfacing as long as possible in order to allow cracking to take place, using the highest penetration binder commensurate with stability, or using a 3 to 6 mm strain relieving layer of ground vulcanised rubber, filler and anionic bitumen emulsion.

CONCLUDING REMARKS

Lean concrete is an essentially British method of construction which has evolved largely as a result of experience and of development work on sites rather than as the result of intensive laboratory research. The marriage of lean concrete and of bituminous materials has made a major contribution to road construction in this country during the past 25 years and, providing that attention is paid to finding methods of dealing with the problem of cracking, there is every reason to suggest that it will continue to be used. Further research is necessary, however, to obtain information applicable to pavement design as the emphasis gradually changes from fully empirical to at least partly analytical.

Regarding cement bound granular material and, even more critically, soil–cement, there is an urgent need to amend the specification approach in this country so as to give positive encouragement to the use of non-traditional material such as industrial waste. Thereby, the country's supply of high quality roadstone can be conserved for use in more demanding applications.

REFERENCES

1. ANDREWS, W. P. Soil–cement roads, 3rd ed., Cement and Concrete Association, Db4, London, 1955.
2. JAMES, J. G. Quantities and prices in new road construction, 1969, A brief analysis of 60 successful tenders, TRRL Report LR 513, Transport and Road Research Laboratory, Crowthorne 1972.
3. BROOKS, J. A. *Quarry Manager's J.*, **56**, 1, 21–9, 1972.
4. DEPARTMENT OF TRANSPORT. Specification for road and bridge works, 5th ed., HMSO, London, 1976.
5. SPARKES, F. N. and SMITH, A. F. *The concrete road: a review of the present day knowledge and practice with some reference to the use of stabilised bases*, Institution of Civil Engineers, London, 1945.
6. MACLEAN, D. J. and ROBINSON, P. J. M. Methods of soil stabilisation and their application to the construction of airfield pavements, Proc. of the Inst. of Civil Engrs, **2**, II, Airport Paper No. 23, 447–502, June 1953.
7. MARKWICK, A. H. D. and KEEP, H. S. The use of low grade aggregates and soils in the construction of bases for roads and aerodromes, Proc. of the Inst. of Civil Engrs, Road paper No. 9, 53, 1942.
8. NORLING, L. T. Minimising reflective cracks in soil–cement pavements: A status report of laboratory studies, Highway Research Road Record: Soil stabilisation, 11 reports, No. 442, 22–33, 1973.
9. BS 812. Methods for sampling and testing of mineral aggregates, sands and fillers, British Standards Institution, London, 1975.

10. Sherwood, P. T. The properties of cement stabilised materials, RRL Report LR 205, Road Research Laboratory, Crowthorne, 1968.
11. BS 1924. Methods of test for stabilised soils, British Standards Institution, London, 1975.
12. Department of Transport. Notes for guidance on the specification for road and bridge works, HMSO, London, 1976.
13. BS 1881. Methods of testing concrete, Part 3 and Part 4, British Standards Institution, London, 1970.
14. Williams, R. I. T. A laboratory investigation of methods of compacting test cubes of dry lean concrete, Technical Report TRA/322, Cement and Concrete Association, London, Jan. 1961.
15. Williams, R. I. T. The effect of cement content on the strength and elastic properties of dry lean concrete, Technical Report TRA/323, Cement and Concrete Association, London, Nov. 1962.
16. Kolias, S. Evaluation of the strength and elastic properties of cement stabilised materials, Ph.D. thesis, Univ. of Surrey, 1975.
17. Lilley, A. A. and Williams, R. I. T. Cement stabilised materials in Great Britain, Highway Research Record No. 442, 1973.
18. Williams, R. I. T. Lean concrete roadbases—a review of British experience, NIRR/PC1 Symposium on cement treated crusher-run bases, Johannesburg, February 1973 (publication pending).
19. Whiffin, A. C. and Lister, N. W. The application of elastic theory to flexible pavements, Proc. Int. Conf. on the struct. design of asphalt pavements, University of Michigan, 20–24th August, 1962, 499–521, 1962.
20. Lister, N. W. and Jones, R. The behaviour of flexible pavements under moving wheel loads, Proc. 2nd Int. Conf. on the struct. design of asphalt pavements, University of Michigan, 7–11th August, 1967, 1021–35, 1967.
21. Lister, N. W. *J. Inst. of Hwy Engrs*, **14**, 2, 21–33, Feb. 1972.
22. Jones, R. *Civ. Eng. Pub. Wks Review*, **58**, 682, 613–17, May 1963; **58**, 683, 777–80, June 1963.
23. Road Research Laboratory. Concrete roads, design and construction, HMSO, London, 1955.
24. Transport and Road Research Laboratory. Road Note No. 29—A guide to the structural design of flexible and rigid pavements for new roads, 3rd ed., HMSO, London, 1970.
25. Milne, M. *J. Inst. Hwy Engrs*, **8**, 3, 234–52, July 1961.
26. Wright, P. J. F. A survey of roads constructed with lean concrete bases, Road Research Laboratory Note No. LN/305/PJFW, February 1963, (not published).
27. Wright, P. J. F. A survey of roads constructed with lean concrete bases, Second Report, Road Research Laboratory Note No. LN/865/PJFW, June 1965, (not published).
28. Brewer, B. and Williams, R. I. T. *Roads and Road Const.*, **46**, 551, 334–9, Nov. 1968; **46**, 552, 377–9, Dec. 1968.
29. Williams, R. I. T. *Surveyor*, 22–7, 2nd July 1976.
30. Morris, D. Construction and maintenance of high speed roads for industrial traffic, International Road Tar Conference, Munich, Germany, Plenary session, 17/19 June 1968. 35–57.

31. McLAREN, D. A survey of roads constructed with cement stabilised bases, Road Research Laboratory Note No. LN/306/D, McL, February 1963, (not published).
32. LEWIS, W. A. and BROAD, B. A. An investigation of the performance of nine major roads having cement bound granular bases, RRL Report LR 196, Road Research Laboratory, Crowthorne, 1968.
33. WRIGHT, M. J. The performance of roads with soil–cement bases, Technical Report TRA 418, Cement and Concrete Association, London, June 1969.
34. WILLIAMS, R. I. T. *Hwys and Road Const. Int.*, March/April 1976.
35. CRONEY, D. and LOE, J. A. Full-scale pavement design experiment on A1 at Alconbury Hill, Huntingdonshire, Proc. of the Inst. of Civil Engrs, **30**, 225–70, Feb. 1965.
36. THOMPSON, P. D., CRONEY, D. and CURRER, E. W. H. The Alconbury Hill experiment and its relation to flexible pavement design, Vol. 1, Proc. of the 3rd Int. Conf. on the structural design of asphalt pavements, 920–37, 1972.
37. LISTER, N. W. Deflection criteria for flexible pavements, TRRL Report LR 375, Transport and Road Research Laboratory, Crowthorne, 1972.
38. WILLIAMS, R. I. T. *J. of the Inst. of Hwy Engrs*, **14**, 2, 5–19, Feb. 1972.
39. WILLIAMS, R. I. T. and PATANKAR, V. D. *Roads and Road Const.* **46**, 542, 34–42, Feb. 1968; **46**, 543, 65–9, March 1968.
40. BOFINGER, H. E. The measurement of the tensile properties of soil–cement, RRL Report LR 365, Road Research Laboratory, Crowthorne, 1970.
41. JOHNSTON, C. D. and SIDWELL, E. H. *Magazine of Concrete Research*, **20**, 65, 221–8, Dec. 1968.
42. GALLOWAY, J. W. and RAITHBY, K. D. Effects of rate of loading on flexural strength and fatigue performance of concrete, TRRL Report LR 347, Department of the Environment, Transport and Road Research Laboratory, Crowthorne, 1973.
43. RAITHBY, K. D. and WHIFFIN, A. C. Failure of plain concrete under fatigue loading—a review of current knowledge, RRL Report LR 231.
44. BONNELL, D. G. R. and HARPER, F. C. The thermal expansion of concrete, Proc. of the Inst. of Civil Engrs, **33**(4), 1949/50.
45. NAKAYAMA, H. and HANDY, R. L. Factors influencing shrinkage of soil–cement, Highway Research Record No. 86, Washington, 1965.
46. CRONEY, D. and JACOBS, J. C. The frost susceptibility of soils and road materials, RRL Report LR 90, Road Research Laboratory, Crowthorne, 1967.
47. KETTLE, R. J. and WILLIAMS, R. I. T. Frost action in cement stabilised colliery shale. Paper presented at the annual meeting of the Transport Research Board, Washington, 1977 (publication pending).
48. BS 1377. Methods of testing soils for civil engineering purposes, British Standards Institution, 1975.
49. BS 882. Aggregates from natural sources for concrete, British Standards Institution, 1965.
50. BANCROFT, M. J. *J. Inst. Hwy Engrs*, **14**, 3, 15–17, March 1972.
51. MINISTRY OF TRANSPORT. (Department of the Environment), Technical Memorandum H7/74, Amendments to the Specification for road and bridge works (1969), (not published).

52. BURKS, A. E. and MAGGS, F. The Cromwell slip-form paver trials, Proc. of the Inst. of Civil Engrs, **36**, 225–71, Feb. 1967. Discussion: Vol. 37, August 1971.
53. GRAHAM, G. and MARTIN, F. R. Heathrow. The construction of high grade quality concrete paving for modern transport aircraft, Proc. of the Inst. of Civil Engrs, Airport Paper No. 1, 117–260, 1964.
54. DEPARTMENT OF THE ENVIRONMENT. Directorate of Civil Engineering Development, Design and evaluation of aircraft pavements, 19, 1971.
55. MINISTRY OF PUBLIC BUILDING AND WORKS. (Department of the Environment), General Specification No. 201, Airfield pavements, London, 142, Directorate of Civil Engineering Development, Standard Specification Clauses, Aircraft pavements, Series 500, Dry lean Concrete.
56. CRONEY, D. The design of concrete road pavements. One-day meeting on concrete roads. Concrete Society Technical Paper PCS 20, 27, 1967.
57. CONCRETE. Record on M69. *J. Concrete Society*. **10**, 9, 12, Sept. 1976.
58. RILEM SYMPOSIUM 1975. *Fibre reinforced cement and concrete*, Vol. 1 and 2. The Construction Press Ltd, Lancaster, 1975/76.
59. EDGINGTON, J., HANNANT, D. J. and WILLIAMS, R. I. T. Steel fibre reinforced concrete. Department of the Environment, BRE Current Paper 69/7, (Building Research Establishment).
60. BOFINGER, H. E. and SULLIVAN, G. A. An investigation of cracking in soil–cement bases for roads, RRL Report LR 379, Road Research Laboratory, Crowthorne, 1971.
61. PATANKAR, V. D. and WILLIAMS, R. I. T. *Hwys and Traffic Engineering*, **38**, 1721, 32–5, Jan. 1970.
62. JONES, R. H. Frost heave damage and its prevention, Chapter 3, in *Developments in Highway Pavement Engineering*—2, P. S. Pell (ed.), Applied Science Publishers, London, 1978.

Chapter 6

SKID RESISTANCE OF BITUMINOUS AND CONCRETE SURFACINGS

G. Lees

The University of Birmingham, UK

SUMMARY

The skid resistance of road and airfield pavements is concerned with the factors which govern the surface's frictional interaction with tyres. It is also concerned with the measurement of these factors in the laboratory and in the field and with methods of (a) designing skid resistant surfacings, and (b) restoring skid resistance to surfacings which have become polished and/or lost macrotexture. In this chapter the first sections are devoted to the direct laboratory and field methods of measurement of skid resistance and to the indirect methods of assessing pavement microtexture and macrotexture. These sections are followed by an account of the influence of vehicle speed, seasonal climatic variation, traffic intensity, braking and cornering and age of the surfacing on measured or experienced skid resistance. The concluding sections deal briefly with the frictional properties of typical conventional bituminous surfacing materials, with modern developments in methods of producing macrotextures in concrete in the plastic state and in the hardened state and finally with some developments of the last two decades in the direction of producing special skid resistant materials.

INTRODUCTION

The interest in skid resistance of road and airfield pavements centres on the relationship of this property with accident risk. Amongst the earliest of systematic studies into this relationship was that reported by Giles.[1]

The same principle of relating accident occurrence to friction values measured on road surfaces has often been used since in many countries, culminating in the kind of sophisticated study which is in progress in the Greater London Council.[2] Here, a programme of regular SCRIM (Sideway force Coefficient Routine Investigation Machine) testing combined with careful analysis of police accident records allows a ready identification of actual and potential risk areas and has enabled the highway authorities to carry out a systematic programme of surface treatment and resurfacing. This and similar approaches[3-7] emphasise the real purpose of all such studies, namely the identification of dangerous surfaces and the prevention of skidding accidents by appropriate treatment.

It will be understood that tyre compound, tyre construction, tread pattern, inflation pressure,[8] brakes of various forms of material and operation (including anti-lock systems),[9] and various vehicle characteristics also play parts of varying degrees of importance in the phenomenon of skid resistance; however, the scope of this chapter clearly excludes their discussion. Even so it is important to add that in general the road surface dominates all other effects in contributing to good or poor skid resistance.

METHODS OF MEASUREMENT OF SKID RESISTANCE

Methods of measurement of skid resistance include both direct and indirect methods, each comprising laboratory and road applications. (Throughout this chapter 'road' will be taken to include airfield pavements except where the latter are separately distinguished.)

Direct Methods
Road
The history of development of vehicles to enable the measurement of road friction includes the use of motorcycle combinations, towed trailers, adapted cars, and specially designed vehicles. The two chief friction parameters measured are Braking Force Coefficient (BFC)—the ratio of vertical load to horizontal braking force, and Sideway Force Coefficient (SFC)—the ratio of vertical load to sideway force acting along the line of the axle of a wheel set at an angle to the line of forward motion of the vehicle. Another measure of friction is to determine the stopping distance of a vehicle in wet conditions and either to give this value or to calculate the wet stopping distance/dry stopping distance ratio (SDR).

It is not intended in this chapter to describe in detail any of these instruments although some are illustrated in Fig. 1. Descriptions are to be found in the following references:

SDR: diagonal braked vehicle,[10] skiddometer.[11]

BFC: skiddometer,[11] front locked wheel car,[12] towed trailer,[11,13] stradograph,[14] universal friction tester.[11,18]

SFC: stradograph,[14] motorcycle combination,[15] fifth-wheel vehicle (Citroen),[15] fifth/sixth-wheel vehicle (SCRIM),[16] universal friction tester.[11,18]

Cornering   Mu meter.[17]
force

Road and Laboratory
One of the simplest and cheapest instruments used in the measurement of friction characteristics of road surfaces has been the Portable Pendulum Tester developed by the British Road Research Laboratory. The ability of this instrument to aid in the identification of high risk road surfaces has been referred to in several publications.[19-21] Early in the development of the pendulum its potential to aid also in the evaluation of rock aggregates in a laboratory accelerated polishing test was realised, leading to the world's first successful test for this property (see Fig. 2). The test for Polished Stone Value (PSV) is well documented,[22-27] the volume of the literature reflecting the usefulness of the test in research and in application in specifications with respect to both natural and artificial aggregates. Its main limitations in road use are:

(i)   its unreliable behaviour on coarse rough surfacings, mentioned by Salt;[15]
(ii)   the small area of road tested;
(iii)   the difficulty of carrying out tests in heavily trafficked sites;
(iv)   its inapplicability to high speed skid resistance.

As discussed later, friction values fall with speed on the majority of surfaces, and typically at different rates for different types of surface, resulting in a change in order of merit for different surfaces at different speeds. It follows that the pendulum, which by its nature is able to give only one value for one surface in a given condition, cannot indicate the whole of the friction versus speed relationship, or any possible change in order of merit of surfaces with speed. Studies by the Transport and Road Research Laboratory[19] have indicated that there is a reasonable correlation between

(a)

(b)

(c)

(d)

Fig. 1.   Skid resistance testing vehicles. (a) TRRL towed trailer; (b) SCRIM; (c) Mu-meter; (d) ASTM towed trailer.

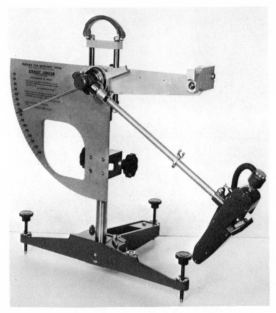

FIG. 2(a).   Transport and Road Research Laboratory Portable Pendulum Tester.

FIG. 2(b).   Accelerated Polishing Machine.

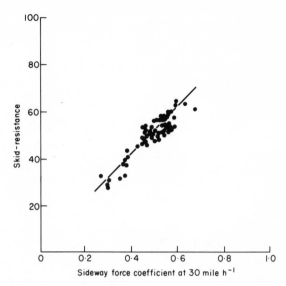

FIG. 3. Comparison of measurements made with the portable tester and the sideway force test car on rough-looking and medium textured surfaces.[19]

pendulum values and SFC (50 km h^{-1}) (see Fig. 3) but that the correlation is poor at high speeds.

Laboratory

Apparatus for measurement of skid resistance properties of surfacing materials has been designed at Purdue University,[28] the Portland Cement Association,[29] the Technical University, Berlin,[30] the University of Birmingham,[31] and a number of other laboratories.

Purdue University: While the apparatus developed by Shupe and Goetz at Purdue[28] (see Fig. 4) is considerably different in construction and operation from the pendulum, it resembles it in that it provides one value of friction coefficient only and that value simulates a low speed skidding condition. (There is no opportunity for build-up of the water wedge known to be responsible for most of the reduction in friction with speed observed in road behaviour due to the large drainage channels cut in the test rubber disc.) The correspondence with low speed skid resistance is suggested by the results shown in Fig. 5 in which it is shown that the skid resistance value (expressed as relative resistance value) for mixes composed of identical aggregate types is greatest for the densest close texture mixes, a

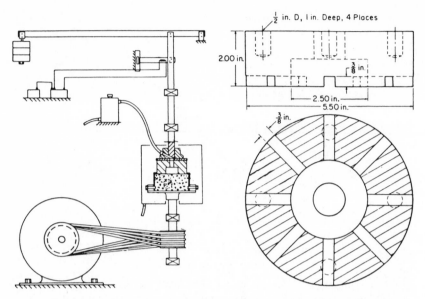

FIG. 4. Relative (skid) resistance value—Purdue University apparatus. *Left:* Schematic diagram of laboratory skid-test apparatus. *Right:* Testing shoe for skid-test apparatus.

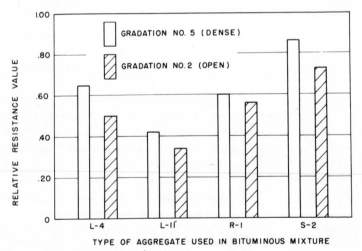

FIG. 5. Relative (skid) resistance value—effect of dense or open texture.

circumstance which would only be true for the low speed condition where surface drainage channels are not necessary.

Technical University of Berlin: The apparatus at the Technical University of Berlin[30] has some similarities to that at Purdue in that a flat disc with rubber sliders is caused to rotate against the upper surface of a test specimen. The essential influences of surface microtexture and macrotexture on wet friction were confirmed in studies largely on model surfaces.

Portland Cement Association: For studies on concrete slabs, Balmer[29] developed an apparatus consisting of a rotating wheel operating at a given speed upon a wetted surface. Frictional forces were measured in terms of the power consumption required to maintain the wheel at constant speed. While some useful results have been obtained by this method it will be noted that a spinning wheel on a wet 'locked' surface is not the equivalent of a locked wheel moving over a wet surface in that in the former case there is no opportunity for build-up of a water wedge as in the latter case.

University of Birmingham: The advance in laboratory study of friction characteristics of surfacing materials, made possible by the Transport and Road Research Laboratory's accelerated polishing machine, was considerable and this test remains the only test enabling reliable routine comparison of the polishing characteristics of road aggregates. However, it suffers from the following limitations:

1. The aggregates tested are coarse single size particles specially selected for near cubical shape; thus it cannot provide any information concerning the effect on skid resistance of aggregate grading or aggregate shape.
2. There is no opportunity in the test to include the effect of different binder types or binder contents.
3. The only means of testing friction properties is by means of the portable pendulum tester which as stated represents low speed skidding effects only.

A need was therefore apparent for a laboratory housed testing machine and method whereby complete bituminous (and concrete) specimens of the widest range of compositions could be subjected to cycles of abrasive wear (wear which could have polishing, roughening or neutral effects) and tested for friction properties over the full range of normal traffic speeds. The Variable Speed Internal Drum Machine[31] (Fig. 6) was developed at the

FIG. 6.   Variable Speed Internal Drum Machine (University of Birmingham).

University of Birmingham to extend the range of laboratory testing to meet
the needs indicated above. Specimens of 'complete' surfacing materials are
mounted on the internal surface of a 1·2 m diameter drum operating in a
vertical plane and subjected to wear/polishing cycles at various slip angles.
The tests for friction are performed at chosen intervals and speeds ranging
from 20 to 100 km h^{-1}. A typical test result is shown in Fig. 7 which
illustrates that both peak (rolling) and locked wheel (slide) values of friction

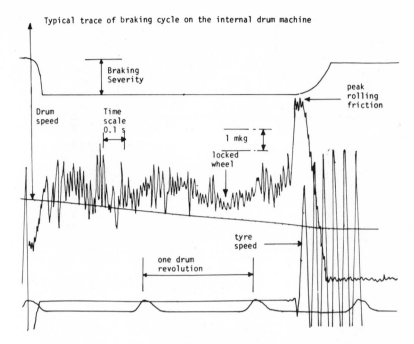

Typical trace of braking cycle on the internal drum machine

FIG. 7.   Variable Speed Internal Drum Machine—typical test chart.

are measured in this test as in road tests of braking force coefficient. Figure 8 illustrates the results achieved to show the effect of varying slip angle on the state of polish of a bituminous surfacing.[32] Figure 9 demonstrates the ability of the machine to differentiate between concrete surface textures tested for wet friction against speed.[33]

Other internal drums have been built at the Federal Institute of Roads, Köln, and at the Technische Hochschule of Karlsruhe and Stuttgart.[34] These appear to have been used primarily for testing the resistance of road surfacing materials to studded tyre wear and for tyre testing, although it is reported[35] that the drum at Köln may be lined with road surfaces of different texture and construction.

Indirect Methods

Microtexture

Only two indirect methods of assessment of the effect of aggregate microtexture exist, namely the use of stereophotography and the use of the scanning electron microscope.

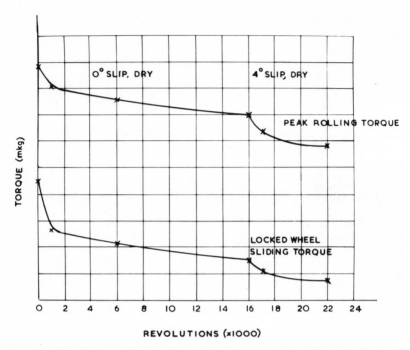

FIG. 8.   Variable Speed Internal Drum Machine—variation of wet friction (at 0°
slip angle) with slip angle of dry polishing cycles on Carboniferous Limestone
aggregate.

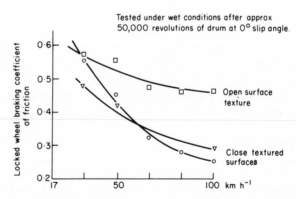

FIG. 9.   Variable Speed Internal Drum Machine—variation of friction with speed.

Stereophotography has been used by Schonfeld[36] and shown to be a reliable indicator of pavement frictional properties. In this method the surface texture is analysed into six components, the Texture Code Number being given as the complete set of six parameter numbers. Two of the parameters are designated as microtextural and the remaining four as macrotextural although one of these, 'Angularity', is recognised as being also in part a microtextural effect. The method requires highly trained personnel and is somewhat time consuming.

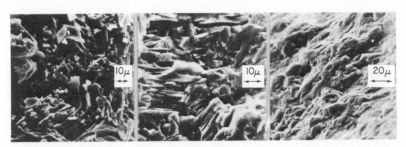

FIG. 10.   Scanning electron micrographs of Leicestershire augite diorite subjected to polishing on the Accelerated Polishing Machine: *Left:* freshly crushed, unpolished—wet skid resistance value 82; *Centre:* after 3 h polishing with coarse emery—wet skid resistance value 72; *Right:* after further 3 h polishing with emery flour—wet skid resistance value 65.

The scanning electron microscope was first used by Williams[8,37] for the study of aggregate microtexture. The level of microtexture which appeared to correlate most closely with the state of polish of aggregates as determined by the pendulum tester was stated to be that most clearly visible at high magnifications of the order of 5000 times. Measurement on such textures which would possess an adequate level of wet friction without resulting in excessive tyre wear showed them to be within the range 10 to 100×10^{-3} mm.

For example, Fig. 10 (left and centre) shows the burring over of the previously sharp cleavage edges of plagioclase felspar crystals of a Leicestershire augite diorite. This followed 3 h of polishing with a coarse emery abrasive during the first stage of testing with the accelerated polishing machine. The effect on pendulum skid resistance is noted in the change of values from 82 to 72, followed by a further drop to a value of 65 (the PSV) brought about by the second stage of polishing with fine emery flour. Tubey and Hosking[38] also adopted this approach to microtexture study.

Macrotexture

While pavement surface macrotexture has an important effect on other engineering properties such as tyre/road noise, vibration, rolling resistance, spray etc., the highway engineer's main interest in this property lies in the effect that macrotexture has on the drainage capacity of a surface under tyre pressures at varying modes of operation (rolling or sliding) and at various speeds. Hence it is the main factor governing the friction/speed relationship.

The *sand patch method* [21] is the earliest quantitative method of assessing pavement macrotexture. In this method a known volume of sand is poured onto the surface to be measured and spread into as nearly circular a patch as possible such that the tips of the aggregate particles just project at the upper level of the sand. The texture depth is measured by volume of sand/area of patch in mm.

While a general correlation between drainage capacity and an average surface voids measurement may exist, there is a fallacy in assuming that the average texture depth so determined may be related precisely to the fall of friction coefficient with speed since unconnected voids in the surface are included in the measurement while they play an idle part in dissipating the water between the tyre and the road surface. Confirmation of this is shown in Table 1 [39] which demonstrates from TRRL results that quite different sand

TABLE 1

THE EFFECT OF MACROTEXTURE ON THE CHANGE IN SKIDDING
RESISTANCE WITH SPEED

Drop in skidding resistance with speed change from 50 *to* 130 $km\,h^{-1}$ %	*Texture depth mm*	
	Flexible	*Concrete*[a]
0	2·0	0·8
10	1·5	0·7
20	1·0	0·5
30	0·5	0·4

[a] When textured predominantly transversely.

patch texture depths produce the same fall in friction with speed. This is according to whether the voids so measured form continuous channels (as in the case of pavements deliberately grooved) or contain a large number of discontinuous and irregular channels (as in the case of the rolled asphalt with coated chippings included in this survey).

FIG. 11.   Gussasphalt—dimpled surface texture.

Different correlations are therefore required for different categories of surface with the consequent implication that categorisation of a surface is required before any correlation may be attempted. It should also not be assumed that only two categories exist as shown in Table 1, although it may be true that these represent almost the extremes of a range. Probably the most extreme case of disconnected voids is the 'dimpled' variety of the German Gussasphalt (Fig. 11) where sand would clearly occupy surface voids but represent no aid to drainage whatever. In fact disconnected voids such as these and those that are sometimes present in rolled asphalts with poor to average chipping distribution (Fig. 12) act as surface reservoirs for water aiding the lubrication of nearby particles and preventing full deformation of the tyre into the road texture. Other limitations of the method are that it is not capable of being used to indicate the drainage characteristics of open texture friction course types of material, where it is desired to compare these with each other or with denser compositions, and that it cannot be used in wet or windy conditions. The method is, however, simple, inexpensive and widely used.

FIG. 12.   Rolled asphalt—poor chipping distribution.

A *grease patch method* of similar principle has also been used on an experimental scale.[40] This method suffers from the same disadvantage as the sand patch, i.e. failure to discriminate between active and idle voids, but in addition suffers in that any method involving putting a highly lubricating material such as grease on road surfaces is unpopular with highway engineers.

The *profile ratio* and *filtered profile ratio* methods of analysis of stereophotographs are described by Sabey.[41] Profile ratio is defined as the ratio of the length of the surface profile along a line to the length of the baseline. The filtered profile ratio is the profile ratio for the tops of the asperities only, over a depth D, below the line of the peaks. These measurements while of use in giving some general indication of macrotexture are linear measurements and not able to provide direct information on two- or three-dimensional drainage characteristics of a surface. A useful summary of these and other methods of surface texture measurement has been compiled by Rose *et al.*[42]

Outflow meters or 'drainage' meters have been in use since 1963 mostly at the research level. The first such meter was developed by Moore and Kummer while working at Pennsylvania State University, the development continuing with Moore working at Cornell,[43] Delft, and Dublin.[44]

The principle is simple; place a hollow cylinder with a rubber annulus at the lower surface upon the surface to be measured, fill the cylinder with water and record the time for a given quantity of water to flow out of the cylinder between the lower surface of the rubber annulus and the pavement texture. While the principle is simple, attention has to be paid to such details as the dimensions of the rubber annulus, the hardness and creep characteristics of the rubber and the load on the rubber, all of which determine the deformation of the annulus into the pavement texture.

Moore also describes other more complex forms of outflow meter in which a constant head of water (instead of a falling head) is used with a pressurised water supply and others in which a constantly decreasing load is employed on the ring during the test to compensate for creep deformation of the rubber during test: this is accomplished by a pneumatic control system. While there are theoretical advantages in the latter, more complex, outflow meters, they unfortunately lose the main practical advantage of portability and ease of operation of the basic simple type. To some extent this has been overcome by mounting the apparatus at the rear of a vehicle as has been done at the Delft University of Technology and at the Centre Expérimental de Recherches et d'Etudes du Bâtiment et des Travaux Publics, Paris.

Discussion of the repeatability of results, the correlation of results with skid resistance measurements by various other field test methods, and the correlation of results with change in skid resistance with speed appear in several papers.[42-45]

A further development in the concept of outflow meters was made by Lees and Katekhda[46] who described a meter with an elliptical 'shoe' instead of a circular annulus (Fig. 13). The purpose of this was not to imitate the shape of a tyre contact patch but to detect anisotropy, if it should exist, in the drainage characteristics of a surface. With a circular annulus the outflow times clearly would not vary with orientation of the meter, even on surfaces with pronounced anisotropy in drainage properties, e.g. grooved surfaces. Since vehicles are known to show different friction/speed gradients depending on whether surfaces are grooved transversely or longitudinally an outflow meter with a circular annulus could not distinguish between these two forms of friction/speed behaviour. This may however be done by an outflow meter with an elliptical shoe since the outflow times are different

FIG. 13. University of Birmingham outflow meter—elliptical shoe.

for the position when the long axis of the ellipse lies parallel to the grooves (or any similar form of anisotropy) or perpendicular to the grooves.

Contactless sensor is the latest development in methods of texture depth measurement, i.e. an optical system using a pulsed semiconductor laser.[47] This apparatus is mounted on a towed trailer and is capable of giving a continuous record. 'Single shot' and repetitive methods gave correlation coefficients with sand patch texture depth of 0·998 and 0·986 respectively. The main disadvantages of the method are:

(i)   the high cost of the apparatus;
(ii)   that as with other linear measurements no direct information is available on two- or three-dimensional drainage (indeed there is doubt as to whether the obtained results on friction courses or grooved surfaces would have any meaning, e.g. on longitudinally grooved surfaces the laser could be reading on the tops of the ridges at one time and in the troughs of the grooves at another).

On the other hand the continuous reading over a large sample of the road surface is a considerable advantage over methods relying upon a few measurements over a small sample of the surface.

THE RELATIONSHIPS BETWEEN WET SKIDDING RESISTANCE AND VEHICLE SPEED

The considerable drop in friction that occurs when a surface is wet has led to a practically total emphasis on studies of wet friction. The nature of the wet friction/speed relationship has been investigated by a number of workers.[10,13,17,20,30] The typical form has been given by Sabey[20] (Fig. 14) and expresses the two fundamental principles, namely that the level of friction for a given speed is a function of the surface microtexture (chiefly the microtexture of the exposed aggregate particles) and that the rate of fall of friction with speed is a function of the surface macrotexture. The latter factor governs, for a given tyre construction and tyre pattern, the relative ease with which bulk surface water may be displaced from the tyre/road contact patch. This latter 'drainage facility' is of increasing importance as vehicle speed increases and the consequent time available for water to be dispelled reduces. A further factor influencing the rate of fall of friction with speed is the manner of tyre operation, i.e. per cent slip (e.g. rolling or locked wheel mode), slip angle, etc. What little evidence there is[13,48] appears to show that the per cent rate of fall of friction with speed is greater in the case of the locked wheel than in the rolling wheel or the sideway force. This would agree with an explanation in terms of the greater displacing force which would be applied to a thick film of water by a rotating tyre rather than a sliding tyre and the consequent lesser opportunity for a wedge of water to build up under the tyre at high speeds. The final stage of this hydraulic wedge action is commonly known as the hydroplaning (or aquaplaning)

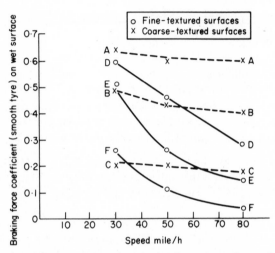

FIG. 14. Change in skidding resistance with speed on six surfaces of the Road Research Laboratory test track.[20]

condition[10] but all stages of reduced friction exist up to the final stage. Many accident cases referred to as due to hydroplaning have not strictly experienced this phenomenon but nevertheless have encountered very low values of friction due to excessive hydrodynamic lubrication.

While the wet friction/speed relationship (just described) in which friction falls with speed is typical, some interesting cases have been reported[41] where (usually after an initial drop) friction rises as speed increases (Fig. 15). No generally acceptable explanation for this phenomenon exists, although it has variously been suggested that it is due to the increasing contribution of a supposed hysteresis component of friction and to an increasing viscous drag effect of thick water films at high speeds. However, it is noticeable that the surfaces on which this phenomenon has been observed are all of the open and harsh textured variety, e.g. surface dressing with crushed rock aggregate, which of all surfaces are least likely to facilitate the build up of thick films of water. On the other hand, such surfaces are those most conducive to cutting and tearing of tyre rubber and this may be the prime cause of the observed rise in friction with speed. A detailed study and explanation of the mechanism is awaited but in view of the known increase in stiffness of rubber with rate of testing it may be supposed that at higher speeds this increase in stiffness encourages less 'draping' of the rubber over aggregate asperities and consequently a higher contact pressure than occurs at lower speeds. The higher pressure may be sufficient to rupture the water films existing at the

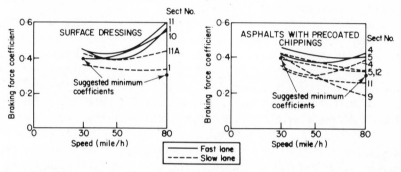

FIG. 15.   Variation in braking-force coefficient with speed on test surfaces on A1.[41]

surface and so encourage a wet cutting and tearing action on the tyre rubber—this being the source of increased friction. The initial drop in friction, observed in many cases in passing from low to medium speed before the upturn occurs at higher speeds, would then be explained as being due to the normal increase in lubrication effect as some portions of the surface develop thicker water films on the aggregate microtexture as speed increases.

The Use of Macrotexture Measurements in Prediction of Friction/Speed Relationships

The concept of combining the use of the pendulum (or a vehicle test at low speed) as an indicator of low speed friction characteristics, and a macrotextural parameter as an indicator of the change in friction with speed has been used with the sand patch method,[21] the profile ratio,[41] and the filtered profile ratio.[41] The correlations so attempted have in part been based upon the belief that the need for high texture depth surfaces is associated with an assumed greater deformation component of friction (mobilising hysteresis energy losses in the tyre) at high speeds. For example the stated reason for adopting a 'filtered' profile ratio in place of the simple profile ratio is that 'in practice only the tops of the asperities will produce local deformations of the tyre tread, and the shape of the surface profile below a certain level will play no part in determining the energy losses set up in the rubber'.[41] An acknowledgement of the importance of drainage characteristics is, however, made in the same paper in the following words added to the comments made on tyre deformation: 'as well as permitting the rapid disposal of the main bulk of the water'. The majority of authors have concentrated on the latter phenomenon as being the prime cause of the fall of friction with speed.

The scatter of results plotted for these relationships is large, suggesting that the relationships would be unreliable indications of high speed performance, when, as suggested, combined with skid pendulum values or a low speed vehicle friction measurement. Furthermore, there is serious objection to plotting these measurements of surface topography against a percentage fall in braking force coefficient from 50 to 130 km h^{-1}, when the individual curves over the whole range of speed contain numerous examples where there is a fall in BFC from 50 to 80 km h^{-1}, followed by a rise in coefficient from 80 to 130 km h^{-1}. There are consequently doubts on the general validity of such a correlation which assumes a linear relationship between friction and speed. In addition it is apparent that even if a valid prediction was made of the skid resistance at 130 km h^{-1} from such a correlation it could not correctly predict the skid resistance value at intermediate speeds in the region of, say, 70 to 110 km h^{-1}.

Since it is apparent as stated above that a different mechanism not associated with drainage must exist to account for a rise of friction with speed it is suggested that these values should not be included where correlation with macrotexture measurements is attempted, whether sand patch, profile ratio or outflow meter measurements.

If such values are so excluded, valid correlations can be expected in all cases but with different equations and with different correlation coefficients.

THE VARIATION OF WET SKID RESISTANCE WITH TIME AND TRAFFIC

It has been well known for a number of years that there is a general trend for road surfacing materials to suffer, to a greater or less extent, a drop in frictional resistance with age and increased traffic intensity. However, Szatkowski and Hosking's work[49] has demonstrated relationships more

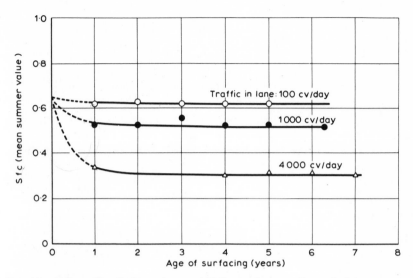

FIG. 16.   Effect of traffic intensity on skidding resistance of a typical motorway standard surfacing.[49]

exact than has previously been known (Fig. 16). These studies have led to the realisation that aggregates of given PSV would tend with time, subject to seasonal variation, towards different values of SFC ($50 \, \text{km} \, \text{h}^{-1}$) for different traffic conditions (Table 2)[39] when used as coated chippings in rolled asphalt. Such a table has enabled specifications, as in Technical Memorandum H16/76,[50] to be framed so that for a given required SFC ($50 \, \text{km} \, \text{h}^{-1}$) in the rolled asphalt, aggregates of different PSV can be selected for use according to the existing and anticipated traffic. Such an approach when linked to the risk rating of the highway situation (i.e. on the identification of high risk locations which have consequently high SFC requirement) (see Table 3[39]) should enable the following two highly desirable aims to be achieved:

(i)   The production of surfaces with friction values related to the degree of hazard of the highway circumstance.

(ii)   The most efficient and economic use of aggregates; the often scarce and expensive highest PSV aggregates should be utilised in the locations where they are most needed and there should be the opportunity to use aggregates of lower, but still acceptable, polishing resistance in situations of lower commercial traffic density and lower risk.

TABLE 2

PSV OF AGGREGATE NECESSARY TO ACHIEVE THE REQUIRED SKIDDING RESISTANCE IN
BITUMINOUS SURFACINGS UNDER DIFFERENT TRAFFIC CONDITIONS

Required mean summer SFC at $50\,km\,h^{-1}$	*PSV of aggregate necessary* *Traffic in commercial vehicles per lane per day*					
	250 or under	1000	1750	2500	3250	4000
0·30	30	35	40	45	50	55
0·35	35	40	45	50	55	60
0·40	40	45	50	55	60	65
0·45	45	50	55	60	65	70
0·50	50	55	60	65	70	75
0·55	55	60	65	70	75	a
0·60	60	65	70	75	a	a
0·65	65	70	75	a	a	a
0·70	70	75	a	a	a	a
0·75	75	a	a	a	a	a
Aggregate abrasion value	not greater than 12			not greater than 10		

[a] SFC values in these traffic conditions are sometimes achievable with aggregates of extreme hardness and very high resistance to abrasion, such as certain grades of calcined bauxite.

The philosophy of the approach is thus to be commended; different opinions may exist however as to the detail of what SFC values should be specified or recommended for particular categories of site and risk rating.

THE VARIATION OF WET SKID RESISTANCE WITH SEASONAL VARIATION AND LOCATION IN THE HIGHWAY

Further detailed studies[31,51] utilising the scanning electron microscope have demonstrated the effect of (i) seasonal variation (Fig. 17) and (ii) location in the highway, i.e. proximity to zones of braking and cornering (Fig. 18). The first of these, the seasonal variation where generally a higher state of polish existing towards the close of a summer period is largely removed during the following winter, must be ascribed to a combination of three effects.

1.   The variation in grading of the detritus lying on the surface.

Evidence[22] has shown this to be coarser in the winter when the wet tyres of vehicles pick up detritus more readily from channels, etc. and carry it onto the surface. During the (usually) drier summer months of the northern temperate zones it is suggested that only the finer wind blown dust will lie on the surface and impart a higher state of polish.

2.   The differential solubility and differential susceptibility to wet weather softening of minerals common in road aggregates (Fig. 19(a)).

3.   The action of frost disruption in porous aggregates and those with well developed mineral cleavage (Fig. 19(b)).

THE ROLE OF SURFACE MICROTEXTURE AND MACROTEXTURE IN WET SKID RESISTANCE

Aggregate Microtexture

The importance of aggregate microtexture in tyre/road friction has been recognised since early research by Knill[52] drew attention to the significance of detailed aggregate petrology in promoting or opposing development of a

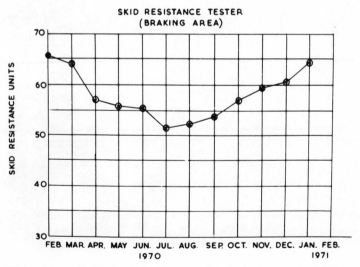

FIG. 17(a).   The variation in skid resistance with time of year, all measurements taken within a braking area on a medium trafficked road.

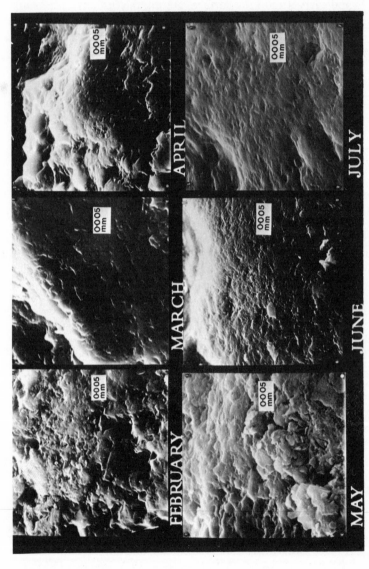

FIG. 17(b).   The changes in microtopography of aggregate taken from the braking area of a medium trafficked road (Warwick bypass).

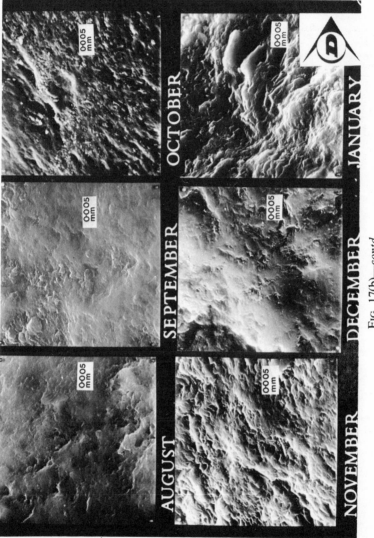

Fig. 17(b)—contd.

TABLE 3

MINIMUM VALUES OF SKIDDING RESISTANCE FOR DIFFERENT SITES

Site	Definition		SFC (at 50 km h⁻¹) Risk rating									
			1	2	3	4	5	6	7	8	9	10
A1 (v. difficult)	(i)	Approaches to traffic signals on roads with a speed limit greater than 40 mile h⁻¹ (64 km h⁻¹)						0·55	0·60	0·65	0·70	0·75
	(ii)	Approaches to traffic signals, pedestrian crossings and similar hazards on main urban roads[a]										
A2 (difficult)	(i)	Approaches to major junctions on roads carrying more than 250 commercial vehicles per lane per day				0·45	0·50	0·55	0·60	0·65		
	(ii)	Roundabouts and their approaches										
	(iii)	Bends with radius less than 150 m on roads with a speed limit greater than 40 mile h⁻¹ (64 km h⁻¹)										
	(iv)	Gradients of 5 % or steeper, longer than 100 m										
B (average)		Generally straight sections of and large radius curves on:										
	(i)	Motorways	0·30	0·35	0·40	0·45	0·50	0·55				
	(ii)	Trunk and principal roads										
	(iii)	Other roads carrying more than 250 commercial vehicles per lane per day										
C (easy)	(i)	Generally straight sections of lightly trafficked roads	0·30	0·35	0·40	0·45						
	(ii)	Other roads where wet accidents are unlikely to be a problem										

[a] Main urban roads would generally be included in Marshall road categories, 1, 2 and 3.

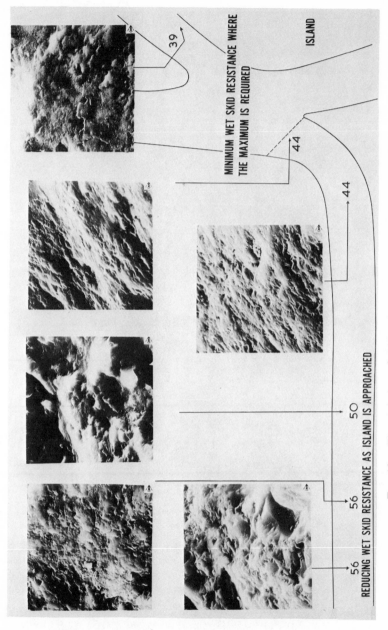

Fig. 18.   The variation of skid resistance with location in the highway.

FIG. 19(a).   Scanning electron micrographs to show effect on microtexture of differential solubility of mineral components of carbonate rock (Carboniferous limestone) after 1 year's natural weathering (without traffic). (i) After testing on the accelerated polishing machine, skid resistance 47.

FIG. 19(a)—*contd.*   (ii) After natural weathering, skid resistance 75.

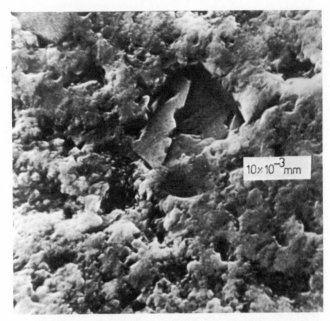

FIG. 19(b). Scanning electron micrograph to show effect of frost action on aggregate microtexture.

state of polish on particle surfaces. Rocks which contained minerals of sufficiently different hardness or which were friable, i.e. consisted of grains rather insecurely cemented together, were found to give high polishing resistance. For example igneous and metamorphic rocks which showed a degree of decomposition by weathering effects gave higher PSV than fresh unweathered rocks due to the lower hardness of the secondary minerals (chlorite, serpentine, kaolinite, sericite, etc.) compared with the primary minerals (quartz and unaltered crystals of felspar, augite, hornblende, etc.). Further studies by Shupe and Lounsbury[53] and Gray and Renninger[54] have demonstrated that even in the generally suspect rock types, limestone and dolomite, a degree of impurity may significantly improve the polishing resistance. The simple relationship shown in Fig. 20 pointed to the poor performance of pure calcite limestones, calcite being a mineral of low hardness (3 on Moh's scale) which polishes easily. While the improvement in polishing resistance correlated well with an increase in the percentage of insoluble residue (which would consist chiefly of both quartz sand grains and clay mineral matter), Gray and Renninger found that an

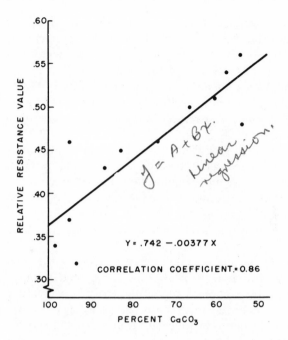

FIG. 20.   Correlation between $CaCO_3$ content and skidding susceptibility.[53]

even better correlation existed if the insolubles measured were restricted to those of sand size, i.e. coarser than 0·05 mm. This would eliminate the clay and silt size mineral matter from consideration which would have little difference in hardness from the calcite, and concentrated attention on the difference in hardness between quartz (7 on Moh's scale) and calcite. They found, however, in addition, that sand size mica flakes (with lower hardness than the carbonate minerals) also led to high skid resistance, i.e. the difference in mineral hardness operated to aid resistance to polishing whether the insoluble residue was harder or softer than the carbonate matrix.

In describing the properties of gritstones, Hawkes and Hosking[55] showed clearly the relationships between petrology, polishing resistance and abrasion resistance amplifying the explanations of Knill[52] and others that the retention of a rough non-polished texture in this category of rocks is due primarily to the dislodgement of weakly cemented grains before any can attain a high state of polish. It follows that there is, in general, an inverse relationship between polishing resistance and abrasion resistance. The skill in choosing aggregates, especially gritstones, for wearing course materials or surface dressing lies in correct engineering judgement, based upon experience, of the balance between the need to employ aggregates which will provide good skid resistance and the requirement that these aggregates will not exhibit an economically unacceptable rate of wear. However, neither polishing resistance nor abrasion resistance are absolute qualities required at the same level irrespective of engineering environment. It has been mentioned above[49, 50] that aggregates of different PSV can produce the same SFC on the road if different traffic conditions exist, but also it should be noted in respect of abrasion resistance that certain aggregates which would have an unacceptably high rate of wear if employed as chippings for surface dressing or open textured macadams, may be quite acceptable if used as a component of dense bituminous mixes where the strength and support of a bituminous mortar can provide protection against wear.

Finally in this section, mention must be made of the comprehensive studies that have been made by Hosking, Tubey and Jacobs.[38, 56–58]

These study the various basic characteristics of grain shape and differential grain hardness which control the polishing resistance of natural aggregates and the means by which artificial aggregates may be composed to simulate these characteristics.

Apart from the effect of aggregate petrology on surface microtexture it has been shown[59] that a reasoned blend of aggregates of different rates of wear as measured by the Aggregate Abrasion Test[23] can preserve surface macrotexture with a view to maintaining an adequately low value of speed-dependence for road friction.

Binder Materials and Binder Content

Stripping properties and weathering properties are important in so far as they affect the degree of exposure of the aggregates to the tyre. While both stripping and weathering of the binder are detrimental to the durability of a mix if occurring excessively, it has been shown[60, 61] that with some mixes a degree of weathering encourages aggregate exposure and hence skid resistance at all speeds (Fig. 21). While Please and Lamb[60, 61] detected significant improvements in both typical rolled asphalt and asphaltic concrete mixes there can be no doubt that the need for rapid weathering binders is greatest for the richer mixes and that for leaner mixes the advantage is less. For certain high stone content mixes the normal wearing action of traffic and weather may be adequate without the need to resort to rapid weathering binders. In fact in the interests of durability such cases

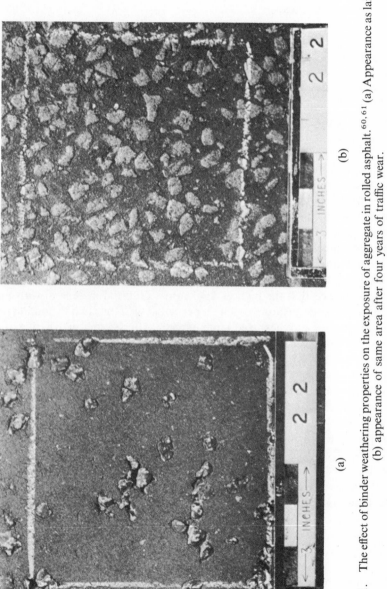

(a)

(b)

FIG. 21.   The effect of binder weathering properties on the exposure of aggregate in rolled asphalt.[60,61] (a) Appearance as laid; (b) appearance of same area after four years of traffic wear.

may be better served by the use of binders with low rather than rapid weathering tendencies.

In those cases, however, where rapid weathering binders are needed, attention in the past has been concentrated on the ability of Trinidad Lake Asphalt when blended with residual bitumens in proportions in the region of 50:50 or 40:60 to impart a rough texture to the mix by its tendency to weather at a more rapid rate than typical road bitumens. The relatively high cost of Trinidad Lake Asphalt and the generally known faster rate of weathering of tars in comparison with residual bitumens led workers of the Road Research Laboratory to develop a so-called Pitch Bitumen blend of approximate ratio 25:75 or 20:80 to substitute a cheaper local product for the imported product. It is not intended in this chapter to discuss the relative economics of the two types of binder or the relative ease or difficulty with which either may be stored, mixed, rolled or receive the coated chippings which are typically applied for British Standard rolled asphalts utilising these binders. Suffice it to say that both have their supporters and their opponents. Please and Lamb[61] compared skid resistance and sand patch texture depth measurements for mixes made with a range of binders including several varieties of experimental and production bitumens. These results showed that the highest SFC values occurred in general with the surfaces of highest texture depth, in particular with the High Oxidation (in Dark) bitumen and the fluxed Lake Asphalt. After 8 years' weathering, the range of texture depths with 12·7 mm chippings at a spread of 6·5 to 7 kg m^{-2} was 0·28 mm for a rich asphalt with a low weathering hard refinery bitumen to 0·89 mm for a comparatively lean asphalt with the most rapid weathering high oxidation bitumen.

In recent years the realisation that not all bitumens had the same resistance to weathering has led to the study of those physical and chemical properties which might affect this property. These studies[62] have shown that a tendency to more rapid weathering correlates with a high permittivity (dielectric constant). The permittivity is an indirect measure of the ratio of asphaltenes to aromatics in the bitumen, the former being more polar than the latter and possessing greater weathering tendencies.

BITUMINOUS SURFACINGS

With low traffic densities and speeds bituminous surfacings evolved in the early part of the 20th century with virtually no consideration being given to skid resistance properties. Accordingly riding quality, durability relative to economic factors, and structural properties were the prime considerations during this period. The increasing importance of skid resistance led to the adaptation of old established design methods and recipes and the development of new methods and formulae, incorporating in both cases the fundamental principles which have been outlined in the previous sections of this chapter.

Accordingly in all mixes the desirability of utilising high PSV aggregates has long been recognised (but regrettably not always by those responsible for the world's highways). Variations exist, however, as explained earlier, in that the requirement for high polishing resistance varies with traffic densities (and can be shown to vary with traffic manoeuvre, e.g. braking and cornering). There are also variations in requirement for polishing resistant aggregate in that where coated chippings are applied to the surface of a bituminous mix as in low/medium stone content rolled asphalts to BS594,[63] Gussasphalt, Topeka, and similar mixes it may be permissible to specify a lower PSV aggregate for the body of the mix than is specified for the surface chippings.

Rolled Asphalt to British Standard 594

Rolled asphalt has been the main trunk road and motorway surfacing in the UK for several decades. Many variations exist in coarse aggregate/fine aggregate ratio, filler content, binder content and in the petrological nature of aggregate and the composition of bituminous binder. Each variation exerts its own effect on skid resistance properties according to the general principles outlined above.

The most frequently used variety of rolled asphalt has been a low stone content variety (typically 30% coarse aggregate content) the surface macrotexture of which, if it were unmodified, would be too low for any high speed road such as the use intended. The application of pre-coated chippings to compensate for this lack of texture has therefore become mandatory for this type of mix and has followed a trend from a light scattering of chippings applied by hand, to the present day heavy rates of application by machine in order to achieve a more uniform distribution (Fig. 22).

Surface macrotexture can thus be varied by (a) variation of size of coated chipping (generally 20 or 14 mm nominal size), (b) variation of rate of spread (as per BS 594—table 16), (c) rolling temperature and rolling technique (BS 594 section 4.2.10), and (d) stiffness of the rolled asphalt matrix by increase of stone content, and/or use of crushed fine aggregate in place of sand, increase of filler/binder ratio and use of high PI binders. The

FIG. 22.   Rolled asphalt-uniform chipping distribution.

latter if used at the mixing temperatures applicable to more normal binders will be stiffer at the time of application of the coated chippings and help to resist embedment. The effect of variations in mix design on the stiffness of rolled asphalt is fully discussed in Chapter 3.

In anxiety to adopt means to offset the excessive chipping embedment which has been apparent in many examples of rolled asphalt in the past, there is a danger that all or too many of the above methods might be adopted at the same time leading to the defect of the other extreme, namely loss of insecurely held chippings by traffic action (Fig. 23(a)). Figure 23(b) illustrates a further suggested mechanism by which coated chippings may be lost, namely by the improper use of unduly 'coked', i.e. overheated chippings.

The technique is thus one that requires careful attention to detail and awareness of all the interrelated factors mentioned above.

Binder weathering properties as applied to BS 594 asphalts have been described earlier. Some weathering of the binder has been shown to be required to prevent the embedment of the chippings into the soft matrix occurring at a faster rate than the weathering of the binder can re-expose them.

Asphaltic Concrete

Asphaltic concretes, manufactured generally to specifications of the

(a)

(b)

FIG. 23.   (a) Dislodgement of inadequately embedded chippings in rolled asphalt.
(b) Dislodgement of coked chippings in rolled asphalt; (left) good quality chippings
(right) coked chippings (TRRL SR240 UC).

Asphalt Institute[64] or to state or national modifications, vary widely in skid resistance properties according to detail of grading design (one size gradings, open gradings or dense gradings), aggregate types available and binder contents and types. While the variations are so numerous as to defy description the most generally understood asphaltic concrete is one composed to a continuous grading and with a dense surface texture. For such mixes the comments which have been made above in regard to aggregate petrology, binder contents and binder type apply. As mentioned, Please and Lamb[61] have shown that rapid weathering binders have a small but statistically significant beneficial effect on the skid resistance properties of asphaltic concretes. However, it may be considered that asphaltic concretes which show such benefit have probably been manufactured with a somewhat too high binder content and that the remedy should rather be to design the mix at a more appropriate slightly lower binder content to counter flushing-up under traffic.

Macadam Type Mixes

The usual understanding of coated macadam is of a high stone content mix with low content of fine aggregate, little or no filler and frequently a high void content. Such mixes do appear in some of the Asphalt Institute publications but more typically appear in British Standard 4987,[65] the current British Standard in which have been combined many of the older standards which separated tar bound from bitumen bound macadams and also had separate standards for fine cold asphalt, etc.

The resistance of aggregate to polishing is as important here as in all other mix types which have been mentioned, but the lower binder content generally means that less importance is attached to rapid weathering of the binder. A well chosen binder content and viscosity grade is however very important to obviate the risk of 'closing-up' or 'flushing-up' which occurs if too much binder is used, especially if of low viscosity. Too little binder especially if of high viscosity grade (i.e. low pen) may lead to fretting and pot-holing with consequent danger to vehicle stability.

Surface Dressings

This chapter is not the place to review surface dressing design and procedures. In fact it is probable that the best summary of the principles and techniques of surface dressing exists in the TRRL's Road Note 39.[66]

So far as skid resistance is concerned there is no doubt that this is one of the most effective and cheapest ways of imparting or restoring it. The reduction in accidents reported for the M4 flyover resurfacing[3] is the clearest possible example of the relationship between accidents and road friction.

The petrological factors concerning skid resistance are as described earlier. So far as size of chippings is concerned no clear evidence exists as to the effect of this parameter, however for equivalent degree of embedment the larger chippings will have a higher texture depth and hence, if laid 'shoulder-to-shoulder', a lower decrease in friction with speed. On the other hand there is theoretical[67] and practical reason to believe that smaller chippings provide a greater real contact to the deformable rubber of tyre treads and hence for low speed conditions, a greater friction. These two factors (amongst others not connected with skid resistance) both need to be taken into account in selection of chipping size.

CONCRETE SURFACINGS

Developments in improving the skid resistance of concrete roads have included the following:

1. Identification of the relative importance of the polishing resistance and wear resistance of the coarse aggregates as compared with the fine aggregates.
2. Developments in producing surface macrotextures in:
    (a) the plastic concrete by brushing and grooving;
    (b) the hardened concrete by grooving, flailing, acid treatment, etc;
    (c) the 'seeding' of chippings onto the surface of the plastic concrete.

1.   The relative importance of resistance to polishing and to wear of coarse and fine aggregates has been dealt with by Weller and Maynard.[68,69] The main conclusion drawn by these workers from their study utilising a laboratory accelerated wear machine of their own design is that in typical concrete mixes where the surface contains a low proportion of exposed coarse aggregate the PSV of the aggregate plays a rather small role in determining the level of skid resistance (as determined with the pendulum), compared with the large influence of the hardness and resistance to polishing of the fine aggregate.

Only in cases where the fine mortar surface is relatively weak, deliberately removed by brushing, or is ultimately worn down by traffic in older concretes does the relative importance of the coarse and fine aggregates reverse as the former begins to predominate in area at the tyre/road contact. This is a fairly obvious conclusion but its importance lies in the recommendation that has followed, namely that certain low PSV coarse aggregates such as typical limestones may be used in normal concrete road surfacings with a low exposure of the coarse aggregate.

Because of the importance placed on the fine aggregate the study also included experiments in which the fine aggregates were varied from dolomitic limestone through dolerite, crushed flint gravel, natural (uncrushed) flint gravel to gritstone and calcined bauxite. A general conclusion was made that the calcined bauxite always performed best in skid resistance and yielded gritty textures with hard particles standing out from the cement paste background. This latter feature also applied to the hard flint gravel sand particles and contrasted with the case where fine aggregate particles abraded more readily, e.g. limestone, dolerite and gritstone, and yielded lower textures. The limestone and dolerite samples generally showed low skid resistance values. The gritstone which had the highest PSV and is known to perform well in bituminous mixes gave disappointing pendulum values after 50 h of dry abrasion cycles (with flint particles as the abrasive), values which while above those of the dolerite and limestone were inferior to those of the flint gravel. However, the skid resistance values for the gritstone actually improved during a further 5 h of wet abrasion with emery flour becoming in general superior to those of the flint gravel and all other aggregates with the exception of the calcined bauxite. This feature seems to indicate that while dry abrasion/polishing produces certain effects, wet abrasion/polishing has different effects and can reverse the order of merit of different concretes. It was also observed that the neat cement paste while polishing considerably under dry abrasion recovered skid resistance markedly under wet abrasion cycles, confirming the effect of water on concrete surfaces.

2. (a) The technique of brushing a transverse texture into the surface of the plastic concrete has been in operation in the UK and elsewhere for several decades.

Weller and Maynard[70] describe the development in brushing techniques from the soft brush method used mainly pre 1964 to the use of harder yard brooms, wire brooms and tined raking units. The latter were made necessary in view of the rapid loss in texture which was becoming evident with the soft brush technique with the increase in intensity and weight of traffic. Sand patch texture depths with soft to medium-soft brush application were generally not greater than 0·38 mm. The new yard brooming and wire brooming techniques were introduced to enable texture depths averaging greater than 0·65 mm to be specified and produced.[71]

The report examines these textures and the methods adopted to produce them, concluding that in the lighter trafficked fast lanes of two motorways and several major trunk roads on which experimental lengths were laid, there was little reduction in texture during the first four years of trafficking. In the heavily trafficked slow lanes, however, a rapid decrease in texture depth was observed on all roads during the first year.

The rubber tined units have been shown to produce the most satisfactory textures in laboratory trials but it is stated that so far only limited success has been achieved with this method on site. Similar conclusions must be drawn with respect to trials which have been carried out with light rollers and steelpipe rollers which have been modified by covering their surfaces with expanded metal or textured rubber surfaces in diamond pattern.

The drive to produce still deeper and more durable textures in the plastic concrete surface led to the evolution of grooving techniques by means of steel ribs welded to the underside of a steel plate.[72] The requirement to drag this plate across the surface in a transverse direction has led to the development of a complete unit to operate at the rear of the concrete 'train' which carries the plate and drags it in a vibrating mode, across the wet concrete (Fig. 24).

The ribs are 6 × 6 mm in cross section producing a deep and rough texture. In order to prevent the occurrence of the high pitched whining noise which had been an unwelcome feature of the sawn groove pattern cut into hardened concrete surfacings that had become polished on the M1 motorway north of London (see later), the ribs welded to the plate were spaced at irregular intervals. This irregularity succeeded in breaking up the constant high frequency noise patterns which had characterised the M1 grooves, but in its place produced an almost equally unwelcome road-roar from the tyres, undergoing a 'hammering' from beneath at the contact with the surface. The obvious improvement in drainage characteristics (and hence in medium to high speed skid resistance) led several authorities to suggest[73] that an increased road noise was an unavoidable penalty to be paid for an improved high speed skid resistance. However, the existence of quiet but highly drainage-effective surfaces such as friction courses and some newly developed textured high friction dense asphalts[59, 74] has shown this not to be so.

However, the drainage efficiency of grooved surfaces is not to be denied and the technique will no doubt continue to be used in open country areas

FIG. 24.   The grooved texture produced by the plastic grooving machine (TRRL
SR 240 UC).

even if as in the UK at present it is not permitted in 'urban' areas where there
have been or may be objections from the local populations.

(b) Treatments to restore skid resistance in hardened concrete polished by
traffic are described in a further report by Weller and Maynard.[75] The trials
referred to were carried out in the summer of 1965 following earlier trials on
airfield runways. Grooves were cut by diamond blades and by silicon
carbide blades and some grooves were produced by a flailing action with
steel flails (Fig. 25). As shown in Table 4 groove depth, width, and spacing
varied and while the pattern was generally transverse one surface was cut to
a diamond pattern.

FIG. 25(a).   Grooves produced by silicon carbide blades. Treatment B3—three-quarter scale.[75]

FIG. 25(b).   Grooves produced by flails. Treatment C1—three-quarter scale.[75]

TABLE 4

THE TREATMENTS USED TO RETEXTURE THE WORN CONCRETE

Treatment	Type of blade	Grooving pattern	Section no's
		Untreated	0
A	Diamond	Grooves 3 mm wide 1·5 mm approx deep 4·5 mm centres	2, 9
B 1	Silicon carbide	Grooves 6 mm wide 3 mm deep 12 mm centres	5
B 2	Silicon carbide	Grooves 9 mm wide 3 mm deep 28 mm centres	6
B 3	Silicon carbide	Two series of cuts at 45° to the direction of traffic Grooves 3 mm wide 3 mm deep 18 mm centres	3, 7
C 1	Steel flails	Heavy machine Grooves 9 mm wide approx. 2 mm deep 25 mm centres	4, 8
C 2	Steel flails	Light machine Grooves as C 1 above	1

The effect of the grooves was to improve substantially the drainage capacity of the surface (with consequent improvement in reducing the rate of fall of skid resistance with speed) and to produce new sharp edges on the sides of the cuts, which by this local improvement in microtexture caused a general rise in level of skid resistance at all speeds.

The immediate improvements in low speed skid resistance (SFC and BFC) were considerable, approximately 75 % in some cases, methods A and B3 being the most effective (see Fig. 26). However, all the treatments reduced in effectiveness with time, presumably due to the polishing of these edges. For example, after 3 years of trafficking the SFC (50 km h^{-1}) values were only approximately 25 % greater than those of the untreated sections. The BFC values at the low speed condition indeed showed virtually no improvement over the untreated surface after 3 years (Fig. 27).

High speed skid resistance also improved considerably with all techniques immediately after operation, the decrease in BFC from 50 to 130 km h^{-1} being, for the most effective treatment B2, only 30 % compared with a 70 % drop for the untreated surface. This improvement in high speed BFC however, observed immediately after treatment was not lost (albeit somewhat reduced as would be expected) during the following three years of trafficking (Fig. 28). Treatments B2, B3 and C2 were particularly effective. In other words the evidence showed that the effect on surface macrotexture of carrying out grooving or flailing operations was more lasting than the effect on surface microtexture.

The studies carried out by Weller and Maynard have been described rather fully in this chapter as representing probably the most thorough studies of their type that have been carried out. In their cases, with the exception of the diamond pattern, all grooves or brush or tine striations have been transverse to the direction of traffic flow. Authorities in other countries, notably the USA, France and Switzerland, have experimented with longitudinal groove or brush textures as well as with transverse textures. Walter Horne[76] has drawn attention to the significant reduction in accidents that followed longitudinal grooving of a highway in California at the location of a tight radius bend. The validity of this evidence is not, however, proof of the superiority of longitudinal grooving over transverse but merely that longitudinal grooving may be effective in increasing skid resistance compared with taking no action to treat the surface. While longitudinal grooves (on an average flat highway) cannot be as effective in encouraging sub-tyre drainage as transverse grooves, the act of cutting grooves as stated above also improves pavement microtexture at the cut edges. This provides an element of 'tram-line' traction as the tyre rubber

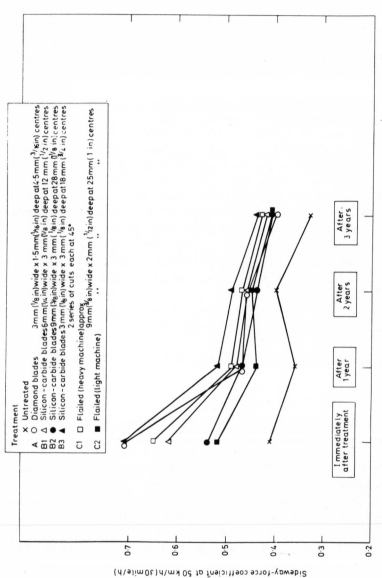

Fig. 26.   The change in sideway-force coefficients at 50 km h^{-1} (30 mile h^{-1}) with time.[75]

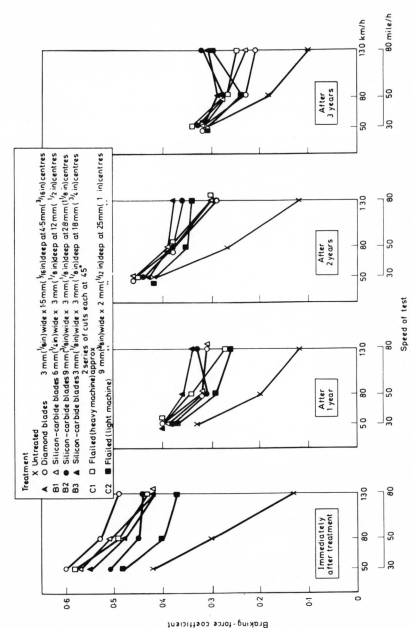

FIG. 27. The braking-force coefficients of the retextured and untreated concrete surfaces.[75]

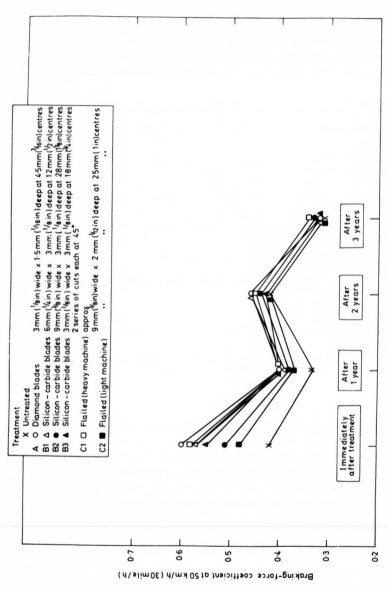

Treatment

X Untreated

A ○ Diamond blades 3mm (1/8in) wide × 1.5mm (1/16in) deep at 4.5mm (3/16in) centres
B1 △ Silicon-carbide blades 6mm (1/4in) wide × 3mm (1/8in) deep at 12mm (1/2in) centres
B2 ● Silicon-carbide blades 9mm (3/8in) wide × 3mm (1/8in) deep at 28mm (1⅛in) centres
B3 ▲ Silicon-carbide blades 3mm (1/8in) wide × 3mm (1/8in) deep at 18mm (3/4in) centres
2 series of cuts each at 45°
C1 □ Flailed (heavy machine) approx.
9mm (3/8in) wide × 2mm (1/2in) deep at 25mm (1in) centres
C2 ■ Flailed (light machine) " " "

Braking-force coefficient at 50 km/h (30 mile/h)

Immediately after treatment | After 1 year | After 2 years | After 3 years

FIG. 28. The change in braking-force coefficient at 50 km h⁻¹ (30 mile h⁻¹) with time.[75]

deforms into the grooves (especially effective in cornering manoeuvres) and, provided rainfall is not so high as to promote flooding, provides a reservoir for water to keep it from the tyre/road contact.

Notwithstanding these favourable judgements on longitudinal grooving there is little doubt that transverse grooving is more effective in promoting sub-tyre drainage, and Horne[10] notes that the high efficiency of a grooved runway at the space shuttle runway at the Kennedy Space Centre, Cape Canaveral

'gives added weight to features long observed on runways grooved with a diamond saw technique; that is, the polished groove channels (from the diamond saw cuts) greatly reduce water flow resistance over water draining through and over the comparatively much rougher texture of conventional surface treatments. In addition, the draining water is forced by the groove channels to take the shortest drainage path (down the grooves) off the runway edge even on runways with longitudinal slope. As a consequence, water drainage from runways grooved with the diamond saw technique is greatly increased over ungrooved runway surfaces.'

Similar conclusions concerning the greater effectiveness of grooved over plane surfaces and of transverse over longitudinal grooving were reached by the PIARC technical committee, 1971.[77]

(c) The 'seeding' of the surface of wet concrete with chippings of high polishing resistance has been developed by the Centre de Recherches Routières in Belgium.[78] It is recognised by the Belgian workers that as for any study of skid resistance the analysis will require years of observation. However, measurements after 6 months of traffic (about 5000 vehicles/day) showed SFC ($50 \, km \, h^{-1}$) values between 0·53 and 0·66 according to PSV of the aggregate chippings. As with the use of coated chippings in bituminous material the technique of seeding cement concrete permits, according to the author, the use of lower PSV aggregates in the body of the concrete.

SPECIAL SKID RESISTANT SURFACINGS

Shellgrip and its Derivatives (Spraygrip, etc.)

Thin surface treatments involving the spreading of artificial aggregates in a bitumen extended epoxy resin binder have been in commercial use in the UK and a few other countries since 1967. As stated by Lamb,[79]

'The combination of refractory grade calcined bauxite and epoxy resin-based binder was first proposed by the British Transport and Road

Research Laboratory and its effectiveness was demonstrated in road trials in 1959. Refractory grade calcined bauxite has a higher resistance to polishing as measured by the Polished Stone Value test than any natural roadstone, coupled with a high abrasion resistance. The epoxy resin binder, being thermo-setting, effectively prevents any embedment of the chippings with the result that in spite of the use of very small chippings (1 to 3 mm size) a remarkably high texture depth can be maintained even under heavy traffic.'

The PSV of calcined bauxite is given as 75 and sand patch texture depths up to 1·5 mm for freshly laid material have been measured, reducing to about 1 mm after a few months of trafficking but remaining stable at these values thereafter. As with other forms of surface dressing, application of Shellgrip does not correct a poor riding quality surface and it needs to be laid on a sound and non-deformed high quality substrate.

The effectiveness of this treatment, however, has been remarkable with a reduction in accident rate of in the order of 60 % (including a significant drop in accidents in dry conditions as well as in the wet) when applied to high risk accident black spots in the Greater London area.[80] Even with a relatively expensive material such as this, the high benefit/cost ratio in accident reduction has fully justified the expenditure in these high risk zones.

Open Graded 'Friction Course'
Open graded plant mix seal coats (various specifications of US highway authorities) and open texture bitumen macadams (Table 3 of the old BS 1621, now incorporated in BS 4987[65]) have been known for several decades.

While not originally designed with any particular thought of imparting high skid resistance, the realisation that an open texture, i.e. pervious material, could have excellent drainage properties and so reduce aquaplaning risk led engineers of the Ministry of Public Building and Works to lay experimental lengths on runways at the Royal Air Force airfield at Valley, Anglesey, during the years 1959 to 1962.[81] The new 'friction course' composition differed from the typical open texture bitumen macadam in that the grading was more tightly controlled—in that only aggregates of certain hard crushed rock Trade Groups were permitted, with stringent limitations on Aggregate Crushing Value, Flakiness Index, and Stripping Resistance and in that $1\frac{1}{2}$ to 2 % of hydrated lime was to be included as filler, further to improve stripping resistance.

Since that time many airfields and many stretches of road have been surfaced with friction course material and have been valued for their spray reduction[74, 82] as well as for their general ability to maintain high levels of friction over a wide speed range. Typically the thickness laid is 20–25 mm. Friction course mixes laid on the A4 at Hammersmith with an epoxy/bitumen binder and with a more open grading than the usual 'Air Ministry' specifications are described by Lamb.[79]

Being a high void content mix (of the order of 20 to 30% air voids) the course is required to be laid on a strong and impermeable foundation, typically a rolled asphalt or asphaltic concrete wearing course.

The water which falls on the upper surface percolates rapidly through the layer until it meets the impermeable course below (or the layer of water built-up thereon) and thence flows laterally outwards. When used on roads it has been customary to leave a channel at the kerb-side to allow the water to drain out freely from the bottom of the friction course, and to leave the gulleys set at the lower surface level, so that a dam effect is not produced. This may have a disadvantage in reducing the effective width of the road for vehicles and is a potential hazard for cyclists and motorcyclists. It is similarly not good practice to paint with bitumen the longitudinal and transverse joints in order to avoid obstructing the lateral flow of water.

Studies have been made[74] of the change in permeability in friction course materials caused by (a) traffic compaction and (b) accumulation of debris, oil etc. These have shown that the majority of the densification and silting up took place in the first four months of trafficking during which period the voids in the mix decreased to approximately two thirds of the original value (i.e. from approximately 25 to 15% air voids). The permeability decreased to between one half and one fifth of the initial value during the first 22 months of trafficking. In spite of these reductions it was concluded that for most sections (except where considerable mud was carried onto the road or where bitumen softening by oil droppings was suspected) little effective decrease in the efficiency of spray reduction was observed.

The durability of such open texture mixes has been variable. Early fears that frost disruption would lead to very short lives proved ungrounded, but nevertheless certain failures have occurred particularly under heavy turning traffic and it may be questioned whether such mixes are suitable for these conditions.

In an attempt to remove certain 'uncertainties and problems' connected with the design of friction course mixes, Smith, Rice and Spelman have contributed a guidance report to the Federal Highway Administration[83] describing a method for determining the most desirable binder content by reference to surface capacity of aggregates.

High Friction Dense Asphalts

A step towards the definition and implementation of factors which affect skid resistance of road surfaces has been made by the introduction in the UK of materials designated as high friction dense asphalts.[59,84] The materials produced to this design are known as Delugrip Road Surfacing Materials which is a registered trade mark of Dunlop Ltd.

Some 150 sites in Great Britain, N. Ireland and in the Irish Republic have now been laid with these materials, including the Hammersmith flyover, a main taxiway with crossing runway at Shannon International airport, Ireland, and many other heavily trafficked sites demanding high skid resistance. Three sites have been laid in 1977 on the Illinois Toll Road near Chicago, USA.

The principles of utilising high polishing resistance aggregate, designing mixes to form surfaces of macrotexture appropriate to the traffic speed and other highway factors pertaining to the site concerned, and of preserving this macrotexture by blending aggregates of differential rates of wear have been combined into a rational method of asphalt mix design.[85]

This method is aimed at producing mixes which combine the skid resistant properties mentioned above with high stability, high resistance to

TABLE 5

WET FRICTION OF DELUGRIP ROAD SURFACES (SCRIM TEST AT $50 \, \mathrm{km \, h^{-1}}$)

Monitored site	Date laid	Date tested	Average SFC
Bostall Hill, Greenwich, London	Jan 1974	29 Mar 1976	74
N22, Carrigrohane Road, Cork	Sept 1974	6 Nov 1975	72
London Road, Croydon, London	Oct 1974	29 Mar 1976	68
A3100, Godalming, Surrey	Nov 1974	May 1975	82
A3100, Godalming, Surrey	Nov 1974	May 1975	(BS 594: 72)
A413, Little Missenden, Bucks	Dec 1974	31 Jul 1975	76
Malone Road, Belfast	Jan 1975	7 Jul 1975	77
Malone Road, Belfast	Jan 1975	7 Jul 1975	(BS 594: 63)
Hammersmith flyover, London	Mar 1975	23 Nov 1975	78
Sydenham by-pass, Belfast	Apr 1975	18 Jun 1975	70
Green Lanes, Enfield, London	Jun 1975	29 Mar 1976	76
Elm Park Road, Harrow, London	Oct 1975	28 Mar 1976	84
Stanmore Hill, Harrow, London	Nov 1975	28 Mar 1976	84

Note: The BS 594 results, where quoted, are for standard asphalt surfacing laid at the same time, at the same sites and utilising the same aggregate as the coated chippings, as has been used in the corresponding Delugrip asphalts.

deformation in wheel tracks, good load distributing properties due to the high stiffness, and a quiet and comfortable running surface. In other words it is believed important when designing skid resistant properties into a surfacing material that other important engineering properties such as noise, rutting, etc. should not be neglected.

While the method has been developed with the objective of obtaining the best use from commonly occurring natural rock aggregates and from conventional bituminous binders, there is nothing exclusive in the method which would make it inapplicable to the use of artificial aggregates or 'exotic' binders such as bitumen extended epoxy resins, etc. It is, however, believed that there is a need for a rationally designed mix (i.e. a non 'recipe' type of mix) or group of mixes, which will use normally available materials and hence be as economical or even more economical than conventional asphalt mixes. By this method continuously graded or gap graded mixes may be designed with equal ease. In the case of gap gradings the gaps may be selected either according to rational principles or be predetermined as those which best suit the aggregate producing industry.

Table 5 lists some of the sites which have been monitored for friction values and gives some of the values obtained.

The latest available figures on accident statistics for the Hammersmith flyover show a reduction from 19 accidents (wet conditions) during the 2 year period before resurfacing with this material to 3 accidents in the 2 years following.

REFERENCES

✻
1. GILES, C. G. The skidding resistance of roads and the requirements of modern traffic, Proc. ICE, **6**, 216–49, 1957.
2. HATHERLY, L. W. and YOUNG, A. E. The location and treatment of urban skidding hazard sites, Transportation Research Record 623, Transportation Research Board, 21–8, 1977.
3. MILLER, M. M. and JOHNSON, H. D. Effect of resistance to skidding on accidents; surface dressing on the elevated section of M4 Motorway, Dept. of the Environment, TRRL Report LR 542, 1973.
4. RUNKLE, S. N. and MAHONE, D. C. Virginia's wet pavement accident reduction program, Transportation Research Record 622, Transportation Research Board, 91–9, 1977.
5. SCHLÖSSER, L. H. M. Traffic accidents and road surface skidding resistance, Transportation Research Record 623, Transportation Research Board, 11–20, 1977.
6. SCHULZE, K. H., GERBALDI, A. and CHAVET, J. Skidding accidents, friction

numbers and the legal aspects involved, Report of PIARC Technical Committee, Transportation Research Record 623, Transportation Research Board, 1–10, 1977.

7. CROWLEY, F. Skidding accidents and road surfaces in Ireland, M.Sc. thesis, Trinity College, Dublin, An Foras Forbartha RS68 Dublin, 1971.

8. WILLIAMS, A. R. The frictional coupling between tyre tread compounds and pavement surfacing materials, Ph.D. thesis, Univ. of Birmingham, 1971.

9. GRIMM, R. A. and BREMER, R. J. Wheel lock control state-of-the-art, Transportation Research Record 621, Transportation Research Board, 83–9, 1977.

10. HORNE, W. B. Status of runway slipperiness research, Transportation Research Record 624, Transportation Research Board, 95–121, 1977.

11. ZOEPPRITZ, H. P. An overview of European measuring methods and techniques, Transportation Research Record 621, Transportation Research Board, 75–82, 1977.

12. ALLBERT, B. J. and WALKER, J. C. Tyre to wet road friction at high speeds, Proc. Inst. Mech. Engrs., 180 (2A No. 4), 1966.

13. LANDER, F. T. W. and WILLIAMS, T. The skidding resistance of wet runway surfaces, Ministry of Transport, RRL. Report LR 184, 1968.

14. The CEBTP Stradograph. Centre Expérimental de Recherches et d'Etudes du Batiment et des Travaux Publics, 12 Rue Briançon 75737 Paris.

15. SALT, G. F. Research on skid resistance at the Transport and Road Research Laboratory (1927–1977), Transportation Research Record 622, Transportation Research Board, 26–38, 1977.

16. HOSKING, J. R. and WOODFORD, G. C. Measurement of skidding resistance: Part I Guide to the use of SCRIM; Part II Factors affecting the slipperiness of a road surface; Part III Factors affecting SCRIM measurements. Dept. of the Environment, TRRL Reports LR 737, 738, 739, 1976.

17. SUGG, R. W. The development and testing of the runway friction meter Mk1 (MU-METER), Procurement Executive, Ministry of Defence, London, 109 pp, 1972.

18. BECKER, R. and HÖRZ, E. Erprobung und Eichung des Universellen Reibungsmessers, Informationen über Straßenbau-und Straßenverkehrs-forschung No. 15, Forschungsgesellschaft für das Straßenwesen, Köln, 1976.

19. GILES, C. G., SABEY, B. E. and CARDEW, K. H. F. Development and performance of the portable skid resistance tester, Dept. of Scientific and Industrial Research, Road Research Technical Paper 66, HMSO, 1964.

20. SABEY, B. E. J. Brit. Granite and Whinstone Federation, 5(2) 7–18, 1965.

21. TRANSPORT AND ROAD RESEARCH LABORATORY. Instructions for using the portable skid-resistance tester, Road Note 27, HMSO, 1969.

22. MACLEAN, D. J. and SHERGOLD, F. A. The polishing of roadstone in relation to the resistance to skidding of bituminous road surfacings, Dept. of Scientific and Industrial Research, Road Research Technical Paper 43, HMSO, 1958.

23. BS 812. Sampling and testing of mineral aggregates, sands and fillers. Part 3, British Standards Institution, London, 1975.

24. HOSKING, J. R. Factors affecting the results of polished stone value tests, Ministry of Transport, RRL Report LR 216, 1968.

25. HOSKING, J. R. and TUBEY, L. W. Aggregates for resin bound skid-resistant road surfacings, Dept. of the Environment, TRRL Report LR 466, 1972.
26. HOSKING, J. R. The role of aggregates in providing skid resistant roads. Symposium. The influence of the road surface on skidding, Univ. of Salford, 1968.
27. VISSER, A. T. The effect of pavement surface properties on the stopping distance of vehicles, National Institute for Road Research, South Africa, Internal Report RC/3/75, 21 pp, 1975.
28. SHUPE, J. W. and GOETZ, W. H. A laboratory method for determining the skidding resistance of bituminous paving mixtures, Proc. ASTM, 58, 1–24, 1958.
29. BALMER, G. J. of the Portland Cement Association, 7(2), 18–23, 1965.
30. SHULZE, K-H. Types of surface texture and their effect on skidding resistance under wet conditions, International Colloquium on the Interrelation of Skidding Resistance and Traffic Safety on Wet Roads, June 1968, Verlag von Wilhelm Ernst und Sohn, Berlin, 553–69, 1970.
31. LEES, G. and WILLIAMS, A. R. Rubber Industry, 8(3) 114–20, 1974.
32. HOLMES, T., LEES, G. and WILLIAMS, A. R. A combined approach to the optimisation of tyre and pavement interaction, Symposium on Tread Wear and Traction, American Chemical Society, Florida, Wear, 20, 241–76, 1972.
33. LEES, G. and TAM, K. K. The design of non-grooved high friction concrete surfacings, Symposium on Skid Resistance, University of Salford, 12 pp, 1975.
34. BRÖDER, K., HAARDT, H. and PAUL, U. Autom. techn. Zeitschr. (ATZ), 75, 39–42, 1973.
35. KELLER, H. Automobil-Industrie, 2, 47–52, 1976.
36. SCHONFELD, R. Pavement surface texture classification and skid resistance—photo interpretation, 325–38, in the Physics of Tire Traction, D. F. Hays and A. L. Browne (eds), Plenum Press, New York, London, 1974.
37. WILLIAMS, A. R. and LEES, G. Qrtly J. Engrg Glgy, 2(3), 217–36, 1969.
38. TUBEY, L. W. and HOSKING, J. R. Synthetic aggregates of high resistance to polishing—Corundum rich aggregates, Dept. of the Environment, TRRL Report LR 467, 1972.
39. SALT, G. F. and SZATKOWSKI, W. S. A guide to levels of skidding resistance for roads, Dept. of the Environment, TRRL Report LR510, 1973.
40. ORDMAN, H. A grease patch method for measuring the depth of texture of road surfaces, Ministry of Transport, RRL Technical Note 122, 1966.
41. SABEY, B. E. Wet road skidding resistance at high speeds on a variety of surfaces on A1, Ministry of Transport, RRL Report LR 131, 1968.
42. ROSE, J. G., HUTCHINSON, J. W. and GALLAWAY, B. M. A summary and analysis of the attributes of methods of surface texture measurements, ASTM committee E-17 Symposium on Skid Resistance, Los Angeles, 1972.
43. MOORE, D. F. A study of tire–surface interaction for the case of rolling on a wet surface, Cornell Aeronautical Laboratory Reports No. YD-1969-V1 and YD-1969-V2, 1965.
44. MOORE, D. F. Design construction and test of a semi-automatic hydraulic texture meter, An Foras Forbartha Teoranta, Dublin, 1976.
45. DOTY, R. N. A study of the sand patch and outflow meter methods of pavement surface texture measurement, Transportation Laboratory, Department of

Transportation, Division of Highways, State of California, Research Report CA-DOT-TL-3126-10-74-24, 1974.

46. LEES, G. and KATEKHDA, I. e. D. Prediction of medium and high speed skid resistance values by means of a newly developed outflow meter, Proc. Ass. of Asphalt Paving Technol., **43**, 436–64, 1974.

47. COOPER, D. R. C. Measurement of road surface by a contactless sensor, Dept. of the Environment, TRRL Report LR 639, 1974.

48. SCHLÖSSER, L. H. M. Tyres and road surfaces, Transportation Research Record 624, Transportation Research Board, 15–26, 1977.

49. SZATKOWSKI, W. S. and HOSKING, J. R. The effect of traffic and aggregate on the resistance to skidding of bituminous surfacings, Dept. of the Environment, TRRL Report LR 504, 1972.

50. DEPARTMENT OF TRANSPORT. Technical Memorandum H16/76, Specification requirements for aggregate properties and texture depth for bituminous surfacings to new roads, London, 1976.

51. HOSKING, J. R. and TUBEY, L. W. Aggregates for resin-bound skid-resistant road surfacings, Dept. of the Environment, TRRL Report LR466, 1972.

52. KNILL, D. C. *J. Appl. Chem.*, **10**, 28–35, 1960.

53. SHUPE, J. W. and LOUNSBURY, R. W. Polishing characteristics of mineral aggregates, Proc. of the First Int. Skid Prevention Conference, 509–37, 1959.

54. GRAY, J. E. and RENNINGER, F. A. Skid resistant properties of carbonate aggregates, National Crushed Stone Association—Special Engineering Report, 44th Annual Meeting of Highway Research Board, Washington DC, USA, 1965.

55. HAWKES, J. R. and HOSKING, J. R. British arenaceous rocks for skid-resistant road surfacings, Dept. of the Environment, TRRL Report LR 488, 1972.

56. HOSKING, J. R. Synthetic aggregates of high resistance to polishing, Part 1, Gritty aggregates, Ministry of Transport, RRL Report LR 350, 1970.

57. HOSKING, J. R. Synthetic aggregates of high resistance to polishing, Part 3, Porous aggregates, Dept. of the Environment, TRRL Report LR 655, 1974.

58. HOSKING, J. R. and JACOBS, F. A. Synthetic aggregates of high resistance to polishing, Part 4, Specially shaped chippings, Dept. of the Environment, TRRL Report LR 656, 1975.

59. LEES, G., KATEKHDA, I. e. D., BOND, R. and WILLIAMS, A. R. The design and performance of high friction dense asphalts, Transportation Research Record 624, Transportation Research Board, 40–51, 1977.

60. PLEASE, A. and LAMB, D. R. Binder properties and the texture of asphalt surfacings, Proc. Ass. of Asphalt Paving Technol., **40**, 324–57, 1971.

61. PLEASE, A. and LAMB, D. R. The role of the binder in the maintenance of resistance to skidding of dense asphaltic surfacings under heavy traffic, Ministry of Transport, RRL Report LR 319, 1970.

62. GREEN, E. H. An acceptance test for Bitumen for rolled asphalt wearing course, Dept. of the Environment, TRRL Report LR 777, 1977.

63. BS 594. Rolled asphalt (hot process) for roads and other paved areas, British Standards Institution, London, 1973.

64. THE ASPHALT INSTITUTE. Specification and construction methods for hot mix asphalt paving, SS1, Maryland, USA.

65. BS 4987. Specification for coated macadam for roads and other paved areas, British Standards Institution, London, 1973.

66. TRANSPORT AND ROAD RESEARCH LABORATORY. Recommendations for road surface dressings, Dept. of the Environment, Road Note No. 39, HMSO, 1972.
67. BOND, R. and LEES, G. A theoretical approach to road surface bulk water drainage requirements, *Tire Science and Technology*, accepted for publication.
68. WELLER, D. E. and MAYNARD, D. P. The use of an accelerated wear machine to examine the skidding resistance of concrete surfaces, Ministry of Transport, RRL Report LR 333, 1970.
69. WELLER, D. E. and MAYNARD, D. P. The influence of materials and mix design on the skid resistance value and texture depth of concrete, Ministry of Transport, RRL Report LR 334, 1970.
70. WELLER, D. E. and MAYNARD, D. P. Methods of texturing new concrete road surfaces to provide adequate skidding resistance, Ministry of Transport, RRL Report LR 290, 1970.
71. MINISTRY OF TRANSPORT. Specification for road and bridge works, HMSO, London, 1969.
72. WEAVER, J. Texturing of concrete pavements, Safety and the concrete road surface, Cement and Concrete Association Symposium, London, 37–42, 1973.
73. MILLARD, R. S. Characteristics of carriageway surfacing, National Conference, Inst. of Hwy Engrs, 22–9, 1973.
74. BROWN, J. R. Pervious bitumen–macadam surfacings laid to reduce splash and spray at Stonebridge, Warwickshire, Dept. of the Environment, TRRL Report LR 563, 1973.
75. WELLER, D. E. and MAYNARD, D. P. Treatments to retexture a worn concrete surface of a high-speed road, Ministry of Transport, RRL Report LR 250, 1969.
76. HORNE, W. B. *Astronaut and Aeronaut*, 5(8), 48–55, 1967.
77. PERMANENT INTERNATIONAL ASSOCIATION OF ROAD CONGRESSES. Report of the Technical Committee on Slipperiness, XIV Congress, Prague, 1971.
78. FUCHS, F. Actual experience regarding the chipping of cement concrete, Transportation Research Record 624, Transportation Research Board, 90–4, 1977.
79. LAMB, D. R. Some UK developments in skid resistant road surfacings, Transportation Research Record 624, Transportation Research Board, 52–62, 1977.
80. HATHERLEY, L. W., MAHAFFY, J. H. and TWEDDLE, A. *J. Inst. Hwy Engrs*, 16(4), 3–12, 1969.
81. JUDGE, R. F. A. *J. of the British Granite and Whinstone Federation*, 4(2), 45–50, 1964.
82. MARTIN, F. R. and JUDGE, R. F. A. *Civ. Eng. Pub. Wks Review*, 1495–505, 1966.
83. SMITH, R. W., RICE, J. M. and SPELMAN, S. R. Design of open graded asphalt friction courses, Federal Highway Administration, Washington DC, Report No. FHWA-RD-74-2, 38 pp, 1974.
84. BOND, R., KATEKHDA, I. e. D., LEES, G. and WILLIAMS, A. R. *J. Inst. Hwy Engrs*, 23(11), 11–20, 1976.
85. LEES, G. The rational design of aggregate gradings for dense asphaltic compositions, Proc. Ass. Asphalt Paving Technol., 39, 60–97, 1970.

INDEX